an introduction to finite mathematics

BRUCE E. MESERVE, University of Vermont

▲ **ADDISON-WESLEY PUBLISHING COMPANY**
Reading, Massachusetts
Menlo Park, California · London · Don Mills, Ontario

This book is in the
ADDISON-WESLEY SERIES IN MATHEMATICS

Gail S. Young and Richard S. Pieters
Consulting Editors

preface

Finite mathematics provides an opportunity to introduce modern mathematics to liberal arts students and to provide basic mathematical tools for the study of social and behavioral sciences. Economic and business applications are very common.

This book is designed for a one-semester course. Properties of sets, elements of logic, uses of numbers, and flow charts are considered and used in Chapter 1 for a discussion of the nature of finite mathematics. Sample spaces and counting (Chapter 2) provide the basis for a study of probability including the introduction of Markov chains in Chapter 3. Vectors and matrices (Chapter 4) provide tools for introductions of linear programming (Chapter 5) and game theory (Chapter 6). Applications are considered throughout the book. Exercises are provided at the end of practically all sections. Review exercises are provided at the end of each chapter.

Numerous illustrative examples are used to provide an introduction to finite mathematics for students who have had at least two years of high school mathematics. Sets of exercises for almost every section provide ample opportunity for practice and exploration. Answers to the odd-numbered exercises are included in the back of the book;

answers to the even-numbered exercises are available in the Instructor's Manual.

Students and colleagues have provided helpful suggestions. I would also like to thank the staff at Addison-Wesley for their suggestions and Gail S. Young of the University of Rochester for his detailed comments on the manuscript.

Burlington, Vermont   B.E.M.
October 1971

contents

finite mathematics   1

Finite mathematics is based upon finite sets. A set is finite if we can count its elements and finish the counting. We start with a review of the vocabulary of sets, consider statements, use statements to define finite sets, and observe the sufficiency of finite sets for most ordinary purposes.

1.1 SETS

Any collection of elements such as

a set of books.
the letters of the English alphabet,
the persons enrolled in this course,
the numbers $\{1, 3, 4, 6\}$

forms a set. The basic property of a set is membership, belonging to, being in, the set. The elements that are in the set are **members** of that set. We use the words "element" and "member" interchangeably.

We write $A = \{1, 2, 3, 4, 5\}$ to indicate that A is another name for the set $\{1, 2, 3, 4, 5\}$. Since the order in which the elements are listed does not affect membership,

$$\{1, 2, 3, 4, 5\} = \{5, 4, 3, 2, 1\}.$$

In general, two sets are **equal sets** if they have the same members. Since repeated listing does not affect membership,

$$\{1, 1, 2, 3, 3, 3, 4, 5\} = \{1, 2, 3, 4, 5\}.$$

The set of **decimal digits** is $\{0, 1, 2, 3, \ldots, 9\}$. The three dots indicate that the specific listing is incomplete. The omissions are *for convenience* since we can complete the list as $\{0, 1, 2, 3, 4, 5, 6, 7, 8, 9\}$.

The set of **whole numbers** is $\{0, 1, 2, 3, 4, \ldots\}$. As before the three dots indicate that the listing is incomplete. However, in this case the three dots are *essential* since it is not possible to make a complete listing with specific names for each of the whole numbers. Rather we must recognize that the pattern in which the first few elements are listed continues indefinitely.

The members of a set may be indicated by a description, a list, or in set-builder notation. For example, we may *describe* a set as

the set of whole numbers,

list as a set of elements

$$\{0, 1, 2, 3, 4, \ldots\},$$

or use **set-builder notation**

$$\{x : x \text{ a whole number}\}$$

(read as "the set of elements x such that x is a whole number").

If $A = \{1, 2, 3, 4, 5\}$, we write $3 \in A$ to indicate that "3 is a member of set A." We write $7 \notin A$ to indicate that "7 is not a member of set A." Whenever a set B is given, we must be able to identify whether or not any given element x is a member of B. In other words, we must be able to identify any given statement of the form $x \in B$ or $x \notin B$ as true or false.

The set that has no members is called the **empty set** or **null set** and is represented by $\{\}$ or $\varnothing$. Notice that the set $\{0\}$ is not the empty set since this set has one element, namely zero. The empty set may arise in many ways. For example, consider the set of 100-year old monkeys in your class, the set of people who went to the moon and returned safely before 1970, the set of odd numbers that are also even numbers.

The empty set enables us to talk about various sets without first determining whether or not each particular set has at least one member.

Many of us answer questions without understanding precisely the
steps that we use to obtain the answer. Patterns of reasoning (certain
ways of obtaining answers) provide a major basis for the power of
mathematics. Thus you should be as interested in how you obtain an
answer as in the answer itself.

Example Arrange the digits of "1492" in order from largest to smallest.
Then describe the steps that you used to solve this problem.

Solution. 9, 4, 2, 1.

Among the steps that you could use are the following:

1. Read the digits 1, 4, 9, 2 in order.
2. Think of the first digit 1 and read the next digit 4.
3. Is 4 larger than 1 ? Yes. Think of 4 and read the next digit 9.
4. Is 9 larger than 4 ? Yes. Think of 9 and read the next digit 2.
5. Is 2 larger than 9 ? No. Think of 9 and read the next digit.
6. There are no more digits; 9 is the largest digit. Therefore 9 is the
   first digit in the desired arrangement of the given digits.
7. The remaining digits are 1, 4, 2. As before 4 is the next largest digit.
8. The remaining digits are 1, 2. As before 2 is the next largest digit.
9. The only remaining digit is 1. When arranged in order from largest
   to smallest, the digits are 9, 4, 2, 1.

. . . .

Exercises

1. Let $B = \{h, e, l, p\}$. Is it true that $a \in B$? Describe the steps that
   you used to answer this question.
2. Let $D = \{d, a, r, t\}$. Is $r \in D$? Describe the steps that you used to
   answer this question.
3. Let A be the set of letters in the word "psychology" and identify
   each statement as true or false:
   a) $b \in A$;   b) $c \in A$;   c) $g \in A$;
   d) $h \in A$;   e) $i \in A$;   f) $k \notin A$;
   g) $l \notin A$;   h) $n \notin A$;   i) $o \notin A$.
4. Arrange the letters of the word "tar" in alphabetical order. Describe
   the steps that you used to obtain your answer.

5. Repeat Exercise 4 for the word "tart."
6. Consider the words "tall" and "table."
    a) Arrange in alphabetical order the letters of each word.
    b) Find the set of letters that are members of both words.
    c) Find the set of letters that are members of at least one of the given words.
    d) Do the two given words have equal sets of letters?
7. Assume that Exercise 6(a) can be done as in Exercises 4 and 5. For each of the other parts of Exercise 6 describe a set of steps that can be used to obtain the answer.

In Exercises 8 and 9 repeat Exercise 6 for:

8. "part" and "trap."
9. "students" and "dents."

10. Describe each set in words:
    a) $\{1, 3, 5, 7, \ldots\}$;   b) $\{2, 4, 6, 8, \ldots\}$;
    c) $\{3, 6, 9, 12, \ldots\}$;   d) $\{7, 14, 21, 28, \ldots\}$.
11. List the first five members greater than 100 in each of the sets in Exercise 10.
12. Identify as true or false and explain the reason for your answer:
    a) $27 \in \{x : x$ is an odd number$\}$;
    b) $321 \in \{x : x$ is a multiple of 3$\}$;
    c) $759 \in \{1, 3, 5, 7, \ldots\}$;
    d) $759 \in \{2, 4, 6, 8, \ldots\}$;
    e) $759 \in \{3, 6, 9, 12, \ldots\}$;
    f) $759 \in \{7, 14, 21, 28, \ldots\}$.
. . . .

1.2 STATEMENTS

Certain sets of words form sentences. These sentences are true:

$1 + 1 = 2.$
Some apples are red.
$\{1, 9, 7, 1\} = \{1, 7, 9\}.$

These sentences are false:

$1 = 0.$
All apples are red.
$\{1, 9, 7, 1\} = \{1, 9, 7, 2\}.$

Sentences that have truth values, that is are either true or false, are called **closed sentences** or **statements**.

Each of these sentences may be either true or false depending upon the replacement used for the variable or pronoun:

$x + 2 = 5$. (True for $x = 3$, false for $x \neq 3$).

He was the first man to step on the moon. (True for Neil Armstrong, false for others.)

Sentences that can be either true or false depending upon the replacements used are called **open sentences**.

In ordinary English usage there are also sentences such as these:

Go to bed.

How are you?

Right!

Such sentences are neither true nor false, are neither closed nor open, and are not considered further in this book.

We shall be primarily concerned with sentences that can be identified as true or false. However, in our discussion of sentences and statements we shall not insist on the narrow interpretation of the word "statement." As in the case of a statement about living things on Mars, the truth of a statement may depend upon definitions or upon information that is not available to us.

Several types of statements will now be considered in an effort to improve our methods of communicating with one another and understanding the statements that we read. Consider the statement:

John is tall and Mary is short.

The connective "and" is used with two statements that we may identify as

p: John is tall.

q: Mary is short.

If the symbol $\wedge$ is used for "and," the original statement becomes

$p \wedge q$: John is tall and Mary is short.

The symbol "$p \wedge q$" is read "p and q." Any statement of the form $p \wedge q$ where p and q represent sentences is a **conjunction** and one form of a *compound statement*.

We use a conjunction when we define the intersection of two sets A and B. The **intersection** $A \cap B$ (read as "A intersect B") is the set of elements x such that x is a member of set A *and* x is a member of set B. Thus the intersection of sets A and B is the set of elements that are members of *both* sets. For example,

$$\{a, p, p, l, e\} \cap \{p, e, a, r\} = \{a, p, e\};$$
$$r \notin \{a, p, p, l, e\} \cap \{p, e, a, r\}.$$

The **union** $A \cup B$ (read as "A union B") is the set of elements x such that x is a member of set A *or* x is a member of set B. Thus the union of sets A and B is the set of elements that are members of *at least one* of the sets. For example,

$$\{a, p, p, l, e\} \cup \{p, e, a, r\} = \{a, e, l, p, r\}.$$

The word "or" is used in the definition of $A \cup B$ in the *inclusive sense* since elements that belong to both sets are included. For any statements q and s the compound statement

q or s,

where "or" is used in the inclusive sense is a **disjunction** and may be written as

$q \vee s$

(read as "q or s") using the symbol "$\vee$" for "or."

Conjunctions and disjunctions are usually expressed in terms of statements p and q, although the letters used are not significant. The truth values for $p \wedge q$ and $p \vee q$ depend upon the truth values of p and q. We consider only statements that have exactly one of the truth values

true, T
false, F.

Thus there are four possible cases for two statements p and q, that is, for any two sentences that have truth values. If p is true, then q may be true or false:

$$p \qquad q$$
$$T \underset{\displaystyle F}{\overset{\displaystyle T}{\diagdown}}$$

If p is false, then q may be true or false:

$$p \qquad q$$
$$F \underset{\displaystyle F}{\overset{\displaystyle T}{\diagdown}}$$

We usually state these four cases in a **truth table**.

p	q
T	T
T	F
F	T
F	F

A table of truth values for $p \wedge q$ may be used to show that $p \wedge q$ is true if p and q are both true; $p \wedge q$ is false in all other cases. This truth table may be taken as a definition of the truth values of $p \wedge q$ relative to the truth values of p and q.

p	q	$p \wedge q$
T	T	T
T	F	F
F	T	F
F	F	F

Each row provides a particular instance of the truth or falsity of $p \wedge q$. The third column provides all possible cases of the truth or falsity of $p \wedge q$.

A table of truth values for $p \vee q$ may be used to show that $p \vee q$ is true if at least one of the statements p, q is true; $p \vee q$ is false if p and q are both false.

p	q	$p \vee q$
T	T	T
T	F	T
F	T	T
F	F	F

The words "and" and "or" serve to join statements to form compound statements and are called **connectives**. In the formal study of statements "not" is also considered to be a connective. For any statement p we write

$\sim p$

(read as "not p") using the **denial symbol** "$\sim$" for "not." The statement $\sim p$ is called the **denial** of p. As in the truth table, if p is true, then $\sim p$ is false; if p is false, then $\sim p$ is true.

p	$\sim p$
T	F
F	T

Frequently two or more connectives are used to form **compound statements**. In such cases we use the definitions of the connectives and indicate the order in which we complete the columns of the truth table by placing letters of the alphabet below the columns.

Example Make a truth table for $(\sim p) \vee \sim q$.

Solution.

p	q	$(\sim p)$	$\vee$	$\sim q$
T	T	F	F	F
T	F	F	T	T
F	T	T	T	F
F	F	T	T	T

      (a)   (c)   (b)

The truth values in column (a) are obtained as the denials of the truth values of p; those in column (b) as the denials of the truth values of q; those in column (c) using the truth values in columns (a) and (b) and the definition of $\vee$.

. . . .

Exercises

1. Let $A = \{1, 3, 5, 7, 9\}$ and $B = \{0, 1, 2, 5, 6\}$.   Then find (a) $A \cap B$; (b) $A \cup B$.

2. Describe the steps used to find the desired sets in Exercise 1.

In Exercises 3, 4, and 5 repeat Exercise 1 for the given sets:

3. $A = \{0, 2, 4, 6, \ldots\}$ and $B = \{1, 3, 5, 7, \ldots\}$.

4. $A = \{0, 1, 2, 3, 4, 5, \ldots\}$ and $B = \{1, 3, 5, 7, 9, \ldots\}$.

5. $A = \{x : x$ is a positive multiple of $3\}$, $B = \{x : x$ is a positive multiple of $4\}$.

6. Consider these statements:

   p: The car is a Ford.
   q: The car is black.

   Statements in terms of p and q may now be translated into English sentences, often in more than one way. For example,

   $p \wedge q$: The car is a Ford and it is black.
   $p \wedge q$: The car is a black Ford.

   Translate each of these symbolic statements into an English sentence:

   a) $q \wedge p$;   b) $\sim p$;   c) $q \wedge \sim p$;
   d) $p \vee q$;   e) $q \vee p$;   f) $q \vee \sim p$.

7. Which of the statements in Exercise 4 are true if the car is a black Oldsmobile?

8. Use the statements

> p: Joe owes me five dollars.
> q: Joe will pay me on Saturday.

and translate into symbolic statements:

a) Joe doesn't owe me five dollars.

b) Joe won't pay me on Saturday.

c) Joe owes me five dollars but he won't pay me on Saturday.

9. Select suitable statements $p, q, r, \ldots$ and write each given statement as a symbolic statement with at least one connective:

a) I would like to buy that red car but I can't afford it.

b) I'll give you the book in class or bring it to your room.

c) Bill is smart but lazy.

d) Don will take Judy or Ruth to the dance.

10. Indicate whether each statement may be considered in the form $p \wedge q$ or in the form $p \vee q$:

a) Either the United States will destroy ignorance, or ignorance will destroy the United States. (W. E. B. Du Bois)

b) He has to be the bride at every wedding and the corpse at every funeral. (Alice Roosevelt Longworth)

c) Taft means well, but he means feebly. (Theodore Roosevelt)

d) Every man is wanted, and no man is wanted much. (Ralph Waldo Emerson)

e) In politics you don't have friends—you have allies. (John F. Kennedy)

f) Some men see things as they are and say why; I see things as they never were and say why not. (Robert F. Kennedy)

Make a truth table for each of these statements:

11. $p \wedge \sim q$.

12. $p \vee \sim q$.

13. $(\sim p) \wedge \sim q$.

14. $\sim (p \wedge q)$.

. . . .

1.3 IMPLICATIONS

Two statements are often connected in an *if-then* relationship. For example,

> If $x + 2 = 7$, then $x = 5$.

This statement has the form

If p, then q.

for

$p: x + 2 = 7.$
$q: x = 5.$

The statement p is said to *imply* the statement q. In other words, if p is true, then q must be true.

Any statement that can be expressed in *if-then* form is a **statement of implication** and may be expressed as

$p \rightarrow q$

(read as "p implies q") using the **implication symbol** "$\rightarrow$." The truth values of $p \rightarrow q$ are given in the next table. Note that any statement of implication $p \rightarrow q$ is *defined* to be true unless p is true and q is false. The acceptance of the statement of implication as true whenever p is false is in accord with the use of such statements by logicians.

p	q	$p \rightarrow q$
T	T	T
T	F	F
F	T	T
F	F	T

Statements of implication may be expressed in several ways. Consider the statement

If $x = 2$, then $x^2 = 4$.

This statement has two parts; the **premise** (or hypothesis) "$x = 2$" and the **conclusion** "$x^2 = 4$." The words "if" and "then" enable us to identify the premise and the conclusion. This identification does not depend upon the order of the parts of the statement. For example, the same statement may be expressed in the form

$$x^2 = 4 \text{ if } x = 2.$$

Sometimes the statement is expressed in the form

$$x = 2 \text{ only if } x^2 = 4.$$

Note that "only if" identifies the conclusion. Two other common forms of statements of implication arise from the fact that the premise is a sufficient condition for the conclusion; the conclusion is a necessary condition for the premise. Then the statement that we have been considering can also be expressed in each of these forms:

$$x = 2 \text{ is sufficient for } x^2 = 4.$$
$$x^2 = 4 \text{ is necessary for } x = 2.$$

Other examples of these common forms of statements of implication are given in Example 1. In this example we are concerned with the form of each statement rather than its truth value. The statements may be true or false.

Example 1 Write in *if-then* form:
 a) Vertical angles are congruent.
 b) I'll pay for the gas, if you'll drive your car.
 c) Ruth is ready by 7 o'clock only if dinner is before 6.
 d) A hot day is a sufficient reason for Bob to take a swim.
 e) A blizzard is necessary for Jack to miss school.
 f) A red sunset implies a good day tomorrow.

Solution.
 a) If two angles are vertical angles, then the angles are congruent.
 b) If you'll drive your car, then I'll pay for the gas.
 c) If Ruth is ready by 7 o'clock, then dinner is before 6.
 d) If it is a hot day, then Bob takes a swim.
 e) If Jack misses school, then there is a blizzard.
 f) If there is a red sunset, then tomorrow will be a good day.

Example 2 Make a table of the truth values of

$$[(p \lor q) \land \sim q] \to p.$$

Solution.

p	q	$[(p \lor q)$	$\land$	$\sim q]$	$\to$	p
T	T	T	F	F	T	T
T	F	T	T	T	T	T
F	T	T	F	F	T	F
F	F	F	F	T	T	F

       (a)   (c) (b) (e) (d)

In Example 2, column (a) of the truth table can be completed using the truth values of p and q and the definition of $\lor$. Column (b) can be completed using the truth values of q and the definition of $\sim$. Column (c) can be completed using the truth values in columns (a) and (b) and the definition of $\land$. Column (d) is simply a copy of the truth values of p. Then column (e) can be completed using the truth values in columns (c) and (d) and the definition of $\to$. Since all the truth values in column (e) are T, the given statement is always true. Any statement that is always true is a **tautology**.

. . . .

Exercises

Identify p and q such that each statement may be expressed in the form $p \to q$.

1. If you don't like the heat, get out of the kitchen. (Harry Truman)

2. To graduate from college it is sufficient to survive.

3. To graduate from college it is necessary to survive.

4. Doris is on time for class only if she skips breakfast.

Complete each truth table:

5. p q $p \to \sim q$
   T T
   T F
   F T
   F F

   (a)(c) (b)

6. p q $[(\sim p) \wedge q] \to (p \to q)$
   (a)   (c) (b) (g) (d) (f) (e)

If $p \to q$ and $q \to p$, then p and q have the same truth values and are called **equivalent statements**. We write $p \leftrightarrow q$ (read as "p is equivalent to q") using the **equivalence symbol** "$\leftrightarrow$" to make a statement of the equivalence of p and q. Complete each truth table:

7. p q $[(p \to q) \wedge (q \to p)] \leftrightarrow (p \leftrightarrow q)$
   (a)   (e) (b)(d) (c) (g)   (f)

8. p q $(p \to q) \leftrightarrow [(\sim q) \to \sim p]$
   (a)   (e)   (b) (d) (c)

The statement $(\sim q) \to \sim p$ is the **contrapositive statement** of $p \to q$. Any statement of implication is equivalent to its contrapositive (Exercise 8). State the contrapositive of each given statement.

9. If John lives in Chicago, then John lives in Illinois.

10. If Ruth is a mathematics major, then she can do algebra problems.

11. If $x + 2 = 5$, then $x = 3$.

12. If $x \neq 2$, then $x^2 \neq 4$.

13. If a triangle is equilateral, then it is isosceles.

Any statement $p \to q$ has an **inverse statement** $(\sim p) \to \sim q$ and a **converse statement** $q \to p$.

14. State the converse of the statement in (a) Exercise 9; (b) Exercise 10. In each case does the converse of a true statement appear to be necessarily true?

15. Repeat Exercise 14 for the inverse statements.

Supplementary Exercises

1. Use a truth table to show that in general a statement $p \to q$ is not equivalent to its converse.

2. Use a truth table to show that in general the converse and the inverse of any statement $p \to q$ are equivalent statements.

The statements in Exercises 3 and 4 are often called **de Morgan's laws for statements**. Use a truth table to show that each statement is a tautology.

3. $[\sim(p \wedge q)] \leftrightarrow [(\sim p) \vee \sim q]$.
4. $[\sim(p \vee q)] \leftrightarrow [(\sim p) \wedge \sim q]$.

Use de Morgan's laws when necessary and state the negation of each given statement:

5. It is not true that Bill can swim and dive.
6. Bob is tall and Ruth is short.
7. Jane will go to the dance or study.
8. That car dealer is neither reliable nor honest.

. . . .

1.4 QUANTIFIERS

Quantifiers are often used to change an open sentence into a closed sentence. Consider the open sentence

$$x + 2 = 9.$$

This sentence is true if $x = 7$ and false if $x \neq 7$. If x can be any whole number, the sentence cannot be identified as true or false. However, this next sentence includes the **existential quantifier** "there exists" and is true:

There exists a whole number x such that $x + 2 = 9$.

We may use the **existential quantifier symbol**

$\exists x$:

(read as "there exists x such that") to express the statement in the form

$\exists x: x + 2 = 9$, where x is a whole number.

Existential quantifiers may be indicated in several ways as illustrated by the following statements:

Someone borrowed my notes.
There is a student who borrowed my notes.
There is at least one student who borrowed my notes.
There are two students who borrowed my notes.

Each of the previous statements includes a statement of the existence of at least one person who borrowed my notes; that is,

$\exists x$: x borrowed my notes, where x is a person.

The **universal quantifier** "for all" may also be used to obtain a sentence with an identifiable truth value. For example, the next sentence is false:

For all whole numbers x, $x + 2 = 9$.

We may use the **universal quantifier symbol**

$\forall x$:

(read as "for all x") to express the statement in the form

$\forall x$: $x + 2 = 9$, where x is a whole number.

Universal quantifiers may be indicated in several ways as illustrated by the following statements:

All students in this class have copies of the textbook.
Every student in this class has a copy of the textbook.
Everyone in this class has a copy of the textbook.

Each of the previous statements is a statement that everyone in a specified universal set (this class) has a copy of the textbook that is,

$\forall x$: x has a copy of the textbook, where x is a member of this class.

Denials of statements involving quantifiers are often misused. Consider the statement:

There is a doctor in the house.

The denial of this statement may be expressed by any one of these equivalent statements:

There is not a doctor in the house.
No one in the house is a doctor.
Everyone in the house is not a doctor.

The last statement illustrates how a universal quantifier may be used to express the denial of a statement involving an existential quantifier.

Next suppose that we start with a statement involving a universal quantifier. For example,

Every girl in the room is a blonde.

This statement is false if there is at least one girl in the room who is not a blonde. Thus the denial of the original statement may be expressed by either of these equivalent statements:

Not every girl in the room is a blonde.
There exists a girl in the room who is not a blonde.

These two statements illustrate how an existential quantifier may be used to express the denial of a statement involving a universal quantifier.

When symbols are used " $\sim \exists x$:" is read "there does not exist x such that" and " $\sim \forall x$:" is read "it is not true for all x that."

. . . .

Exercises

State using symbols for quantifiers:

1. There exists a whole number x greater than 100.
2. Not all whole numbers x are greater than 100.
3. All whole numbers are greater than -1.
4. There does not exist a whole number less than 0.

In Exercises 5 through 8 consider the set of whole numbers $\{0, 1, 2, 3, \ldots\}$. State without using symbols for quantifiers:

5. $\exists x: x^2 = 1$, where x is a whole number.
6. $\sim \exists x: x^2 = 2$, where x is a whole number.
7. $\forall x: x^2 \geq 0$, where x is a whole number.
8. $\sim \forall x: x^2 > 0$, where x is a whole number.

9. Use an existential quantifier and replace each sentence by a related sentence that can be identified as true or false:
   a) $7 - x = 25$, where x is a whole number.
   b) Mathematics assignments are too long.
10. Use a universal quantifier and replace each sentence given in Exercise 9 by a related sentence that can be identified as true or false.

11. Restate each sentence in words using either "there exist(s)" or "for all":
    a) No one is home tonight.
    b) Some courses are worth taking for credit.
    c) All four tires on this car are flat.
    d) Some one in this class did not pass in a paper.
12. State in words the denial of each statement given in Exercise 11.

. . . .

1.5 FINITE SETS

Two sets are *equal sets* if they have the same members. Two sets are *equivalent sets* if they have the same number of members. To determine whether or not two sets have the same number of members we may count the members of each set or we may simply pair off (one-to-one) each member of one set with a member of the other set. The sets are equivalent if all members of each set are used in the pairing of elements. If the sets are equivalent, the pairing of elements is described as placing the sets in a **one-to-one correspondence**. A set that can be placed in a one-to-one correspondence with a set $\{1, 2, 3, 4, \ldots, n\}$ of whole numbers is a *finite set*.

In a one-to-one correspondence each member of each set is paired with exactly one element of the other set. For example, the set $\{A, B, C\}$ may be placed in a one-to-one correspondence with the set $\{1, 2, 3\}$ as in the next array.

$$\{A, \qquad B, \qquad C\}$$
$$\updownarrow \qquad\quad \updownarrow \qquad\quad \updownarrow$$
$$\{1, \qquad 2, \qquad 3\}$$

The sets $\{P, Q, R, S\}$ have *not* been placed in a one-to-one correspondence in the following array since Q and R are both paired with the same element B.

$$\{P, \qquad Q, \qquad R, \qquad S\}$$

$$\{A, \qquad B, \qquad C\}$$

Consider the sets

$$\{a, b, c, d, e\}$$
$$\{\triangle, \ \square, \ \square, \ \bigcirc, \ \diagup\ \}$$

If we count the elements of each set, then we place each set in a one-to-one correspondence with the set

　　{1, 2, 3, 4, 5}.

For example, consider the one-to-one correspondences indicated by the double arrows:

　　{*a, b, c, d, e*}　　　　{△, ☐, ☐, ○, ▱ }
　　 ↕ ↕ ↕ ↕ ↕　　　　　 ↕ 　↕ 　↕ 　↕ 　↕
　　{1, 2, 3, 4, 5}　　　　{1 　2 　3, 　4, 　5}

If we combine these two correspondences, we have

　　{*a,　b,　c,　d,　e*}
　　 ↑ 　↕ 　↕ 　↕ 　↕
　　{1,　2,　3,　4,　5}
　　 ↕ 　↕ 　↕ 　↕ 　↕
　　{△, ☐, ☐, ○, ▱}

The set of numbers can be omitted. Then we have the one-to-one correspondence

　　{*a,　b,　c,　d,　e*}
　　 ↕ 　↕ 　↕ 　↕ 　↕
　　{△, ☐, ☐, ○, ▱ }

　　　Any two sets that can be placed in a one-to-one correspondence are defined to be **equivalent sets**. As in the previous paragraph any two sets with the same number of elements can be placed in a one-to-one correspondence and are equivalent sets.
　　　The counting numbers are the members of the set

　　{1, 2, 3, 4, 5, 6, . . . }.

The counting numbers are used in their stated order to determine the number of elements in a set. For example, the one-to-one correspondence

　　{*a, b, c, d, e*}
　　 ↕ ↕ ↕ ↕ ↕
　　{1, 2, 3, 4, 5}

shows that $\{a, b, c, d, e\}$ has 5 elements, since 5 is the last (largest) counting number used in the one-to-one correspondence. The number of elements of a set is the **cardinal number** of the set. Thus the set $\{a, b, c, d, e\}$ has cardinal number 5. If $A = \{a, b, c, d, e\}$, we write

$$n(A) = 5$$

(read as "cardinal number of A is 5"). Any two sets with the same cardinal number have the same number of elements and are equivalent sets. Any two equivalent sets have the same cardinal number.

The whole numbers are the members of the set

$$\{0, 1, 2, 3, \ldots\}.$$

The empty set is defined to have cardinal number 0. Any set that has a whole number as its cardinal number is a **finite set**.

A set that is not a finite set is an **infinite set**. As tor finite sets one-to-one correspondences are used to determine whether infinite sets are equivalent. Consider the correspondence

$$\{1, \; 2, \; 3, \; 4, \; 5, \ldots, \; n, \ldots\}$$
$$\updownarrow \; \updownarrow \; \updownarrow \; \updownarrow \; \updownarrow \qquad \updownarrow$$
$$\{2, \; 4, \; 6, \; 8, \; 10, \ldots, \; 2n, \ldots\}$$

This one-to-one correspondence shows that the set of all counting numbers is equivalent to the set of even counting numbers. We could not determine this by counting. Indeed, the property of a set being equivalent to a part of itself after some elements have been removed seems a bit strange to many people. However, from the example one sees that after the odd counting numbers have been removed from the set of counting numbers, there are just as many elements left as there were before. This is the characteristic property of infinite sets.

Let $A = \{1, 2, 3, 4, 5\}$ and $B = \{1, 3, 5\}$. Then each element of B is an element of A; that is, B is a **subset** of A. Similarly, A is a subset of A and, by definition, the empty set is a subset of every set A. We use the symbol " $\subseteq$ " for "is a subset of" and write

$$B \subseteq A, \qquad A \subseteq A, \qquad \varnothing \subseteq A.$$

The distinction between the given sets A and B arises from the fact that there exist elements such as 2 and 4 of A that are not elements of B. In general, if B is a subset of A and there is at least one element of A that is not an element of B, then B is a **proper subset** of A, written $B \subset A$. Then the characteristic property of infinite sets may be stated as follows: Any set that is equivalent to one of its proper subsets is an infinite set. In this book we shall be primarily concerned with finite sets, that is, sets that are not equivalent to any of their proper subsets.

. . . .

Exercises

Show a one-to-one correspondence from one set to the other:

1. $\{t, a, n\}$ and $\{s, u, n\}$.
2. $\{2, 4, 6, 8, 10\}$ and $\{5, 10, 15, 20, 25\}$.
3. $\{3, 6, 9, \ldots, 21\}$ and $\{1, 2, 3, \ldots, 7\}$.
4. $\{1, 3, 5, 7, \ldots, 99\}$ and $\{2, 4, 6, 8, \ldots, n, \ldots, 100\}$.
5. $\{5, 10, 15, 20, \ldots\}$ and $\{1, 2, 3, \ldots, n, \ldots\}$.

In Exercises 6 through 12 identify each set as finite or infinite. If a set is finite, find its cardinal number:

6. $A = \{2, 4, 6, 8, 10\}$.
7. $B = \{1, 3, 5, \ldots, 99\}$.
8. $C = \{5, 10, 15, \ldots, 5280\}$.
9. $D = \{5, 10, 15, \ldots\}$.
10. $E = \{1, \frac{1}{2}, \frac{1}{3}, \frac{1}{4}, \ldots\}$.
11. $F = \{x : x \text{ a whole number less than } 101\}$.
12. $G = \{x : x \text{ an even whole number}\}$.

13. Insert the appropriate symbol "$\subseteq$" or "$\subset$":
    a) $\{t, o, n\} \underline{} \{n, o, t\}$;
    b) $\{t, o, e\} \underline{} \{t, o, t, e\}$;
    c) $\{h, a, t\} \underline{} \{t, h, a, t\}$;
    d) $\{r, o, v, e\} \underline{} \{c, l, o, v, e, r\}$.
14. Use "$\not\subset$" for "is not a proper subset of" and insert the appropriate symbol "$\subset$" or "$\not\subset$":
    a) $\{s, t, o, p\} \underline{} \{p, o, s, t\}$;
    b) $\{l, i, p\} \underline{} \{p, i, l, l\}$;
    c) $\{s, l, i, p\} \underline{} \{l, i, s, p\}$;
    d) $\{s, h, i, p\} \underline{} \{h, i, p, s\}$;
    e) $\{t, a, n, k, s\} \underline{} \{t, h, a, n, k, s\}$.
15. Use "$\neq$" for "is not equal to" and repeat Exercise 14 for the symbols "$=$" or "$\neq$."

16. List the 4 subsets of $\{a, b\}$.

17. List the 8 subsets of $\{a, b, c\}$.

18. List the 8 subsets of $\{r, a, t\}$.

. . . .

1.6 FLOWCHARTS

In finite mathematics we are concerned with processes that can be completed in a finite number of steps. Such sequences of steps may be represented graphically by **flowcharts**. For example, in Exercise 1 of Section 1.1 you were asked to describe the steps that you used to decide whether $a \in B$, where $B = \{h, e, l, p\}$. You could have used the flowchart in Fig. 1.1 and the steps described therein.

Diamond shaped boxes are used for questions in accord with the conventions of most people who use flowcharts. Rectangular boxes have been used for convenience for all statements.

Each question used in the flowchart can be answered "yes" or "no" and the appropriate next box is shown for each answer. The chart has been based upon the assumption that it is known that $n(B) = 4$. Under this assumption the answer $a \in B$ or $a \notin B$ obtained simply by following the steps indicated by the flowchart will be the correct answer. The next flowchart (Fig. 1.2) may be used for any finite set B; that is, any set B with a whole number n as its cardinal number.

Note in Fig. 1.2 that we keep asking essentially the same question. We can eliminate the need for repeating the statement of the question by introducing a counter as in Fig. 1.3.

The steps in the use of the flowchart in Fig. 1.3 can be listed for any given set B. Suppose

$$B = \{b, e, g, a, t\}.$$

Start with the first rectangle and follow the arrows:

1. (first box) Read B.

2. (second box) Write $\{b, e, g, a, t\}$
   $$\updownarrow \;\; \updownarrow \;\; \updownarrow \;\; \updownarrow \;\; \updownarrow$$
   $$\{1, 2, 3, 4, 5\}$$

   and determine that $n = 5$.

3. (third box) Let $c = 0$.

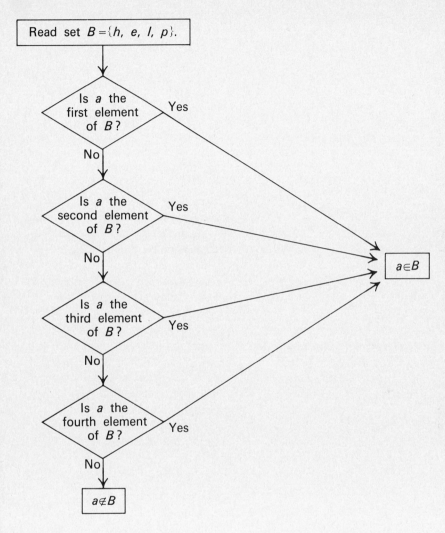

Fig. 1.1

4. (first diamond) Is $5 > 0$? Yes. Therefore we go to the second diamond (Fig. 1.3).

5. (second diamond) Is a the first element b of B? No. Therefore we go to the box at the bottom of the chart.

6. (last box) Let $c = 1$.

7. (back to first diamond) Is $5 > 1$? Yes, go to the second diamond.

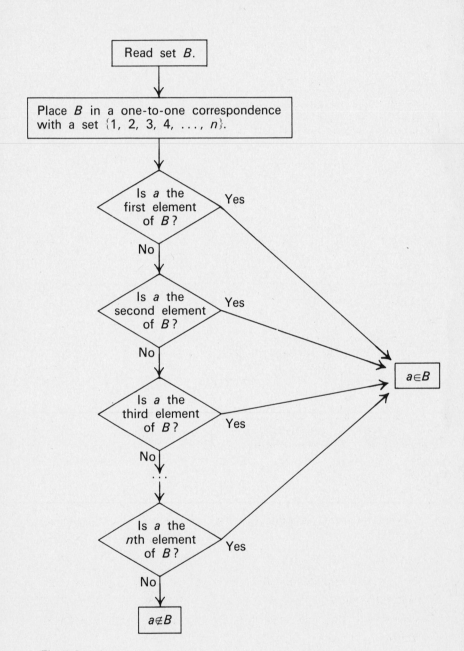

Fig. 1.2

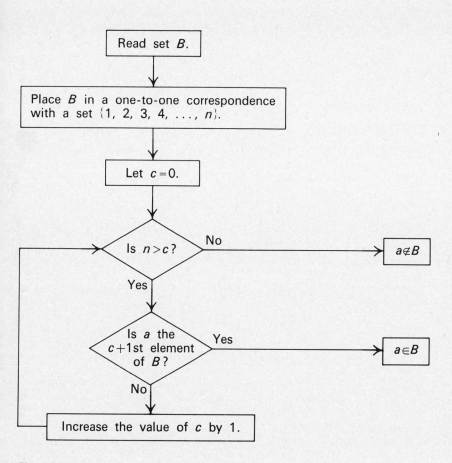

Fig. 1.3

8. (second diamond) Is a the second element e of B? No, go to the last box.

9. (last box) Let $c = 2$.

10. (back to the first diamond) Is $5 > 2$? Yes, go to the second diamond.

11. (second diamond) Is a the third element g of B? No, go to the last box.

12. (last box) Let $c = 3$.

13. (back to the first diamond) Is $5 > 3$? Yes, go to the second diamond.

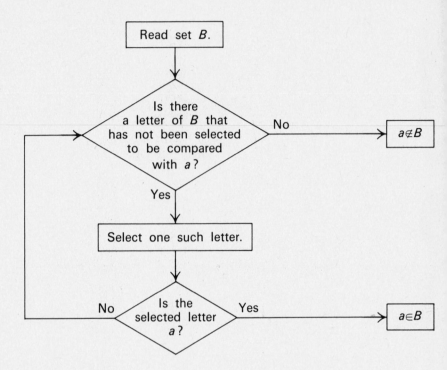

Fig. 1.4

14. (second diamond) Is a the fourth element a of B? Yes, go to the
    next to the last box.

15. (next to the last box) $a \in B$.

   In this flowchart the question "Is a the $(c + 1)$st element of B?"
in the second diamond is asked over and over again until either there
are no more elements of B to ask about or a is identified as an element of
B. The sequence of three steps (first diamond, second diamond, and
last box) that were repeated forms a **loop**. Whenever a flowchart
contains a loop, there must be at least one way of getting out of the
loop. In the previous flowchart there are two ways of getting out of the
loop: from the first diamond if $n \not> c$ and from the second diamond if a
is the $(c + 1)$st element of B. In other words, if the answer to the
question in the first diamond is "no," then $a \notin B$ and we are through; if
the answer is "yes," we proceed to the question in the second diamond.
If the answer to this question is "yes," then $a \in B$ and we are through;
if the answer is "no," then we proceed to the last box and back to the
first diamond with the next value of c. Since B is a finite set, the loop
will be repeated at most a finite number n times.

Flowcharts are often used to indicate the structure of a procedure involving a sequence of steps. For example, many people use flowcharts as they prepare instructions for an electronic computer. We shall use flowcharts primarily to find the structure or clarify the steps that we are using to solve problems.

Just as there are often several correct procedures for carrying out a given task, there are often several correct but very different appearing flowcharts. For example, Fig. 1.4 shows another use of a loop to determine whether $a \in B$ for a given set B. In this case the procedure comes to an end if and only if $a \in B$ or the set B has a finite number of letters.

. . . .

Exercises

1. Prepare a flowchart without a loop for determining whether $t \in S$, where $S = \{h, a, m\}$.

2. Repeat Exercise 1 using a flowchart with a loop.

3. List the steps that would be followed to use the flowchart developed in Exercise 1 for the given problem.

4. List the steps that would be followed to use the flowchart developed in Exercise 2 for the given problem.

Prepare a flowchart for solving:

5. Exercise 2 of Section 1.1.

6. Exercise 3(a) of Section 1.1.

7. Exercise 3(b) of Section 1.1.

8. Exercise 16 of Section 1.5.

9. Exercise 18 of Section 1.5.

. . . .

1.7 USES OF NUMBERS

Numbers that are used to indicate *how many* elements there are in a finite set are cardinal numbers. Numbers that are used to indicate the *order* of the elements of a finite set, such as the pages of this book, are called **ordinal numbers**. We even have special words to use when speaking of order: first, second, third, fourth, fifth, ... Still another use of numbers is for *identification*. For example, consider Social

Security numbers. Most uses of numbers fall into one of these three categories:

    cardinal numbers,
    ordinal numbers,
    numbers for identification.

Operations such as addition and multiplication upon numbers are important primarily for cardinal numbers. Consider the question:

    How far is it from New York to San Franscisco?

The answer might be stated as:

    Five hours of travel by jet airplane.
    Three thousand miles.
    Three hours of change in time zones.

Each answer involves a cardinal number 5, 3, 3. Each answer is expressed in terms of some unit:

    one hour of travel by jet airplane,
    one thousand miles,
    one hour of change in time zone.

Each answer is an approximation to the nearest one of these units and each answer could be made more *precise* by considering smaller units. For example, the distance to the nearest hundred miles might be stated as

    twenty-eight hundred miles

or as

    2.8 thousand miles.

Whichever statement is used, the answer is basically a count (28) of hundreds of miles.

A few measurements, such as an I.Q. (intelligence quotient), are used for comparisons without a consistent unit of measure. However, most measurements depend upon

    a unit of measure

and

    a count of a number of such units.

Thus most measurements involve cardinal numbers. Since each measurement is to the nearest unit, each measurement may be in error by at most half of a unit and is an approximation. Accordingly, the numbers used to express the measures are often called **approximate numbers**.

· ·

Exercises

1. Identify the use of each indicated number as cardinal, ordinal, or for identification.
   a) Bill has *two* copies of this text.
   b) IBM stock went up *1¾* points today.
   c) My office is at *41* North Prospect Street.
   d) This book may be used in Math. *7*.
   e) My car license plate is *7216*.
   f) The assignment for tomorrow is on page *35*.
   g) My speech book has *475* pages.

2. For each part of Exercise 1 in which a unit of measure was used, identify that unit of measure.

3. Name at least five different units of:
   a) linear measure,   b) area measure,
   c) volume measure,   d) angular measure.

4. Each of these measurements may be expressed as a cardinal number of some unit. For example, 1.23 feet may be expressed as 123 hundredths of a foot. In each case identify the cardinal number (such as 123) and the smallest unit of measure used (such as hundredths of a foot):
   a) $5\frac{1}{4}$ inches,   b) 5.2 miles,
   c) 2 hours 35 minutes,   d) 2°35′ (for an angle),
   e) $4\frac{1}{3}$ yards.

5. The size of the smallest unit used is an indication of the **precision** of a measurement. A measurement of 2 inches is *more precise* than a measurement of 2.5 feet since 1 inch is smaller than one-tenth of a foot. In any set of measurements the measurement in terms of

the smallest unit of measure is the most precise. Select the most precise measurement:

a) 4.5 yards, 65 feet, 2 yards;

b) 5.23 miles, 5,372 yards, 257 meters;

c) 1.34 days, 5 hours, 7 hours 35 minutes.

6. The number of decimal digits needed to express the number of the smallest units considered is an indication of the **accuracy** of a measurement. For example, 5 hours 22 minutes has 1 minute as its smallest unit and represents $5(60) + 22$, that is, 322 minutes. Thus a measurement of 5 hours 22 minutes has one-minute precision and three-digit accuracy. Similarly, 173.5 feet has one-tenth foot precision and four-digit accuracy. Find the precision and the accuracy of each of these measurements:

a) $3\frac{1}{4}$ inches,   b) 25.3 feet,
c) 276.01 miles,   d) 3 days and 4 hours,
e) 256 thousand people.

7. Decimal expressions for approximate numbers show their precision and accuracy. For example,

2.5 has two-digit accuracy and precision 0.1;
2.50 has three-digit accuracy and precision 0.01;
0.025 has two-digit accuracy and precision 0.001.

Assume that each number is approximate and state its accuracy and precision:

a) 3.51,   b) 17.250,
c) 0.015,   d) 0.0123.

8. A special notation is needed to extend the procedure used in Exercise 7 for integers. For example, the population of a city is stated as 210,000. Without further information we have no idea whether the precision is ten-thousands, thousands, hundreds, tens, or ones. To avoid this problem we introduce **scientific nota-tion** and express each number as the product of a number x $(1 \le x < 10)$ and a power of ten. For example, 210,000 to the nearest ten-thousand is 2.1×10^5; 210,000 to the nearest hundred is 2.100×10^5. Remember that $10^3 = 1000, 10^2 = 100$, $10^1 = 10$, $10^0 = 1$, $10^{-1} = 0.1$, $10^{-2} = 0.01$, and so forth. Express each number in scientific notation:

a) 56,

b) 73.2,

c) 350 to the nearest ten,

d) 6,000,000 to the nearest ten-thousand.

1.8 APPROXIMATIONS

In finite mathematics we may represent the number $\frac{1}{3}$ as a fraction, but we do not use the infinite decimal expansion

0.33333333333333333 . . . .

In other words, our symbols for decimal numerals include only a finite number of digits. However, we have considerable freedom in selecting the precision that we shall use.

We use the symbol " $\approx$ " for "is approximately equal to" and write

$\frac{1}{3} \approx 0.33$

to the nearest hundredth. We may also write

$\frac{1}{3} \approx 0.333\ 333\ 333$

to the nearest billionth. However, in all cases there must be a smallest unit of precision. This restriction to finite decimals is not a serious practical handicap. For example, all electronic digital computers have such a restriction and still operate with amazing effectiveness.

Suppose that the smallest unit of precision for a particular problem is given as 0.001. Then we may arbitrarily express, for example,

$$7 = 7.000,$$
$$\tfrac{1}{2} = 0.500,$$
$$\tfrac{4}{3} \approx 1.333,$$
$$\sqrt{3} \approx 1.732,$$
$$\pi \approx 3.142.$$

Integers, fractions, and irrational numbers, such as $\sqrt{3}$ and π, all appear as decimals to the nearest thousandth.

Basically, we round off to the nearest thousandth. For example,

$$2.0003 \approx 2.000,$$
$$0.0008 \approx 0.001,$$
$$0.0004 \approx 0.000.$$

Numbers such as 0.0025 and 4.1435 require special consideration. Frequently the situation in which the number is used indicates whether we should round up or down. For example, in ordering materials we might round up to be sure that we had enough. When the situation does not indicate a procedure for rounding off, we shall round ...5000... *to the nearest even digit*; then

$$0.0025 \approx 0.002,$$
$$4.1435 \approx 4.144.$$

This approach is recommended by scientific organizations including the American National Standards Institute to avoid accumulating excessive surpluses (or shortages) by always rounding up (or down).

The principle underlying examples such as $0.0004 \approx 0.000$ can be illustrated very concretely. Suppose that you have $5 to the nearest dollar. How much money do you have (to the nearest dollar) if you find a quarter? Without changing the unit by which you describe the money that you have, the best possible statement is still that you have $5. The same would be true if you spent a quarter. In other words, *to the nearest dollar*

$$\$5 + \$0.25 \approx \$5,$$
$$\$5 - \$0.25 \approx \$5.$$

One problem with approximations arises from the vague notion of many people that mathematics is an *exact* science. Some parts of mathematics are exact. However, approximations, probability, and statistics are *not* among the exact parts of mathematics. Approximations remain approximations, approximate numbers remain approximate, and computations with approximate numbers may decrease their precision. (See Exercises 13, 14, and 15.)

Approximations arise in geometry as well as in arithmetic. In arithmetic any number that is less than half of the specified smallest unit of precision under consideration is treated as 0 and disregarded. In geometry distances receive a corresponding treatment. Suppose that the smallest unit of distance for a particular problem is one tenth of an inch. Then a number line appears as a set of dots one tenth of an inch apart. When viewed from a distance the line appears solid. However, the individual dots appear when the line is considered in greater detail. See Fig. 1.5.

The representation of figures by finite sets of dots is illustrated by all figures on a television screen. Thus the approach can be very effective and useful.

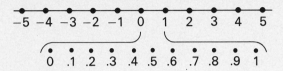

Fig. 1.5

....

Exercises

Round off to the nearest whole number:

1. a) 25.60,   b) 78.35.
2. a) 125.51,   b) 2.49.

One of the most important uses of approximations is in *estimation*. For example, if you find the product 7.5 × 8.2 on a desk calculator or a slide rule, you get the digits 615. Then you estimate the answer as approximately 8 × 8, or 64, and place the decimal point to obtain 7.5 × 8.2 = 61.5. There are, of course, other methods for determining the location of the decimal point. Add zeros as needed and use estimation to place the decimal point for each of these examples:

3. a) $(2.1)^2$ __ 441;   b) $(300)^2$ __ 9.
4. a) $(0.005)^2$ __ 25;   b) $(0.01)^3$ __ 1.
5. a) $(0.2)^3$ __ 8;   b) $\sqrt{0.25}$ __ 5.
6. a) $\sqrt{250,000}$ __ 5;   b) $\sqrt{0.0004}$ __ 2.
7. a) $\sqrt[3]{8,000}$ __ 2;   b) $\sqrt[4]{0.0016}$ __ 2.
8. a) 2.4 × 5.25 __ 126;   b) 0.3 × 500 __ 15.
9. a) 0.25 × 80 __ 2;   b) 0.05 × 80 __ 4.
10. a) 250 ÷ 0.5 __ 5;   b) 675 ÷ 0.09 __ 75.

In making computations with approximate data the rule for addition and subtraction is that the *precision* cannot be increased. Thus for any sum (or difference) the answer is assumed to be as precise as the least precise of the numbers used. For example,

$$\begin{array}{r} 20.35 \\ 16.2 \\ +\ \ 4.015 \\ \hline \approx 40.6 \end{array} \qquad \begin{array}{r} 16.372 \\ -\ \ 5 \\ \hline \approx 11 \end{array}$$

Assume that the given numbers are approximate and find:

11. a)   152.46   b)   2.00174
            70.2   0.523
        +   2.015   + 0.0015

12. a)   275.56   b)   625.7
           −252.3   −   4.002

The rule for multiplication, division, and the extraction of roots of approximate numbers is that the *accuracy* cannot be increased. Thus any product, quotient, or root is assumed to be as accurate (two-digit accuracy, three-digit accuracy, etc.) as the least accurate approximate number used. For example, for approximate numbers

$$\sqrt{2} \approx 1; \qquad \sqrt{2.0} \approx 1.4; \qquad \sqrt{2.000} \approx 1.414.$$

Assume that the given numbers are approximate and find:

13. a) 2.0×5.1;   b) 27.5×0.04.

14. a) $\sqrt{0.250}$;   b) $\sqrt{0.64}$.

15. a) $5.200 \div 0.26$;   b) $6.528 \div 0.020$.

. . . .

1.9 THE NATURE OF FINITE MATHEMATICS

Finite mathematics is concerned with sets that have a finite (whole number) of elements, numbers that can be expressed using a finite number of decimal places, curves that can be represented by a finite number of points, and other finite collections of elements. Finite sets have the property that their elements can be isolated, considered individually. No finite set is equivalent to one of its proper subsets.

The restriction to finite sets appears severe but actually provides the basis for such powerful tools as the representation of numbers for an electronic digital computer and the presentation of pictures on a television tube. At an elementary level finite mathematics includes all measurements. In general, the simplification of all mathematics to finite mathematics leaves us with a very powerful tool whose usefulness we shall explore.

Our explorations include sample spaces and counting in Chapter 2 followed by extensive use of sample spaces and applications of counting procedures in the study of probability (Chapter 3). Finite ordered sets of numbers serve as vectors and finite rectangular arrays of numbers serve as matrices in Chapter 4. Vectors and matrices have many applications and also serve very effectively as tools for the study of linear programming (Chapter 5) and game theory (Chapter 6). Each of these last two chapters is a very brief introduction to a relatively new area of mathematics that is widely used, especially with electronic computers to do the computations.

These explorations do *not* exhaust the scope of finite mathematics. Other topics could have been selected. The selection in this book has been designed to present an elementary and orderly sequence of topics that can be studied in a single semester. This sequence can be meaningfully terminated either with the linear programming (Chapter 5) or with the final chapter on game theory. The explorations of game theory depend upon some of the previous considerations of probability, vectors, matrices, and linear programming.

. . . .

REVIEW EXERCISES FOR CHAPTER 1

1. List the first five numbers greater than 1,000 that are in the set $\{0, 7, 14, 21, \ldots\}$.

2. Let $A = \{2, 3, 5, 7\}$ and $B = \{1, 3, 5, 7, 9\}$. Then find
   a) $A \cap B$,   b) $A \cup B$.

3. Make a truth table for the statement $p \rightarrow [q \lor (p \land \sim q)]$.

4. State the contrapositive of the statement:
   If the car is not a sedan, then the car is not mine.

5. State the denial of the statement:
   Some textbooks are not easy reading.

6. Consider the sets $\{m, a, p, l, e\}$ and $\{p, a, l, m, s\}$.
   a) Are the sets equal?   b) Are the sets equivalent?

7. Write in *if-then* form:
   a) $x = -1$ is sufficient for $x^2 = 1$.
   b) $x + 1 = 5$ only if $x = 4$.

8. Consider the statement $\{p, a, t\} \underline{\quad} \{t, a, p, e\}$ and insert the proper symbol:
   a) $\subseteq$ or $\subset$,   b) $=$ or $\neq$.

9. Show a one-to-one correspondence of the set $\{t, a, p, e\}$ and the set $\{t, r, a, p\}$.

10. List the subsets of $\{p, i, e\}$.

11. Identify the set $A = \{2, 3, 5, 7, 11, 13, 17, 19\}$ as finite or infinite. If the set is finite, find its cardinal number.

12. List the steps used to do Exercise 11 of these review exercises.

13. Prepare a flowchart for solving Exercise 11 of these review exercises.

14. Identify the use of each number as cardinal, ordinal, or for identification.

   a) Joan's room is on the *third* floor.

   b) John has already driven his car *6,000* miles.

15. Select the most precise measurement:

   27 inches,   2.2 feet,   0.8 yards.

16. Give the accuracy and the precision of the approximate number 2.735.

17. Add zeros as needed and use estimation to place the decimal point:

   $(4.9)^2$ ___ 2401.

18. Round off 0.2039 to the nearest hundredth.

19. Consider the given numbers as approximate numbers and find the sum

   $$\begin{array}{r} 752.6 \\ 25.37 \\ + \quad 4.001 \\ \hline \end{array}$$

20. Consider the given numbers as approximate numbers and find:

   a) 3.5 × 0.2;   b) 9.6 ÷ 2.

sample spaces and   2
counting

Finite sample spaces are a particular application of finite sets. Relations among finite sets in tree diagrams, Venn diagrams, and partitions of a set are considered. Ways of counting ordered sets (permutations) and also unordered sets (combinations) are discussed with their own applications and in preparation for the study of probability in Chapter 3.

2.1 SAMPLE SPACES

"Decisions, decisions, decisions" probably we have all heard exclamations of frustrations at the choices to be made. Sometimes in desperation, at other times for the "sport of it," we withdraw from making the decision. For example, we might flip a coin, roll a die, roll a pair of dice, or select a card from a deck of playing cards. The actual events among which a decision is to be made provide a sample space for that decision. Similarly, the set of all possible outcomes of an activity such as flipping a coin or rolling a pair of dice is a sample space for that activity. In general, the set of all possible outcomes for any situation is a **sample space**.

In many colleges students may elect either to take a course pass-fail or to be given a grade in the course. For this decision the sample space has two elements

{pass-fail, grade}.

If a student elects to take a course pass-fail, then the usual sample space for his status at the end of the course also has two elements

{pass, fail}.

If a student elects to receive a grade in a course, the usual sample space for his status at the end of the course has five elements

{A, B, C, D, F}.

Any specified subset of the set of possible outcomes is an **event**. In particular, each outcome may be considered as an event. Sample spaces are of special interest as we consider the likelihood (probability) of individual events. For example, the probability of heads when a fair coin is flipped is $\frac{1}{2}$. The sample space consists of two events: heads and tails. The qualification "fair" is used to imply that the two events are equally likely.

In any sample space of two events the relative probabilities are often stated as *odds*. For example, the odds for heads when a fair coin is flipped are 1 to 1; that is, 1 head to 1 tail (not head). Whenever odds are stated, the events should be *mutually exclusive* (they can not both occur) and also *exhaustive* (at least one must occur). A statement of odds of 1 to 1 for heads is a statement that the coin has one chance of heads for each chance of failing to be heads. That is, on the average (or in the long run) one out of two flips would be heads and one would be tails. In other words, the probability of heads is $\frac{1}{2}$ and the probability of tails is $\frac{1}{2}$.

Consider the rolling of a single unbiased die. The qualification "unbiased" is used in contrast to "loaded." If a die is unbiased, then each element of the sample space

{1, 2, 3, 4, 5, 6}

is as apt to occur as any other; that is, the events are equally likely. Unless otherwise specified all dice are hereafter assumed to be unbiased.

Suppose that a person rolls a die to get a 2. Success can occur in one way {2}. Failure can occur in five ways {1, 3, 4, 5, 6}. The odds for success are 1 to 5. The odds for failure are 5 to 1. The probability of success is $\frac{1}{6}$, one chance out of 6 equally likely chances. The probability of failure is $\frac{5}{6}$, five chances out of 6.

Suppose that a person rolls a die to get a number greater than 4. Success can occur in two ways {5, 6}. Failure can occur in four ways

{1, 2, 3, 4}. The probability of success is $\frac{2}{6}$, that is, $\frac{1}{3}$. The probability of failure is $\frac{4}{6}$, that is, $\frac{2}{3}$.

In any sample space of equally likely events the **probability** of an event A, written $P_r(A)$, is the ratio of the number of ways in which the event A can succeed (happen) to the total number of possibilities;

$$P_r(A) = \frac{\text{number of successes}}{\text{number of possibilities}} = \frac{s}{n}.$$

Notice that this definition requires that the possibilities be equally likely. For example, if the possibilities (events) are equally likely for the sample space

{pass, fail},

the probability of passing is $\frac{1}{2}$. If the possibilities (events) are equally likely for the sample space

{A, B, C, D, F},

the probability of passing with a grade of A, B, C, or D is $\frac{4}{5}$. There is also an assumption that any event A either occurs or does not occur. If $P_r(A) = \frac{4}{5}$ for passing, then $P_r(\tilde{A}) = \frac{1}{5}$ for not passing, that is, failing. If $P_r(B) = \frac{1}{6}$ for rolling a 2 with a single die, then $P_r(\tilde{B}) = \frac{5}{6}$ for not rolling a 2. These assumptions are expressed by the equations

$$P_r(A \cap \tilde{A}) = 0 \qquad (A \text{ and } \tilde{A} \text{ do not both occur})$$

$$P_r(A \cup \tilde{A}) = 1 \qquad (A \text{ or } \tilde{A} \text{ must occur})$$

$$P_r(\tilde{A}) = 1 - P_r(A) = 1 - \frac{s}{n} = \frac{n-s}{n}$$

The **odds** for an event is the ratio $s/(n-s)$ of the number of successes to the number of failures.

. . . .

Exercises

Identify the sample space for drawing one card from an ordinary deck of 52 cards in terms of:

1. The color of the card.
2. The suit of the card.

3. The number (or name) disregarding suit of the card.

Suppose that one unbiased coin is flipped:
    4. What are the odds for tails?
    5. What is the probability of tails?

Suppose that one card is drawn from an ordinary deck of 52 cards. What are the odds for obtaining:
    6. a) A black card?   b) a diamond?
    7. a) The ace of spades?   b) a king?

If one card is drawn from an ordinary deck of 52 cards, what is the probability of obtaining:
    8. a) A black card?   b) a diamond?
    9. a) The ace of spades?   b) a king?
  10. a) A face card (jack, queen, or king)?
       b) a card that is not a face card?

Study the following sample space for flipping a penny (heads H_p, tails T_p) and a dime (heads H_d, tails T_d):
$$\{H_pH_d, \qquad H_pT_d, \qquad T_pH_d, \qquad T_pT_d\}.$$
  11. What is the sample space for flipping the penny:
      a) by itself?
      b) with the dime if the dime is heads?
      c) with the dime if the dime is tails?
  12. What is the sample space for flipping the dime:
      a) by itself?
      b) with the penny if the penny is heads?
      c) with the penny if the penny is tails?
  13. What is the cardinal number of the sample space for flipping:
      a) the penny?   b) the dime?   c) the penny and the dime?
  14. Suppose that the two coins are flipped:
      a) How many equally likely possibilities (outcomes, events) can occur?
      b) What is the probability of each of these outcomes?
      c) What is the probability that the coins will match (both heads or both tails)?
      d) What is the probability of at least one head?
      e) What is the probability of exactly one tail?

Suppose that a coin is flipped and a die is rolled.
15. What is the sample space for the die:
     a) by itself ?
     b) with the coin if the coin is heads?
     c) with the coin if the coin is tails?
16. What is the sample space for the coin:
     a) by itself ?
     b) with the die if the die is 3?
     c) with the die if the die is 5?
17. What is the sample space for the coin and the die?
18. What is the cardinal number of the sample space for:
     a) the coin?   b) the die?   c) the coin and the die?
Consider a red die with a sample space $\{R_1, R_2, R_3, R_4, R_5, R_6\}$ and a green die with a sample space $\{G_1, G_2, G_3, G_4, G_5, G_6\}$.
19. What is the sample space for rolling the two dice?
20. What is the probability of:
     a) R_1G_1?   b) R_6G_6?
     c) R_2R_3?   d) R_aG_b, where $a + b = 3$?
     e) R_aG_b, where $a + b = 7$?   f) R_aG_b, where $a + b = 11$?
21. What is the cardinal number of the sample space when:
     a) two dice are rolled?   b) three dice are rolled?
     c) three coins are flipped?   d) four coins are flipped?
     e) n coins are flipped?

. . . .

2.2 TREE DIAGRAMS

The possible outcomes when two coins are flipped may be found by
following the branches of the diagram in Fig. 2.1. The outcomes from
rolling a die and flipping a coin may be found using the branches of the

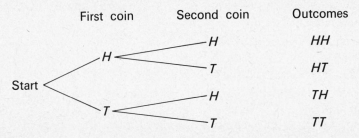

Fig. 2.1

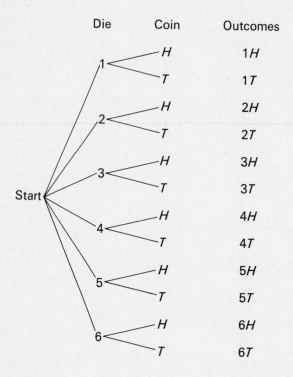

Die	Coin	Outcomes

Fig. 2.2

diagram in Fig. 2.2. The outcomes are listed beside each of the diagrams to show how the diagram may be used to obtain the elements of each sample space. The diagrams are called **tree diagrams**. They provide a very useful tool for displaying the possibilities (outcomes) for an event or an experiment.

The **Cartesian product** $A \times B$ (read as "A cross B") of two sets A and B is the set of all possible ordered pairs (a, b) of elements such that $a \in A$ and $b \in B$. For example, if $A = \{1, 2, 3\}$ and $B = \{s, t\}$, then

$$A \times B = \{(1, s), (1, t), (2, s), (2, t), (3, s), (3, t)\}.$$

These elements of the Cartesian product $A \times B$ may be obtained as outcomes using a tree diagram (Fig. 2.3) with a column for A and a column for B.

Now look again at the first tree diagram in this section. The sample space for flipping two coins may be considered in the form

$$\{(H, H), (H, T), (T, H), (T, T)\}$$

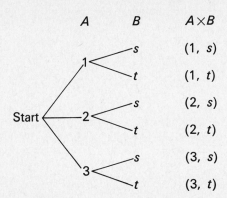

Fig. 2.3

and thus as $\{H, T\} \times \{H, T\}$. Similarly, from the second tree diagram the sample space for rolling a die and flipping a coin may be considered in the form $\{1, 2, 3, 4, 5, 6\} \times \{H, T\}$. In each of these cases, a sample space for the two events may be obtained by taking a Cartesian product of the sample spaces of the individual events. In such cases, the sample spaces for the separate events form a **basis** for the sample space of the two events.

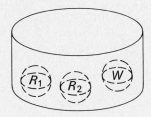

Fig. 2.4

Next consider a bowl that contains two red balls (R_1 and R_2) and one white ball W as shown in Fig. 2.4. The sample space for selecting one ball from the bowl is

$$\{R_1, R_2, W\}.$$

The experiment of selecting one ball, replacing the ball in the bowl, and selecting a second ball may be described as selecting two balls *with replacement*. See Fig. 2.5. The first event E_1 is the selection of the first ball and has sample space

$$S_1 = \{R_1, R_2, W\}.$$

The second event E_2 is the selection of the second ball and occurs after

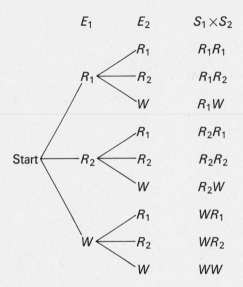

$$E_1 \qquad E_2 \qquad S_1 \times S_2$$

Fig. 2.5

the ball selected for E_1 has been replaced. Then the sample space for E_2 is

$$S_2 = \{R_1, R_2, W\}.$$

The sample space for the two events is $S_1 \times S_2$, the Cartesian product of S_1 and S_2 as in Fig. 2.5.

The Cartesian product of the sample spaces for the individual events in the selection of two balls with replacement provides a sample space for the experiment consisting of the two events. This result depends upon the fact that the first ball was replaced before the second ball was drawn.

Let the first event E_1 of an experiment be the selection of one ball from a bowl that contains three balls R_1, R_2, and W. Let the second event E_2 be the selection of a second ball *without replacing* the ball that was selected in the first event. Then E_1 has sample space $S_1 = \{R_1, R_2, W\}$ as before but the possibilities for E_2 depend upon the outcome of E_1. The sample space for the selection of two balls without replacement may be obtained from the tree diagram in Fig. 2.6.

The sample space for the experiment of selecting two balls without replacement is

$$\{R_1R_2, R_1W, R_2R_1, R_2W, WR_1, WR_2\}.$$

Note that this experiment for selecting two elements from a bowl

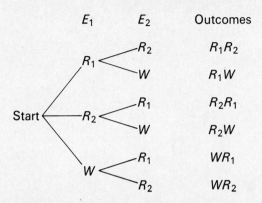

Fig. 2.6

without replacement has a sample space with 6 elements. The experiment for selecting two balls with replacement has a sample space with 9 elements. The sample spaces of the separate events E_1 and E_2 in the selection of two balls with replacement each have 3 elements and the Cartesian product of these two sample spaces has 9 elements.

In the selection of two balls without replacement no ball could be selected twice and thus R_1R_1, R_2R_2, and WW do not occur. The fact that the sample space for the two events is not the same as the Cartesian product of the sample spaces of the individual events with replacement indicates that the outcome of the second event *depends* upon the outcome of the first event. In other words, the events are **dependent events**. Two events are **independent events** if they are not dependent events, that is, if the Cartesian product of the sample spaces of the individual events with replacement may be used as a sample space for the two events.

. . . .

Exercises

In Exercises 1 through 16 use a tree diagram to obtain a sample space for each experiment.

1. A penny is flipped $\{H_p, T_p\}$ and a dime is flipped $\{H_d, T_d\}$.
2. A penny is flipped, a dime is flipped, and a quarter is flipped.
3. A penny is flipped. If the penny comes up heads, a dime is flipped. If the penny comes up tails, the experiment ends.
4. A penny is flipped. If the penny comes up heads, a dime is flipped. If the penny comes up tails, a die is rolled.
5. A coin is flipped again and again until either heads or tails has occurred twice.

6. Three coins are flipped or one coin is flipped three times.

7. A manufacturer of toy automobiles makes toys in three styles (convertible, sedan, station wagon) and each style is available in each of four colors (red, blue, buff, and black). Make a tree diagram with columns for style and color. Then list the possible outcomes. Notice that a complete set of the outcomes is a complete set of samples of the toys manufactured.

8. Merchants are particularly concerned with the number of items that must be stocked in order to provide customers with a complete selection.

   a) Use a tree diagram to obtain a list of the items that need to be stocked (outcomes) if a certain style of ladies' snow boot is available in sizes 5 through 10, black only, medium width only.

   b) How many pairs of boots are needed for just one complete set?

9. Find the number of items (use a tree diagram if necessary) needed for a complete set of the following:

   a) Ladies' ski boots sizes 5 through 10, whole and half-sizes $(5, 5\frac{1}{2}, 6, 6\frac{1}{2}, \ldots, 10, 10\frac{1}{2})$, medium width only, color mocha.

   b) Men's gloves sizes small, medium, large, extra large; colors tan or black.

   c) Men's shirts in three color patterns (blue and white, green and white, red and white) and sizes small, medium, large, and extra large.

   d) Scottish plaid shirts in four sizes (small, medium, large, extra large) and four tartans (Cluny, Beatrice, Black Watch, and Dress Campbell).

   e) Men's ski boots sizes 7 through $12\frac{1}{2}$, whole and half-sizes, medium width only, colors black or brown.

10. Students may take the laboratory for a certain chemistry course at 8, 10, 12, or 2 o'clock on Tuesday or Thursday or at 8 or 10 on Saturday. Use a tree diagram with columns for days and hours to obtain a sample space for the availability of the laboratory.

All subsets of the set $\{a, b\}$ may be obtained using a tree diagram as follows:

	a	b	Outcomes	Subsets
		{ }	{ }∪{ }	{ }
	{ }	{b}	{ }∪{b}	{b}
Start		{ }	{a}∪{ }	{a}
	{a}	{b}	{a}∪{b}	{a, b}

Use a tree diagram to find the subsets of:

11. $\{p, q\}$.

12. $\{a, b, c\}$.

Probabilities may be noted on each branch of a tree diagram and multiplied to find the probability of each outcome. For the flipping of two coins we have:

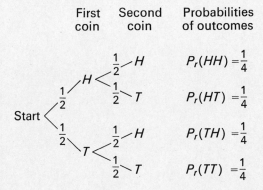

	First coin	Second coin	Probabilities of outcomes
		H	$P_r(HH) = \frac{1}{4}$
	H	T	$P_r(HT) = \frac{1}{4}$
Start		H	$P_r(TH) = \frac{1}{4}$
	T	T	$P_r(TT) = \frac{1}{4}$

Use a tree diagram to find the probability of each outcome when:

13. A coin is flipped and a die is rolled.

14. Three coins are flipped.

A tree diagram may be used to show all possible pairs of truth values for two statements p and q:

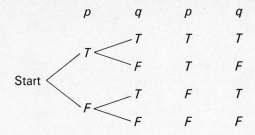

Use a tree diagram to identify all possible:

15. Triples of truth values for three statements p, q, r.

16. Quadruples of truth values for four statements p, q, r, s.

. . . .

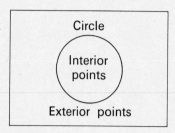

Fig. 2.7

2.3 VENN DIAGRAMS

Any triangle, circle, square, or other simple closed plane curve is the common boundary of its set of *interior points* and its set of *exterior points* (Fig. 2.7). The points of the curve are neither interior points nor exterior points. The union of a triangle and its interior points is a **triangular region**. The union of a circle and its interior points is a **circular region**. See Fig. 2.8.

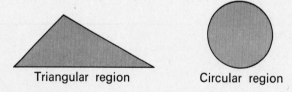

Triangular region   Circular region

Fig. 2.8

Consider a circular region. Every point of the plane is either a point of the circular region or an exterior point of the circle. These two sets of points are mutually exclusive and exhaustive relative to the plane. These sets of points may be used to represent events that either occur or do not occur. For example, we assume that when a coin is flipped the outcome is either heads or not heads (namely, tails). The flipping of a single coin may be represented by the diagram in Fig. 2.9.

Each point of the circular region represents an instance of heads. Each exterior point of the circular region represents an instance of tails. Note that *all* possibilities are represented on the diagram. Such diagrams are called **Venn diagrams**. Venn diagrams may, as we shall see in the exercises, be used for one, two, three, or more independent events that

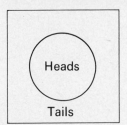

Fig. 2.9

either occur or do not occur. In each case, there must be regions for all possible outcomes. The truth of a given statement may be considered as an event.

Venn diagrams are often described in terms of sets of points or other elements. The set of all elements under discussion at any time is often called the **universal set** r for that discussion. For example, the set of all possible outcomes is the universal set for a sample space. The region, usually rectangular, in which a Venn diagram is drawn is the universal set for that diagram. If a single circular region P is used in the Venn diagram (Fig. 2.10), then the points of r that are not points of P are the exterior points of P and form the set $\tilde{P}$, the **complement** of P with respect to r. The circular boundary of $\tilde{P}$ is dashed to show that the points of the circle are not points of $\tilde{P}$.

Fig. 2.10

Any region P has these two properties:

$$P \cup \tilde{P} = r, \qquad P \cap \tilde{P} = \varnothing.$$

The corresponding properties of statements are these:

$P \vee \tilde{P}$ is always true,
$P \wedge \tilde{P}$ is never true.

The corresponding properties of events are these:

$$P_r \,(E \text{ or not } E) \,=\, 1,$$
$$P_r \,(E \text{ and not } E) \,=\, 0.$$

. . . .

Exercises

1. Any open sentence p is assumed to be either true T or false F. Draw a Venn diagram with a single circular region. Label the circular region p to indicate that the points of this region represent circumstances in which p is true. Label the set of exterior points $\sim p$ to indicate that these points represent circumstances in which p is false.

2. Consider the set of numbers $r = \{-3, -2, -1, 0, 1, 2, 3\}$. Copy the diagram for Exercise 1 and write the numerals for the elements of r in the proper regions if p is the statement $x \leq 0$.

3. Repeat Exercise 2 for the statement $x^2 < 4$.

4. The given diagram may be used as a Venn diagram with two circular regions P and Q. Copy the diagram and label the four regions $P \cap Q, P \cap \tilde{Q}, Q \cap \tilde{P}, \tilde{P} \cap \tilde{Q}$.

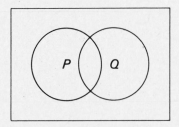

5. The Venn diagram for Exercise 4 may be used to show the truth values of statements p and q. Let the points of the region P represent the instances in which p is true; let the points of Q represent the instances in which q is true.

   a) Copy the diagram and label each region with an ordered pair of truth values for p and q; that is, use TT, TF, FT, FF from the truth tables for p and q.

   b) Copy the diagram and label each region with one of the following statements that is true for the instances represented by the points of that region, $p \wedge q, p \wedge \sim q, (\sim p) \wedge q, (\sim p) \wedge \sim q$.

Copy the Venn diagram for Exercise 4 and shade the region(s) representing instances in which the given statement is true:

6. a) $\sim p$;   b) $p \vee q$.

7. a) $p \vee \sim q$;   b) $(\sim p) \vee \sim q$.

Copy the Venn diagram for Exercise 4, represent each of the given statements on a Venn diagram, and observe the *tautology* (same regions shaded) that indicates that the statements are equivalent:

8. $p \rightarrow q$; $(\sim p) \vee q$.

9. $p \rightarrow q$; $(\sim q) \rightarrow \sim p$. (*Note:* Exercise 9 shows the equivalence of a statement of implication and its contrapositive.)

10. $(\sim p) \rightarrow \sim q$; $q \rightarrow p$. (*Note:* Exercise 10 shows the equivalence of the inverse and the converse of a statement of implication.)

11. $(\sim p) \wedge \sim q$; $\sim(p \vee q)$.

12. $(\sim p) \vee \sim q$; $\sim(p \wedge q)$. (*Note:* The equivalence of the statements in Exercise 11 and the equivalence of the statements in Exercise 12 are **de Morgan's laws for statements.**)

Copy the Venn diagram for Exercise 4, shade a diagram for each member of the equation, and note their equivalence (**de Morgan's laws for sets of points**):

13. $\tilde{P} \cap \tilde{Q} = (\widetilde{P \cup Q})$.

14. $\tilde{P} \cup \tilde{Q} = (\widetilde{P \cap Q})$.

The given diagram may be used as a Venn diagram with three circular regions P, Q, and R. These regions determine eight regions.

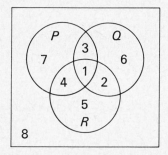

15. Identify each of the eight regions by its number and as an intersection of three of the sets P, Q, R, $\tilde{P}$, $\tilde{Q}$, $\tilde{R}$.

16. Let the points of the region P represent the instances in which the statement p is true. Similarly, let Q and R represent the instances of the truth of statements q and r. Then identify each of the eight regions by its number and by an ordered triple of truth values for the statements p, q, and r corresponding to the instances represented by the points of the region.

With reference to the Venn diagram for Exercises 15 and 16 list the number(s) of the region(s) representing instances in which the given statement is true:

17. $p \wedge (q \vee r)$.
18. $(p \wedge q) \vee r$.
19. $p \to (q \vee r)$.
20. $(\sim p) \vee (q \to r)$.

The region S intersects each of the eight regions of the Venn diagram for Exercises 15 and 16. The new Venn diagram has sixteen regions as numbered on the figure.

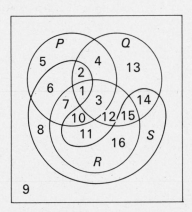

21. Identify each region by its number and as an intersection of four of the sets P, Q, R, S, $\tilde{P}$, $\tilde{Q}$, $\tilde{R}$, $\tilde{S}$.
22. List the number(s) of the region(s) representing instances in which the given statement is true:

   a) $p \wedge q$;   b) $(q \wedge r) \wedge s$;
   c) $(p \vee q) \wedge (r \vee s)$;   d) $(p \wedge q) \vee (r \wedge s)$.

23. Make a flowchart for making a Venn diagram with:

   a) one circular region;   b) two circular regions;
   c) three circular regions.

2.4 PARTITIONS

Two sets A and B are **disjoint sets** if $A \cap B = \emptyset$. Any subdivision of a given set C into disjoint subsets A and B such that $A \cup B = C$ is a *partition* of the set C. For example, A and $\tilde{A}$ form a partition of the universal set $\mathscr{r}$ for any set A. The set S_1 of even integers and the set S_2 of odd integers form a partition of the set W of integers.

A partition of a set may involve more than two subsets. For example, the set of integers may be partitioned according to the remainder when the number is divided by 6:

$$T_1 = \{\dots, -18, -12, -6, 0, \; 6, 12, 18, \dots\},$$
$$T_2 = \{\dots, -17, -11, -5, 1, \; 7, 13, 19, \dots\},$$
$$T_3 = \{\dots, -16, -10, -4, 2, \; 8, 14, 20, \dots\},$$
$$T_4 = \{\dots, -15, \;\; -9, -3, 3, \; 9, 15, 21, \dots\},$$
$$T_5 = \{\dots, -14, \;\; -8, -2, 4, 10, 16, 22, \dots\},$$
$$T_6 = \{\dots, -13, \;\; -7, -1, 5, 11, 17, 23, \dots\}.$$

In general, a collection of subsets $S_1, S_2, S_3, \dots, S_n$ of a set $\mathscr{r}$ forms a **partition** of $\mathscr{r}$ if

$$S_i \cap S_j = \emptyset \quad \text{for} \quad 0 \leq i < j \leq n,$$

and

$$S_1 \cup S_2 \cup S_3 \cup \cdots \cup S_n = \mathscr{r};$$

that is, if the subsets S_i are disjoint and exhaustive. The subsets in a partition are often called the **cells** of the partition. Note that a partition of a sample space into nonempty subsets corresponds to mutually exclusive and independent events (Section 2.1).

Two partitions $\{S_1, S_2\}$ and $\{T_1, T_2, T_3, T_4, T_5, T_6\}$ have just been considered for the set W of integers. Note that

$$S_1 = T_1 \cup T_3 \cup T_5 \quad \text{and} \quad S_2 = T_2 \cup T_4 \cup T_6.$$

Since each T_i is a subset of an S_j, the partition $\{T_1, T_2, T_3, T_4, T_5, T_6\}$ is called a *refinement* of the partition $\{S_1, S_2\}$.

We next form another partition of W. Let

$$R_1 = \{\dots, -9, -6, -3, 0, 3, 6, \; 9, \dots\},$$
$$R_2 = \{\dots, -8, -5, -2, 1, 4, 7, 10, \dots\},$$
$$R_3 = \{\dots, -7, -4, -1, 2, 5, 8, 11, \dots\}.$$

Since $R_1 \cup R_2 \cup R_3 = W$ and $R_i \cap R_j = \emptyset$ for $1 \leq i < j \leq 3$, the set $\{R_1, R_2, R_3\}$ is a partition of W. Since

$$R_1 = T_1 \cup T_4, \qquad R_2 = T_2 \cup T_5, \quad \text{and} \quad R_3 = T_3 \cup T_6,$$

the partition $\{T_1, T_2, T_3, T_4, T_5, T_6\}$ is a refinement of the partition $\{R_1, R_2, R_3\}$.

There is also a relationship among the three partitions $\{S_1, S_2\}$, $\{R_1, R_2, R_3\}$, and $\{T_1, T_2, T_3, T_4, T_5, T_6\}$. Basically each T_i may be expressed in the form $S_i \cap R_k$, and each such intersection is one of the sets T_j. In particular, we have

$$\begin{array}{ll}
S_1 \cap R_1 = T_1, & S_2 \cap R_1 = T_4, \\
S_1 \cap R_2 = T_5, & S_2 \cap R_2 = T_2, \\
S_1 \cap R_3 = T_3, & S_2 \cap R_3 = T_6.
\end{array}$$

Possibly in recognition of the ordered pairs as in a Cartesian product, the partition $\{T_1, T_2, T_3, T_4, T_5, T_6\}$ is called the **cross partition** of the partitions $\{S_1, S_2\}$ and $\{R_1, R_2, R_3\}$.

Several applications of partitions are considered in the exercises. Other applications will arise throughout this book.

· ·

Exercises

1. Consider the sample space $S = \{HH, HT, TH, TT\}$ for flipping two coins.

   a) Is $\{S_1, S_2\}$ a partition of S, where $S_1 = \{HH, TT\}$ and $S_2 = \{HT, TH\}$?

   b) Describe an event E that has S_1 as its sample space.

2. Indicate whether or not each set of subsets is a partition of a universal set $\mathscr{r}$:

   a) $\{P, \tilde{P}\}$;   b) $\{P \cap Q, \tilde{P}, \tilde{Q}\}$;

   c) $\{P \cap Q, \tilde{P} \cap Q, P \cap \tilde{Q}, \tilde{P} \cap \tilde{Q}\}$.

3. Form a cross partition of the partitions:

   a) $\{P, \tilde{P}\}$ and $\{Q, \tilde{Q}\}$;

   b) $\{P \cap Q, P \cap \tilde{Q}, \tilde{P} \cap Q, \tilde{P} \cap \tilde{Q}\}$ and $\{R, \tilde{R}\}$.

4. Consider the partition into four cells in the figure at the top of page 55. The cardinal number of each cell is given. Find:

   a) $n(A \cap \cup B)$;   b) $n(A)$;   c) $n(B)$;

   d) $n(A \cup B)$;   e) $n(\tilde{A})$;   f) $n(\mathscr{r})$.

   g) Does $n(A) + n(\tilde{A}) = n(\mathscr{r})$?

   h) Does $n(A \cup B) = n(A) + n(B)$?

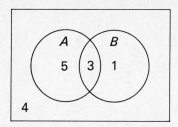

5. Repeat Exercise 4 for the next given figure.

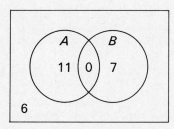

6. For any set A we assume that $n(A) \geq 0$ and recognize that $n(A) + n(\tilde{A}) = n(\nu)$ since each element of ν belongs to exactly one of the sets A, $\tilde{A}$. Explain why it appears reasonable to assume that:

a) if $A \cap B = \varnothing$, then $n(A) + n(B) = n(A \cup B)$,

b) for any sets $A, B, n(A) + n(B) = n(A \cup B) + n(A \cap B)$,

c) if $\{S_1, S_2, \ldots, S_k\}$ is any partition of ν, then

$$n(S_1) + n(S_2) + n(S_3) + \cdots + n(S_k) = n(\nu).$$

7. The cardinal number of a partitioned set can be found if the cardinal number of each cell is known. For example, a penny and a dime were flipped together many times. The results, as shown in the Venn diagram at the top of page 56, were as follows:

Penny	Dime	Number of occurrences
heads	heads	40
heads	tails	32
tails	heads	23
tails	tails	25

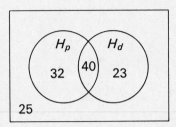

How many times were the two coins flipped?

8. If the cardinal number of a partitioned set is known and the cardinal number of all but one cell is known, then the cardinal numbers of the remaining cell may be found. For example, among 250 girls at Lane High School 5 girls play both hockey and softball, 20 play hockey but not softball, and 35 play softball but not hockey.
   a) Draw a Venn diagram and note that $n(\nu) = 250$.
   b) Determine how many of the girls play neither softball nor hockey.

9. At George's school 130 boys went out for football or baseball, 50 went out for football, and 90 went out for baseball. Consider the Venn diagram with a region F for the set of boys who went out for football and a region B for the set of boys who went out for baseball. Note that $n(F \cup B) = 130$, $n(F) = 50$, and $n(B) = 90$. How many boys went out for both football and baseball?

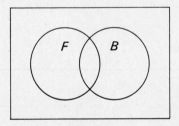

10. Assume that all members of this class will either pass or fail. Then the set P of those who pass and the set $\tilde{P}$ of those who fail is a partition of the class. Similarly, the members of the class may be partitioned as girls G and boys $\tilde{G}$.
    a) Draw a Venn diagram and label the cells of the cross partition.
    b) If there are 45 members of the class and 29 of these are girls, how many are boys?
    c) If also only 13 boys pass, how many of the boys fail?

d) If also only 41 members of the class pass, how many of the girls pass?

e) Copy the Venn diagram from part (a) and label each cell with its cardinal number.

11. A survey of 150 people revealed that 70 bought regular gasoline and 52 bought premium.

a) Draw a Venn diagram letting R be the set of people who bought regular gasoline and P be the set of people who bought premium gasoline. If 5 people bought both kinds, label each cell of the Venn diagram with its cardinal number.

b) How many people did not buy any gasoline?

12. At John's school there are 175 students with 115 students studying mathematics, 40 studying mathematics and physics, and 55 studying neither mathematics nor physics.

a) Draw a Venn diagram.

b) How many students are studying physics but not mathematics?

13. Partitions may be used for more than two sets. Consider the sets of students taking French, German, and Spanish at a certain school. In the given Venn diagram each cell is labeled with its cardinal number. How many students are taking:

a) French?   b) German?
c) French and German?   d) French or German?
e) French or Spanish?   f) Spanish but not German?

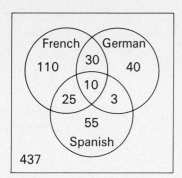

14. At Bob's school there are 205 students.

a) Represent the following data on a Venn diagram: 5 students are studying mathematics, physics, and chemistry; 26 are studying mathematics and chemistry (note that 5 of these are studying all three subjects); 45 are studying mathematics and physics (note that this means that 40 are studying mathematics and physics but not chemistry); no one is studying physics and chemistry but not mathematics; 52 are studying physics (we know that 5 are studying all three subjects, 40 mathematics and physics but not chemistry, and 0 physics and chemistry without mathematics; thus 7 are studying physics but neither mathematics nor chemistry); 30 are studying chemistry; and 96 are not studying any of the three subjects.

b) How many are studying mathematics but neither physics nor chemistry?

15. As in Exercise 14 it is easiest to start with the intersections of the sets in labeling each cell with its cardinal number.

a) Draw a Venn diagram for the following data and label each cell with its cardinal number: A survey of student preferences among the soft drinks orange, grape, and ginger ale at one college indicated that 225 bought orange, 150 bought grape, 300 bought ginger ale, 125 bought orange and ginger ale, 90 bought grape and ginger ale, 35 bought orange and grape, and 20 bought all three flavors.

b) How many of the students surveyed bought at least one of the soft drinks?

Partitions are often used to indicate whether or not the data from a survey is consistent. At times it is possible to determine whether a person who was supposed to make a survey actually did the work or simply submitted some figures.

16. As in Exercise 15 one thousand students are surveyed, 450 bought orange, 300 bought grape, 250 bought ginger ale, 50 didn't buy any of the soft drinks, 10 bought all three, 40 bought orange and ginger ale, 30 bought orange and grape, and 20 bought grape and ginger ale. Is this data consistent?

17. Don reported that he flipped three coins (a penny, a nickel, and a dime) one hundred times. All three coins had heads 18 times, the penny and the nickel both had heads 30 times, the penny and the dime both had heads 25 times, the nickel and the dime both had heads 27 times, the penny had heads 55 times, the nickel had heads 52 times, the dime had heads 47 times, and all three had tails 10 times. Is this data consistent?

18. A young stock broker was asked to use the following procedure for reporting on his success in predicting changes in prices of various stocks. Fifty common stocks with which he had been working were selected. Three intervals of time A, B, and C were selected. Over each interval of time he was to look up in his records

the predictions that he had made for the price increase (or not increase, possibly decrease) for each stock and compare his prediction with what actually happened. The young broker reported that his predictions had been correct for all three time intervals on 10 stocks, for A and B on 25 stocks, for A and C on 18 stocks, for B and C on 32 stocks, and for at least two of the three time intervals for each of the selected stocks. Is his data consistent?

....

2.5 PERMUTATIONS OF DISTINCT ELEMENTS

A list (arrangement, ordering) of n elements, each element being included exactly once, is a **permutation** of these n elements. Unless otherwise specified the permutation is assumed to be along a straight line (a linear ordering). To find a permutation of n elements we select a first element, then select a second element, and so forth. A tree diagram may be used to show all possible permutations.

For two elements $\{a, b\}$ the first element may be selected in two ways, the second element is the remaining element, and there are two permutations. See Fig. 2.11.

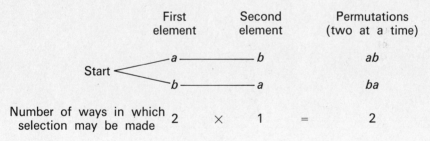

Fig. 2.11

For three elements $\{a, b, c\}$ the first element may be selected in three ways, the second element may be selected in two ways, the third element is the remaining element, and there are six permutations. See Fig. 2.12.

For a given set of four distinct elements the first element can be selected in four ways. For each of these selections the second element can be selected in three ways. For each of these selections the third element can be selected in two ways. For each of these selections the fourth element can be selected in only one way; it is the remaining

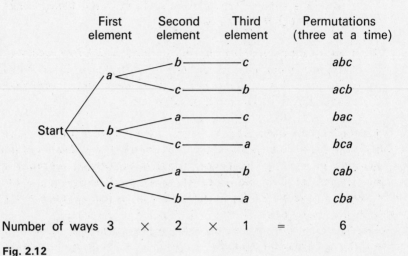

First element	Second element	Third element	Permutations (three at a time)
	b — *c*		*abc*
a	*c* — *b*		*acb*
	a — *c*		*bac*
Start — *b*	*c* — *a*		*bca*
	a — *b*		*cab*
c	*b* — *a*		*cba*

Number of ways 3 × 2 × 1 = 6

Fig. 2.12

element. Thus there are twenty-four permutations of four distinct elements;

$$4 \times 3 \times 2 \times 1 = 24.$$

In general, for a given set of *n* distinct elements the number of permutations is given by a product of the form

$$n \times (n - 1) \times (n - 2) \times (n - 3) \times \cdots \times 2 \times 1.$$

Such products occur so frequently that a special symbol *n*! (read as "*n* **factorial**") is used;

$$n! = n(n - 1)(n - 2)(n - 3) \cdots 2 \times 1.$$

Thus as from a tree diagram *there are n! permutations of n distinct elements.* This property is extended to the empty set by *defining* $0! = 1$.

The procedure used for counting the number of permutations of *n* distinct elements is a special case of the following **counting principles:**

1) If one event can occur in n_1 ways and for each of these outcomes a second event can occur in n_2 ways, then the two events can occur in $n_1 n_2$ ways.

2) If one event can occur in n_1 ways, for each of these outcomes a second event can occur in n_2 ways, for each of these outcomes a third event can occur in n_3 ways, and so forth, then a sequence of k events can occur in $n_1 n_2 n_3 \ldots n_k$ ways.

For any set of n distinct elements for any whole number $r \leq n$ the counting principles may be used to find the number of ordered subsets of r elements each, that is, the number of **permutations of n elements taken r at a time**. Consider the set of vowels $V = \{a, e, i, o, u\}$. The set of ordered pairs of distinct vowels is the set of permutations of the elements of V taken two at a time. See Fig. 2.13.

The selection of the r elements of any permutation of n elements taken r at a time may be made in $n(n - 1)(n - 2) \ldots (n - r + 1)$ ways as shown in the array:

Elements:	First	Second	Third	. . .	rth
Ways:	$n \times$	$(n - 1) \times$	$(n - 2)$	. . .	$(n - r + 1)$

This product represents $_nP_r$, the number of **permutations of n elements taken r at a time**. Note that

$$_nP_r \times (n - r)! = n!,$$

and thus

$$_nP_r = \frac{n!}{(n - r)!}.$$

The counting principle may also be used for permutations that are not along a straight line. Consider the permutations of n people around a round table as in Fig. 2.14. In each case it is helpful to seat one person, A, as a reference person and to consider the other people counter-clockwise (or clockwise) from this reference person. In general, for permutations of n people around a table, one person is seated as a reference person, there are $n - 1$ ways to seat the person on his right, $n - 2$ ways to seat the next person, and so forth. Thus

there are $(n - 1)!$ permutations of n people around a round table.

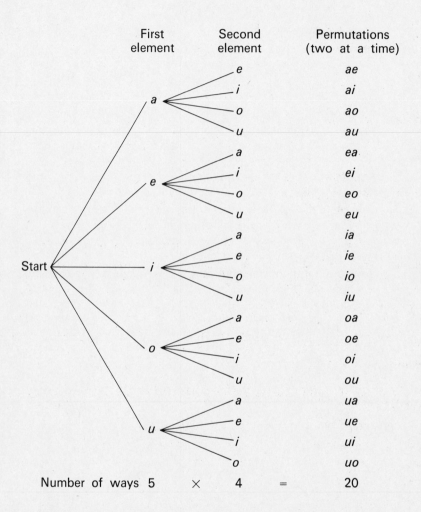

Fig. 2.13

The previous example has been specifically stated for people around a round table since the situation is different for keys on a circular key ring. The key ring may be turned over. For $n \geq 3$ turning over the key ring makes different (clockwise versus counter-clockwise) arrangements of people around the table correspond to the same arrangement of keys on a key ring. Thus

for $n \geq 3$ there are $\dfrac{(n-1)!}{2}$ permutations of n distinct keys on a circular key ring.

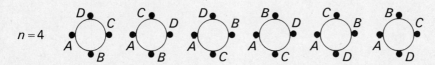

Fig. 2.14

. . . .

Exercises

Make a tree diagram and list the permutations of the elements of the set $\{a, b, c, d\}$:

1. One at a time.
2. Two at a time.
3. Three at a time.
4. Four at a time.

Find:

5. a) $3!$;   b) $4!$.
6. a) $6!$;   b) $10!$.

Write out the factors and simplify:

7. a) $\dfrac{6!}{4!}$;   b) $\dfrac{10!}{9!}$.

8. a) $\dfrac{9!}{5!\,4!}$;   b) $\dfrac{10!}{7!\,3!}$.

Find:

9. a) $\dfrac{25!}{24!}$;   b) $\dfrac{52!}{50!\,2!}$.

10. a) $\dfrac{52!}{49!\,3!}$;   b) $\dfrac{52!}{40!\,12!}$.

In Exercises 11 and 12 write as a quotient of factorials:

11. a) 6×5;   b) $10 \times 9 \times 8$.
12. a) 52×51;   b) $52 \times 51 \times 50 \times 49$.
13. Assume that there are three good routes for driving from Boston to New York. In how many ways can one drive one of these routes from Boston to New York and return by a different one of these routes.
14. In how many ways can four people be arranged to have a picture taken
    a) if they line up in a row?
    b) if one is seated and the others stand in back?
15. Repeat Exercise 14 for five people.
16. Each statement on a certain quiz is to be designated as true or false. In how many ways can the entire quiz be answered if there are
    a) three statements?
    b) five statements?
    c) ten statements?

In Exercises 17 and 18 find the number of permutations of:

17. a) Six people around a round table,
    b) six keys on a key ring.
18. a) Ten people around a round table,
    b) ten keys on a key ring.
19. A seminar room has 12 chairs. In how many ways can seats be selected if there are
    a) 3 people in the seminar?   b) 7 people in the seminar?
20. Six people are ready to play tennis. If the first person named in each pair is to serve first, in how many ways can the pairs of people to play together be named?
21. A committee of three is to be selected from a group of ten people. The first named person is to be chairman and the second named person recorder for the committee discussions. How many such committees can be named?
22. Forty runners enter a race for which the first place winner, second, third, and fourth places are recognized. How many such sets of winners are theoretically possible?
23. Two hundred students entered a contest for which the top ten contestants would be reported by rank. Express the possible number of such outcomes (excluding ties) of the contest as a product of integers. Do not simplify.

. . . .

2.6 COUNTING

The counting principle (Section 2.5) can be used in a wide variety of circumstances. For example, suppose a state with a small population decided to make each car license plate consist of a letter from our alphabet followed by a four-digit decimal numeral in which repeated digits are allowed. The letter could be selected in 26 ways and each of the four digits could be selected in 10 ways. The number of possible car license plates would be $26 \times 10 \times 10 \times 10 \times 10$, that is, 260,000.

Another counting situation arises when we seek the number of subsets of r elements, without regard to the order of the r elements that can be obtained from a set of n distinct elements, that is, the number $_nC_r$ of **combinations of n elements taken r at a time.** For example, there are 6 permutations of the elements of the set $\{a, b, c\}$ taken two at a time. For any given ordered pair ab there is one other ordered pair ba that consists of the same elements; $\{a, b\} = \{b, a\}$. Thus the 6 permutations consist of 3 pairs of permutations with the same elements. In other words,

$$_3C_2 = \frac{_3P_2}{_2P_2} = \frac{6}{2} = 3.$$

A tennis club has 25 members. In how many ways can pairs be selected for a game of tennis? The number $_{25}C_2$ is sought. We know that $_{25}P_2 = 25 \times 24$ and for any two members $_2P_2 = 2$. For example selecting Ruth and Doris to play results in the same game as selecting Doris and Ruth to play. Then

$$_{25}C_2 = \frac{_{25}P_2}{_2P_2} = \frac{25 \times 24}{2 \times 1} = 25 \times 12 = 300.$$

A permutation of n elements taken r at a time is an *ordered subset* of r elements. A combination of n elements taken r at a time is a subset (no order implied) of r elements. The elements of any set of r elements may be order in $_rP_r$ ways. Therefore

$$_nC_r = \frac{_nP_r}{_rP_r} = \frac{n(n-1)(n-2)\cdots(n-r+1)}{r(r-1)(r-2)\cdots 1}.$$

If we multiply numerator and denominator by $(n-r)!$, we obtain

$$_nC_r = \frac{n!}{(n-r)!\,r!}.$$

Since $0! = 1$, $_nC_0 = n!/(n!\,0!) = n!/n! = 1$, the number of sub-sets with no elements, that is, the empty set.

Example   Find the number of combinations of 25 things taken 5 at a time.

Solution. $_{25}C_5 = \dfrac{25!}{20!\,5!} = \dfrac{25 \times 24 \times 23 \times 22 \times 21}{5 \times 4 \times 3 \times 2 \times 1} = 53{,}130.$

The expression $_nC_r$ is written in many books as $\binom{n}{r}$. We shall try to avoid extra notation and stick to the $_nC_r$ for the number of com-binations of n things r at a time.

Permutations in which repeated elements are allowed are con-sidered as permutations with specified numbers of elements of the same kind. For example, cards with the letters E, L, E, M, E, N, T may be considered as having three of one kind and one each of four other kinds. If the cards were all distinct such as $E_1, L, E_2, M, E_3, N, T$ there would be $7!$ permutations of the cards. Since there are $3!$, that is, 6, permutations of the cards E_1, E_2, E_3, each of the $7!$ permutations is one of a set of 6 permutations that look alike (are indistinguishable) when the subscripts on the E's are removed. For example, consider

$E_1\ L\ E_2\ M\ E_3\ N\ T$
$E_1\ L\ E_3\ M\ E_2\ N\ T$
$E_2\ L\ E_1\ M\ E_3\ N\ T$
$E_2\ L\ E_3\ M\ E_1\ N\ T$
$E_3\ L\ E_1\ M\ E_2\ N\ T$
$E_3\ L\ E_2\ M\ E_1\ N\ T$

Thus there are $7!/3!$ distinguishable permutations of the 7 cards with 3 of a kind. Since $1! = 1$, we also have

$$\frac{7!}{3!} = \frac{7!}{3!\,1!\,1!\,1!\,1!\,1!}.$$

In general, the number of distinguishable permutations of n elements with n_1 of one kind, n_2 of another kind, n_3 of another kind, . . . , and n_k of another kind is

$$\frac{n!}{n_1!\,n_2!\,n_3!\cdots n_k!}.$$

Finally, there are many situations in which a desired count is obtained by counting a more extensive set and subtracting. For example, in how many ways can five books be arranged in a row side by side on a shelf if two of the books cannot be beside each other since their colors clash? The five books can be arranged on the shelf in 5! ways. The two books can be together in 2! ways. With the two books together there are four elements that can be arranged in 4! ways. Thus 2!4! of the 5! arrangements are unacceptable. There are 5! − 2!4!, that is, 120 − 2 × 24, or 72, acceptable arrangements.

. . . .

Exercises

1. Use only letters from our alphabet. How many people can have different initials if each person has as his initials:
    a) two letters (not necessarily different)?
    b) three letters (not necessarily different)?

2. Explain why at least fifty people must have the same initials in a city with a million people where each person has three letters from our alphabet as his initials.

3. How many five-digit numbers can be formed from the digits 1, 2, 3, 4, 5:
    a) if each digit is used only once?
    b) if each digit may be used as many times as needed?

4. How many distinct necklaces can be formed using (assume that beads of the same color are alike):
    a) five red beads, six yellow beads, and four green beads?
    b) five red beads, three yellow beads, three blue beads, and four green beads?

5. Two couples are playing bridge.
    a) In how many ways can one person be selected to answer the phone?
    b) In how many ways can three people be selected to get the refreshments?

6. Five students are on a camping trip.
    a) In how many ways can two be selected to use the canoe?
    b) In how many ways can three be selected to use the rowboat?

7. A committee of two Republicans and two Democrats is to be selected from seven Republicans and nine Democrats. In how many ways can the committee be selected?

8. The expression $n!/[r!\,(n-r)!]$ is used for ${}_nC_r$. Show that:
    a) ${}_nC_n = 1$;   b) ${}_nC_0 = 1$;   c) ${}_nC_r = {}_nC_{n-r}$.

9. In how many ways can six students be assigned to three double rooms:
   a) if any two may room together?
   b) if it is not desirable for one particular pair to room together?

10. In how many ways can the five starting positions on a basketball team be filled:
    a) from ten men who can play any position?
    b) from two men who can play center and eight other men who can play any of the other positions?
    c) from two men who can play center, five other men who can play either of the two forward positions, and four other men who can play either of the two guard positions?

11. In a certain state license plates consist of two letters from our alphabet followed by five decimal digits.
    a) How many different license plates are possible?
    b) How many different license plates would be possible using three letters and four digits?
    c) In part (b) how many different license plates would be "lost" whenever a particular permutation of three letters was excluded as inappropriate?

12. In how many ways can a team that plays nine football games end the season with five wins, three losses, and one tie?

13. In how many ways can three boys and four girls sit in a row if the boys and girls must alternate?

14. In how many ways can four boys and four girls sit around a table if the boys and girls must alternate?

Supplementary Exercises

1. Use a symbol of the form $_pC_q$ to designate the number:
   a) of subsets with no elements of a set with five elements;
   b) of subsets with six elements of a set with seven elements;
   c) of subsets with five elements of a set with nine elements.

2. A set of n elements is given. For $0 < r \leq n$ find an expression for the number of subsets:
   a) of r elements each,
   b) of $n - r$ elements each.
   c) Explain the relationship between the answers for parts (a) and (b) in terms of sets and their complements in the universal set of n elements.

3. Find:
   a) $_1C_1 + {}_1C_0$,
   b) $_2C_2 + {}_2C_1 + {}_2C_0$,
   c) $_3C_3 + {}_3C_2 + {}_3C_1 + {}_3C_0$.

4. Let S be a set with n elements.
   a) Apply the counting principle to the selection or rejection of each element of S to show that S has 2^n subsets.
   b) Find $_nC_n + {}_nC_{n-1} + {}_nC_{n-2} + \cdots + {}_nC_3 + {}_nC_2 + {}_nC_1 + {}_nC_0$.

5. Assume that a four-digit number must start with a digit different from zero. In our ordinary decimal system of numeration:
   a) how many four-digit numbers are there?
   b) how many four-digit numbers are divisible by 5?
   c) how many four-digit numbers are divisible by 2?

6. Express as a quotient of factorials (do not expand) the possible number of ways in which 52 playing cards can be divided evenly among four players.

7. Let S be a set with $n + 1$ elements. Then the number of subsets of S with r elements is $_{n+1}C_r$. Let t be a particular element of S. There are $_nC_r$ subsets of S with r elements that do not contain t. Also there are $_nC_{r-1}$ subsets of S with $r - 1$ elements that do not contain t. By taking t with each of these $_nC_{r-1}$ subsets we have $_nC_{r-1}$ subsets of S that do contain t. Then the number $_{n+1}C_r$ of subsets of S with r elements must be equal to the sum of the number $_nC_r$ of these subsets of S that do not contain t and the number $_nC_{r-1}$ of these subsets of S that do contain t, that is

$$_{n+1}C_r = {}_nC_r + {}_nC_{r-1}.$$

Prove this relation from their algebraic representations.

. . . .

2.7 THE BINOMIAL THEOREM

A binomial has two terms. The binomial theorem is usually stated for a power of a binomial such as $(x + y)^n$, where n is a whole number and $x + y \neq 0$. We shall be particularly concerned with the coefficients

$$
\begin{array}{lll}
n = 0 & (x + y)^0 = & 1 \\
n = 1 & (x + y)^1 = & 1x + 1y \\
n = 2 & (x + y)^2 = & 1x^2 + 2xy + 1y^2 \\
n = 3 & (x + y)^3 = & 1x^3 + 3x^2y + 3xy^2 + 1y^3 \\
n = 4 & (x + y)^4 = 1x^4 + 4x^3y + 6x^2y^2 + 4xy^3 + 1y^4
\end{array}
$$

and, in general, we have the binomial theorem

$$(x + y)^n = x^n + nx^{n-1}y + \frac{n(n-1)}{1 \cdot 2}x^{n-2}y^2 + \cdots$$
$$+ nxy^{n-1} + y^n.$$

If we make an array from the coefficients of the powers of $(x + y)$ we have Pascal's triangle

```
            1
          1   1
        1   2   1
      1   3   3   1
    1   4   6   4   1
  1   5  10 [10   5 ] 1
1   6  15  20 [15 ] 6   1
```

We can extend Pascal's triangle for as many rows as we wish since each element is equal to the sum of the numbers above it on the previous row.

This pattern such as $15 = 10 + 5$ as outlined in the array is technically a consequence of the relation $_{n+1}C_r = {_n}C_r + {_n}C_{r-1}$ (Section 2.6, Supplementary Exercise 7). The coefficients for $(x + y)^0$ and $(x + y)^1$ need no explanation. For $(x + y)^n$, where $n \geq 2$ we note the number of ways in which x^r could be obtained as a factor. For example, if $n = 2$, then $(x + y)^2 = x^2 + 2xy + y^2 = (x + y) \times (x + y)$. The x^2 term arose in one way by selecting x from both binomial factors, $_2C_2 = 1$. An xy term arises in two ways since x can be selected from exactly one of two factors in two ways, $_2C_1 = 2$ and hence the term is $2xy$. The y^2 term arose in one way by not selecting x from each of the binomial factors, $_2C_0 = 1$. Thus we may write

$$(x + y)^2 = {_2}C_2x^2 + {_2}C_1xy + {_2}C_0y^2.$$

Similarly,

$$(x + y)^3 = {_3}C_3x^3 + {_3}C_2x^2y + {_3}C_1xy^2 + {_3}C_0y^3$$
$$(x + y)^4 = {_4}C_4x^4 + {_4}C_3x^3y + {_4}C_2x^2y^2 + {_4}C_1xy^3 + {_4}C_0y^3$$

and, in general, the binomial theorem may be expressed in the form

$$(x + y)^n = {_n}C_nx^n + {_n}C_{n-1}x^{n-1}y + {_n}C_{n-1}x^{n-2}y^2 + \cdots + {_n}C_0y^n.$$

In each case note that x can be selected from exactly r binomial factors in $_nC_r$ ways and in each of these circumstances y is selected from the other $n - r$ binomial factors. Thus there is a term $_nC_r x^r y^{n-r}$ for $0 \le r \le n$. Since $_nC_r = {_nC_{n-r}}$ (Section 2.6, Exercise 8(c)), the binomial theorem may also be expressed in the form

$$(x + y)^n = {_nC_0}x^n + {_nC_1}x^{n-1}y + {_nC_2}x^{n-2}y^2 + \cdots + {_nC_n}y^n.$$

In this form it is easy to observe that there are $n + 1$ terms and the $(r + 1)$ term is $_nC_r x^{n-r}y^r$.

Example 1 Find the 8th term of $(x + y)^{12}$.

Solution. Here $r + 1 = 8$, $r = 7$, and the 8th term is $_{12}C_7 x^{12-7}y^7$, that is, $792x^5y^7$ since

$$\frac{12!}{7!\,5!} = \frac{(12)(11)(10)(9)(8)}{(5)(4)(3)(2)(1)} = 792.$$

Example 2 Find the first four terms of $(a + 2b)^{17}$.

Solution. $(a + 2b)^{17} = a^{17} + 17a^{16}(2b) + \dfrac{(17)(16)}{(1)(2)} a^{15}(2b)^2$

$$+ \frac{(17)(16)(15)}{(1)(2)(3)} a^{14}(2b)^3 + \cdots$$

$$= a^{17} + 34a^{16}b + 544a^{15}b^2 + 5440a^{14}b^3$$

$$+ \cdots.$$

Exercises

In Exercises 1 through 8 find the first four terms of:
1. $(x + y)^{10}$.
2. $(a + b)^{12}$.
3. $(a - b)^6$.
4. $(c - d)^{12}$.
5. $(a + 2b)^7$.
6. $(a - 2b)^8$.
7. $(a - 2b)^{11}$.
8. $(2x + 3y)^6$.

9. Write out a Pascal's triangle for $n = 1$ to $n = 12$.

In Exercises 10 through 13 find:
10. The 5th term of $(c + d)^{12}$.
11. The 10th term of $(a + 2b)^{12}$.

12. The 6th term of $(x - y)^{11}$.

13. The 8th term of $(2x - y)^{11}$.

14. Use the binomial theorem for $x = y = 1$ to show that

$$_nC_n + {}_nC_{n-1} + {}_nC_{n-2} + \cdots + {}_nC_2 + {}_nC_1 + {}_nC_0 = 2^n.$$

The first four terms of $(1 + x)^n$ are

$$1 + nx + \frac{n(n - 1)}{1 \times 2} x^2 + \frac{n(n - 1)(n - 2)}{1 \times 2 \times 3} x^3.$$

Use as many of these terms as necessary to find to four decimal places:

15. $(1.02)^5$.

16. $(1.0015)^3$.

17. $(2.02)^6$, that is, $[2(1.01)]^6$.

18. $(1.98)^5$, that is, $[2(1 - 0.01)]^5$.

. . . .

2.8 THE MULTINOMIAL THEOREM

The binomial theorem (Section 2.7) was based upon the $n!/[(n - r)!\,r!]$ ways of selecting one element exactly r times from n binomial factors. The number $n!/[(n - r)!\,r!]$ may be considered either as $_nC_r$ or as the number of permutations of n elements with r of one kind and $n - r$ of another kind (Section 2.6). The multinomial theorem may be considered as an extension of this second point of view.

Consider $(x + y + z)^5$ and think of the five trinomial factors. The element x may be selected from each of the trinomial factors in exactly one way;

$$\frac{5!}{5!\,0!\,0!} = 1.$$

The terms $x^2 y z^2$ arise from selecting x from two trinomials, y from one, and z from two;

$$\frac{5!}{2!\,1!\,2!} = \frac{(5)(4)(3)(2)(1)}{(2)(1)(1)(2)(1)} = 30.$$

The terms $y^2 z^3$ arise from not selecting x from any of the trinomials, selecting y from two trinomials and selecting z from three trinomials;

$$\frac{5!}{0!\,2!\,3!} = 6.$$

Each term of the expansion of $(x + y + z)^5$ is of the form

$$\frac{5!}{a!\,b!\,c!}\, x^a y^b z^c,$$

where $a + b + c = 5$ and all possible such terms occur in the expansion. In general, $(x + y + z)^n$ is equal to the sum of all possible terms of the form

$$\frac{n!}{a!\,b!\,c!}\, x^a y^b z^c,$$

where $a + b + c = n$. Similarly, for any multinomial, $(x_1 + x_2 + \cdots + x_k)^n$ is equal to the sum of all possible terms of the form

$$\frac{n!}{n_1!\,n_2!\cdots n_k!}\, x_1^{n_1} x_2^{n_2} x_3^{n_3} \cdots x_k^{n_k},$$

where $n_1 + n_2 + n_3 + \cdots + n_k = n$.

The expression $n!/(n_1!\,n_2!\cdots n_k!)$ arises frequently and is often designated by

$$_nC_{n_1 n_2 \cdots n_k} \qquad \text{or by} \qquad \binom{n}{n_1 n_2 n_3 \cdots n_k}.$$

In any of their forms these coefficients of the multinomial theorem enable us to write down any specified term of the expansion of a power of a multinomial.

Example Find the term of the expansion of $(x + y + z + w)^5$ that involves $xz^2 w^2$.

Solution. $\dfrac{5!}{1!\,2!\,2!}\, xz^2 w^2 = 30xz^2 w^2.$

· ·

Supplementary Exercises

1. Find the $x^2 y^5$ term of $(x + y)^7$ using:
   a) the binomial theorem,   b) the multinomial theorem.
2. Repeat Exercise 1 for the $x^3 y^5$ term of $(x + y)^8$.

3. In how many ways can ten people be assigned to offices:

   a) if there are ten offices and one person is assigned to each office?

   b) if there are seven offices, three people are assigned to one large office, two people to another office, and one person to each of the other offices?

4. Let $x_1 = x_2 = \cdots = x_k = 1$ and explain why for any given values of $n, n_1, n_2, n_3, \ldots, n_k$ such that $n_1 + n_2 + \cdots + n_k = n$, the sum of all possible multinomial coefficients

$$\frac{n!}{n_1!\, n_2! \cdots n_k!}$$

is k^n.

The result obtained in Exercise 4 may be interpreted as the number of ways in which n elements can be used to form k subsets. Find the number of ways in which:

5. Three different elements may be placed in:

   a) 1 box;   b) 2 boxes;   c) 3 boxes.

6. Five different elements may be placed in:

   a) 2 boxes;   b) 3 boxes.

. . . .

REVIEW EXERCISES FOR CHAPTER 2

1. Suppose that one card is drawn from an ordinary deck of 52 cards. What are the odds for obtaining:

   a) the queen of clubs?

   b) an ace?

   c) the jack, queen, or king of diamonds?

2. As in Exercise 1 what is the probability of obtaining:

   a) the queen of clubs?

   b) an ace?

   c) the jack, queen, or king of diamonds?

3. What is the cardinal number of the sample space when:

   a) three distinguishable dice are rolled?

   b) five distinguishable coins are flipped?

4. Use a tree diagram to obtain a sample space for the experiment consisting of the following two events. A bowl contains three red balls (R_1, R_2, R_3) and two white balls (W_1, W_2). One ball is withdrawn and then without replacing this ball, a second ball is drawn.

5. Copy the given Venn diagram and shade the region(s) representing instances in which the given statement is true.

   a) $(\sim r) \lor s;$ b) $\sim(r \lor s);$ c) $r \to s.$

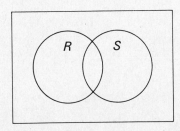

6. Make a Venn diagram for three regions, P, Q, and R and shade the region(s) for each set of points:

   a) $P \cup (Q \cap R);$ b) $\tilde{P} \cap (Q \cup R).$

7. Consider the partition into four cells in the figure. The cardinal number of each cell is given. Find:

   a) $n(R \cup S);$ b) $n(\tilde{R} \cup S).$

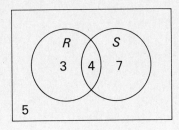

8. In how many ways can:

   a) seven different books be arranged in a row on a shelf ?

   b) five different trees be arranged for planting in a circle ?

9. A set of 12 distinct items is given.

   a) How many permutations of 3 items each are there from the set of 12 items ?

   b) How many combinations of 3 items each are there from the set of 12 items ?

   c) How many subsets of the set of 12 items have exactly 3 items ?

10. A box contains one dozen very large eggs of which three have double yolks. In how many ways can two eggs be selected such that:

   a) both eggs have double yolks?

   b) neither egg has a double yolk?

   c) exactly one egg has a double yolk?

   d) at least one egg has a double yolk?

11. How many subsets of the set {0, 1, 2, 3, 4, 5} contain:

   a) 0?   b) 0 and 1?

12. How many three-digit numbers can be formed using the digits 1, 3, 5, 7, 9:

   a) if repetitions are not allowed?

   b) if repetitions are allowed?

13. Assume that the first digit of a four-digit number cannot be zero. How many four-digit numbers can be formed using the digits 0, 1, 2, 3, . . . , 9:

   a) if repetitions are not allowed?

   b) if repetitions are allowed?

14. In each part of Exercise 13 how many of the four-digit numbers are odd numbers?

15. How many ten letter arrangements ("words") can be made using the letters of the word "combinations."

16. Find $(0.99)^3$ as $(1 - 0.01)^3$.

17. Find the first four terms of $(x + 2y)^5$.

18. Find the fifth term of $(x - y)^7$.

19. Find $(1.03)^5$ to the nearest thousandth.

20. Prove that $_nC_n - _nC_{n-1} + _nC_{n-2} - _nC_{n-3} + \cdots + (-1)^n{}_nC_0 = 0$.

probability   3

Probabilities are considered informally by practically everyone—the probability of rain tomorrow, the probability of needing a coat today, the probability of catching a certain bus, the probability of crossing the street safely, and so forth. Social sciences and physical sciences are all making increasing use of probabilities and stochastic processes. The formal study of almost any subject now requires some familiarity with probability.

This chapter with its brief introduction of probability, Markov chains, and stochastic processes completes the first major stage in our introduction of finite mathematics.

3.1 PROBABILITY MEASURES

The likelihood of an event occurring may be described in terms of either its odds or its probability (Section 2.1). The probability of an event A was defined in terms of a sample space of equally likely possibilities as

$$P_r(A) = \frac{\text{number of successes}}{\text{number of possibilities}} = \frac{s}{n}.$$

In general, the probability of an event is a number $P_r(A)$ the **probability measure** of the event, such that $0 \leq P_r(A) \leq 1$, $P_r(A) = 0$ if the event cannot happen (set of successes is the empty set), and $P_r(A) = 1$ if the event cannot fail to happen (set of successes is equal to the set of possibilities).   As in Section 2.1 if $P_r(A) = p$, then $P_r(\tilde{A}) = 1 - p$ and the odds for A are p to $1 - p$.

When an unbiased die is rolled the probabilities of the six faces are the same, each is $\frac{1}{6}$. In general, when all elements of the sample space have the same probability, the individual events are said to be **equi-probable events** and the sample space is said to have a **uniform probability distribution**.

Example 1   Indicate the probabilities as weights on the branches of a tree diagram for first rolling a die and then flipping a coin.

Solution.   See Fig. 3.1.   As in Section 2.1 the outcomes of the two events considered in Example 1 may be listed from the tree diagram. Also note that the probability of each outcome is the product of the probabilities indicated as weights on the branches leading to that out-come. The tree diagram in Fig. 3.1 also illustrates the fact that if there are branches leading *from* a point, then the sum of the weights on those branches must be 1.

The sample space for an event serves as the universal set for the possibilities.   Each element of the sample space has a probability and each subset of the sample space has a probability, namely, the sum of the probabilities of its elements.   Note that the probability of a subset is the probability of an event being an element of that subset.

Example 2   Find the probability of each subset of the sample space for flipping two unbiased coins.

Solution.   The sample space is $\{HH, HT, TH, TT\}$.   Each element of the sample space has probability $\frac{1}{4}$. The subsets of the sample space may be obtained as in Section 2.2 using a tree diagram.   The probability of each subset is the probability of the result of flipping two coins being an element of that subset.   Thus the empty set has probability 0 and the probability of each subset is the sum of the probabilities of its elements.

See Fig. 3.2.   The sum of the probabilities of the subsets in Fig. 3.2 is not 1 because the subsets do not represent mutually exclusive and exhaustive events; that is, the subsets do not form a partition of the sample space (Section 2.4).

Example 3   Two cards are drawn from an ordinary deck of 52 cards. Find the probability that both are aces.

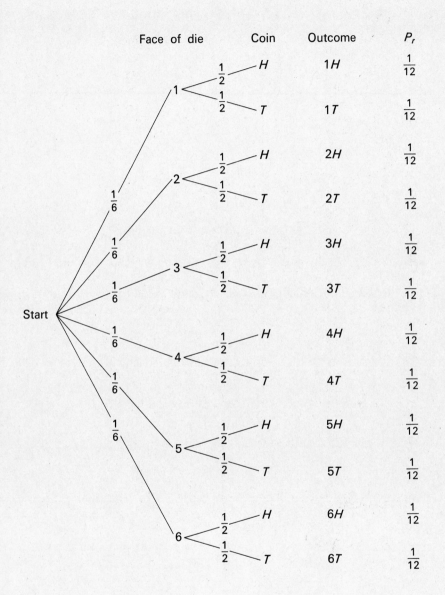

Fig. 3.1

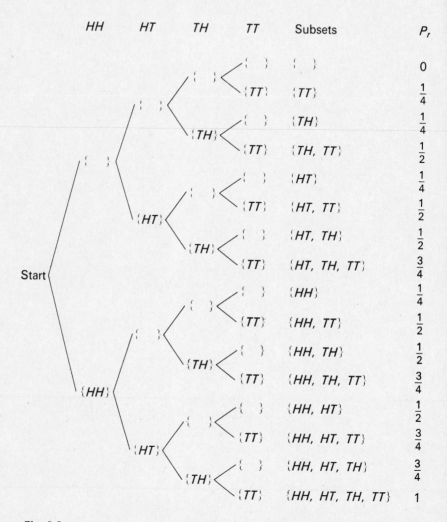

Fig. 3.2

Solution. The first card may be drawn in 52 ways. For each of these ways the second card may be drawn in 51 ways. By the counting principle (Section 2.5) the two cards may be drawn in 52 × 51 ways. Two aces may be drawn in 4 × 3 ways. The probability of drawing two aces is

$$\frac{4 \times 3}{52 \times 51}, \text{ that is, } \frac{1}{13 \times 17} \quad \text{or} \quad \frac{1}{221}.$$

. . . .

Exercises

1. A single unbiased die is rolled. What is the probability of rolling:
   a) 2 or 5?   b) 1, 2, or 6?   c) 2, 3, 4, 5, or 6?

2. Three coins are flipped. The first two coins are unbiased. The third coin has probability $\frac{2}{3}$ heads, $\frac{1}{3}$ tails. Make a tree diagram and find the probability of each outcome for flipping the three coins.

3. John feels that he has an 80 percent chance of passing this course if he passes the first hour exam and a 50 percent chance of passing the course if he fails the first hour exam. He has a 50–50 chance of passing the first hour exam. Find:
   a) the probability of each element of the sample space for his work on the first hour exam and the course;
   b) the probability of John's passing the course.

4. Three coins are flipped. The first two are unbiased. The third has two heads. Find a sample space for the possibilities and the probability of each element of the sample space.

5. Two cards are drawn from an ordinary deck of 52 cards. Find the probability that both are clubs.

6. The letters of the word "probability" are placed in a hat. One letter is drawn from the hat. List the elements of the sample space and indicate the probability of each possible outcome.

7. Two dice are rolled and the sum of their top faces is found. Make a sample space and indicate the probability of each possible outcome.

8. If six people are seated in a row at random, what is the probability that two particular people will be seated together?

9. If six people are seated around a round table at random, what is the probability that two particular people will be seated together?

10. a) Copy the Venn diagram for the flipping of two unbiased coins and label each region with its probability.
    From the Venn diagram find the probability of (b) at least one head, (c) two heads, (d) at most two heads, (e) three heads.

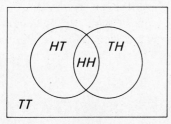

11. Repeat Exercise 10 for this Venn diagram for the flipping of three unbiased coins.

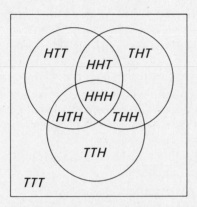

12. Repeat Exercise 10 for the flipping of two coins that are each biased $\frac{2}{3}$ heads and $\frac{1}{3}$ tails.

Identify each statement as true or false. Exercises 10, 11, and 12 may be used to find examples of each true statement and **counter-examples** (examples for which the statement is false) for each false statement.

13. The sum of the probabilities of the cells of any partition of a sample space is 1.

14. The sum of the probabilities of any two subsets of a sample space is equal to the probability of the union of the subsets.

15. The sum of the probabilities of any two cells of a partition of a sample space is equal to the probability of the union of the cells.

16. For any two events E_1 and E_2

$$P_r(E_1) \geq P_r(E_1 \text{ and } E_2).$$

17. For any two events E_1 and E_2

$$P_r(E_1) + P_r(E_2) - P_r(E_1 \text{ and } E_2) = P_r(E_1 \text{ or } E_2).$$

18. For any two events E_1 and E_2 if

$$P_r(E_1) + P_r(E_2) > 1, \qquad \text{then} \qquad P_r(E_1 \text{ and } E_2) > 0,$$

that is, the two events can both occur and thus are **consistent events.**

The following exercises are related to the classic birthday problem. Neglecting February 29 there are 365 possible days for each person's birthday. Suppose that all possibilities are equally likely. Then if two people are selected at random, the probability that their birthdays are different is $\frac{365}{365} \times \frac{364}{365}$, that is, approximately 0.997. The probability that no two will have the same birthday in a group of ten people is $\frac{365}{365} \times \frac{364}{365} \times \frac{363}{365} \times \frac{362}{365} \times \frac{361}{365} \times \frac{360}{365} \times \frac{359}{365} \times \frac{358}{365} \times \frac{357}{365} \times \frac{356}{365}$, that is, approximately 0.883. Similarly, the probability that no two people will have the same birthday is approximately

    0.589 for 20 people,
    0.524 for 22 people,
    0.493 for 23 people,
    0.431 for 25 people,
    0.294 for 30 people,
    0.109 for 40 people,
    0.030 for 50 people.

Suppose that you are in a random group of the specified number of people. (a) What is the approximate probability that at least two will have the same birthday? (b) What are the approximate odds (expressed in the form of the ratio of an integer to 100) that at least two people will have the same birthday?

19. 10.   20. 20.   21. 22.   22. 23.
23. 25.   24. 30.   25. 40.   26. 50.
. . . .

3.2 CONDITIONAL PROBABILITY

Two coins are flipped. The probability that both are heads is $\frac{1}{4}$ as shown in the Venn diagram (Fig. 3.3) where the events associated with each of the four cells has probability $\frac{1}{4}$. Suppose that we know that the first coin is heads. Thus we know that only the shaded region in the diagram is to be considered. With this advance information there are only two equally likely possibilities HT and HH. Each of these now has probability

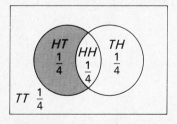

Fig. 3.3

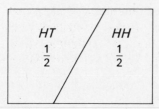

Fig. 3.4

$\frac{1}{2}$. See Fig. 3.4. Thus given that one coin is heads, the probability that both coins are heads is $\frac{1}{2}$ instead of $\frac{1}{4}$. The probability of one event subject to the condition that another event has occurred is called **conditional probability** and may be written in the form $P_r(E_2 \text{ given } E_1)$. Many texts write this as $P_r(E_2 \mid E_1)$. We use the word "given" to avoid learning a new symbol.

The problem of drawing two aces in drawing two cards from an ordinary deck of 52 cards may be used to illustrate the relationship of conditional probability to the probabilities that we have already studied. Let E_1 be the drawing of an ace on the first draw, E_2 the drawing of an ace on the second draw without replacement. Then

$$P_r(E_1) = \tfrac{4}{52} = \tfrac{1}{13}, \qquad\qquad P_r(E_2 \text{ given } E_1) = \tfrac{3}{51} = \tfrac{1}{17},$$
$$P_r(E_1 \text{ and } E_2) = (\tfrac{1}{13}) \times (\tfrac{1}{17}) = \tfrac{1}{221}$$

as obtained by a different method in Example 3 of Section 3.1.

The relation that has just been used is often expressed as the **multiplication theorem for probabilities**

$$P_r(E_1 \text{ and } E_2) = P_r(E_1)P_r(E_2 \text{ given } E_1). \tag{1}$$

If $P_r(E_1) \neq 0$, this formula may be expressed in the form

$$P_r(E_2 \text{ given } E_1) = \frac{P_r(E_1 \text{ and } E_2)}{P_r(E_1)}. \tag{2}$$

The multiplication theorem is frequently used when the probability of two events is desired and the probability of the second event is affected by the first event. Note that if $P_r(E_2 \text{ given } E_1) = P_r(E_2)$, then

$$P_r(E_1 \text{ and } E_2) = P_r(E_1)P_r(E_2). \tag{3}$$

Suppose that two dice are rolled. Let E_1 be the showing of 2, 4, or 6 on the first die and E_2 be a 1 or a 5 on the second die. The sample space for the two events is the Cartesian product of the sample spaces {1, 2, 3, 4, 5, 6} for each die as shown in Fig. 3.5. The cardinal number of this sample space is 36.

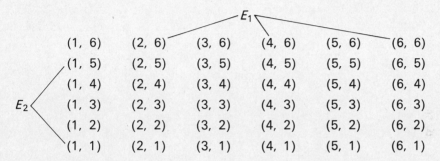

(1, 6)	(2, 6)	(3, 6)	(4, 6)	(5, 6)	(6, 6)
(1, 5)	(2, 5)	(3, 5)	(4, 5)	(5, 5)	(6, 5)
(1, 4)	(2, 4)	(3, 4)	(4, 4)	(5, 4)	(6, 4)
(1, 3)	(2, 3)	(3, 3)	(4, 3)	(5, 3)	(6, 3)
(1, 2)	(2, 2)	(3, 2)	(4, 2)	(5, 2)	(6, 2)
(1, 1)	(2, 1)	(3, 1)	(4, 1)	(5, 1)	(6, 1)

Fig. 3.5

For the first die the probability of E_1 is $\frac{3}{6}$, that is, $\frac{1}{2}$. For the sample space for the two events E_1 is represented by elements in the second, fourth, and sixth columns and has probability $\frac{18}{36}$, that is, $\frac{1}{2}$. Similarly, $P_r(E_2) = \frac{1}{3}$ which may be obtained either as $\frac{2}{6}$ or as $\frac{12}{36}$. The sample space for the two events E_1 and E_2 is

   {(2, 1), (2, 5), (4, 1), (4, 5), (6, 1), (6, 5)}.

Since this sample space is the Cartesian product {2, 4, 6} × {1, 5} of the sample spaces of E_1 and E_2, the events E_1 and E_2 are independent events as defined in Section 2.2. Since the sample space for the two events has cardinal number 6,

   $P_r(E_1 \text{ and } E_2) = \frac{6}{36} = \frac{1}{2} \times \frac{1}{3} = P_r(E_1)P_r(E_2)$

and the formula (3) holds.

Formula (3) holds for any two independent events. However, the formula may also hold for two events that are not independent in the sense considered in Section 2.2. Let E_1 be the drawing of a club from an ordinary deck of 52 cards. Let E_2 be the drawing of a king. Then

   $P_r(E_1) = \frac{13}{52},$ $P_r(E_2) = \frac{4}{52},$

   $P_r(E_2 \text{ given } E_1) = \frac{1}{13} = P_r(E_2),$

and

$$P_r(E_2 \text{ and } E_1) = \tfrac{1}{52} = \tfrac{13}{52} \times \tfrac{1}{13} = P_r(E_1)P_r(E_2).$$

In this case formula (3) holds for events since $P_r(E_2)$ is the same over the sample space of the entire deck as it is over the sample space of E_1. In other words, the probability of E_2 is independent of E_1 even though the sample space of E_2 is not independent of E_1. Any two events such that formula (3) holds are called **probability independent events**. As in the case of the example of flipping two coins, any two independent events are probability independent events.

. . . .

Exercises

1. A coin is flipped. What is the probability that it is a head given that it is not a tail?

2. A die is rolled. What is the probability that it is 2 given that:

   a) it is an even number?   b) it is at most 2?
   c) it is not 5?

3. A card is drawn from an ordinary deck of 52 cards. What is the probability that it is a king or a queen given that:

   a) it is a club?   b) it is not 1, 2, 3, 4, 5?

4. The employment situation in a certain town is given in the table below.

	Employed	Unemployed
Male	450	50
Female	200	300

Find the probability that:

a) an employed person is female;

b) an unemployed person is male;

c) a male is unemployed.

Color \ Box	A	B
Red	3	1
Blue	1	2
Green	2	3

Colored balls are distributed in boxes A and B as in the table at the bottom of page 86. Assume that the boxes are equally likely to be chosen. A box is selected and a ball is selected from that box. Find:

5. a) $P_r(A)$, that is, the probability that box A is selected;
    b) P_r(blue), that is, the probability that a blue ball is selected;
    c) $P_r(A$ and blue).
6. a) P_r(blue given A);   b) P_r(blue given B).
7. a) $P_r(B$ given blue);   b) $P_r(A$ given blue).
8. a) $P_r(A$ given red);   b) $P_r(B$ given red).

Assume that in a certain community the probability that a man smokes is $\frac{3}{10}$; the probability that a woman smokes is $\frac{4}{10}$; the probability that a man smokes given that his wife does is $\frac{7}{10}$.

9. Use the multiplication theorem for probabilities to find the probability that a woman and her husband both smoke.

10. Use the result obtained in Exercise 9 and formula (2) to find the probability that a woman smokes given that her husband does.

11. Use the formula stated in Exercise 17 of Section 3.1 to find the probability that at least one person of a married couple smokes.

Three candidates A, B, and C are running for the same office. The probability of A winning is $\frac{5}{10}$, of B winning is $\frac{4}{10}$, and of C winning is $\frac{1}{10}$. Just before the election C withdraws.

12. Relative to the result of the election the withdrawal of C can be considered what event? What was the probability of that event?

13. What is the probability of A winning given that C has withdrawn?

14. What is the probability of B winning given that C has withdrawn?

There are three cards in a hat. One card is blue on both sides, one card is yellow on both sides, and one card is blue on one side and yellow on the other. A card is drawn from the hat and observed to be blue on one side.

15. What is the probability that this card is also blue on the other side?

16. What is the probability that this card is yellow on the other side?

. . . .

3.3 BAYES' THEOREM

We now express the formula (2) of Section 3.2 for conditional probability in terms of a sample space S with S_1 the sample space for E_1 and S_2 the sample space for E_2. Then $\widetilde{S}_2$ is the sample space for not E_2, where $S_2 \cap \widetilde{S}_2 = \varnothing$ and $S_2 \cup \widetilde{S}_2 = S$; in other words $\{S_2, \widetilde{S}_2\}$ is a partition of S. Also $\{S_1 \cap S_2, S_1 \cap \widetilde{S_2}\}$ is a partition of S_1. Note in Fig. 3.6 that

$$S_1 = (S_1 \cap S_2) \cup (S_1 \cap \widetilde{S_2}),$$

and since $(S_1 \cap S_2) \cap (S_1 \cap \widetilde{S_2}) = \varnothing,$

$$n(S_1) = n(S_1 \cap S_2) + n(S_1 \cap \widetilde{S_2}).$$

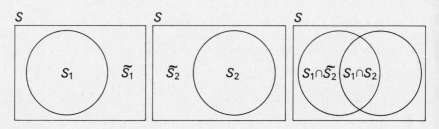

Fig. 3.6

Then

$$P_r(E_1) = n(S_1)/n(S),$$

$$P_r(E_2 \text{ and } E_1) = n(S_1 \cap S_2)/n(S),$$

$$P_r(E_2 \text{ given } E_1) = \frac{P_r(E_2 \text{ and } E_1)}{P(E_1)}$$

$$= \frac{n(S_1 \cap S_2)/n(S)}{n(S_1)/n(S)}$$

$$= \frac{n(S_1 \cap S_2)/n(S)}{n(S_1 \cap S_2)/n(S) + n(S_1 \cap \widetilde{S_2})/n(S)}$$

$$= \frac{P_r(E_2 \text{ and } E_1)}{P_r(E_1 \text{ and } E_2) + P_r(E_1 \text{ and not } E_2)}.$$

In this form the conditional probability of E_2 given E_1 is equal to $P_r(E_2 \text{ and } E_1)$ divided by the sum of the probabilities of E_1 and each element of the partition $\{S_2, \widetilde{S_2}\}$ of the sample space. Bayes' Theorem is simply an extension of this result to any partition of the sample space such that E_2 has a cell of the partition as its sample space.

In general, let $\{S_1, S_2, \ldots, S_n\}$ be a partition of a sample space S with associated events $E_1, E_2, \ldots E_n$. Let E be any event such that $P_r(E) \neq 0$ and the sample space T of E is a subset of S. Then

$$T = (T \cap S_1) \cup (T \cap S_2) \cup (T \cap S_3) \cup \cdots \cup (T \cap S_n),$$

the intersections with S_i form a partition of T, and

$$P_r(E) = P_r(E \text{ and } E_1) + P_r(E \text{ and } E_2) + P_r(E \text{ and } E_3)$$
$$+ \cdots + P_r(E \text{ and } E_n).$$

The conditional probability of any one of the events E_h given E is

$$P_r(E_h \text{ given } E) = \frac{P_r(E_h \text{ and } E)}{P_r(E)}$$

and may be expressed in the form

$$P_r(E_h \text{ and } E) = \frac{P_r(E_h \text{ and } E)}{\begin{array}{c} P_r(E_1 \text{ and } E) + P_r(E_2 \text{ and } E) \\ + P_r(E_3 \text{ and } E) + \cdots + P_r(E_n \text{ and } E) \end{array}} . \quad (4)$$

The equation (4) is one form of **Bayes' Theorem.**

Example Red, white, and blue balls are placed in three boxes as indicated in the array. A box is selected and a ball is selected from that box. If the ball is red, what is the probability that box C was the selected box?

Ball \ Box	A	B	C
Red	3	5	1
White	1	3	5
Blue	6	2	4

Solution. In the language of Bayes' Theorem the problem is to find the probability that the selected box is C given that the selected ball is red. Consider the events

E_1: box A is selected,
E_2: box B is selected,
E_3: box C is selected,
E: the ball is red.

Then

$$P_r(E_1 \text{ and } E) \text{ is } \tfrac{3}{30},$$
$$P_r(E_2 \text{ and } E) \text{ is } \tfrac{5}{30},$$
$$P_r(E_3 \text{ and } E) \text{ is } \tfrac{1}{30}.$$

By Bayes' Theorem

$$P_r(E_3 \text{ given } E_1) = \frac{\tfrac{1}{30}}{\tfrac{3}{30} + \tfrac{5}{30} + \tfrac{1}{30}} = \frac{1}{9}.$$

The probability that box C was selected is $\tfrac{1}{9}$.

The multiplication theorem for probabilities (Section 3.2) may be used to express Bayes' Theorem in terms of conditional probabilities:

$$P_r(E_h \text{ given } E)$$

$$= \frac{P_r(E_h)P_r(E \text{ given } E_h)}{\begin{array}{c} P_r(E_1)P_r(E \text{ given } E_1) + P_r(E_2)P_r(E \text{ given } E_2) \\ + \cdots + P_r(E_n)P_r(E \text{ given } E_n) \end{array}}. \quad (5)$$

This form of Bayes' Theorem could not have been used directly in the Example since we did not know the probabilities of selecting the various boxes. If it is known that the events $E_1, E_2, \ldots, E_n$ are equally likely, then $P_r(E_1) = P_r(E_2) = \cdots = P_r(E_n)$ and for this special case Bayes' Theorem may be expressed in the form

$$P_r(E_h \text{ given } E)$$

$$= \frac{P_r(E \text{ given } E_h)}{P_r(E \text{ given } E_1) + P_r(E \text{ given } E_2) + \cdots + P_r(E \text{ given } E_n)}. \quad (6)$$

This form of Bayes' theorem may be used for the problem in the example. Since there were the same number of balls in each box, the same answer is obtained:

$$P_r(E_3 \text{ given } E) = \frac{0.1}{0.3 + 0.5 + 0.1} = \frac{1}{9}.$$

. . . .

Exercises

The distribution of red, white, and blue balls in three boxes is shown in the array. A box is selected and a ball is selected from that box. Assume that the boxes are equally likely to be chosen and the balls are equally likely to be chosen.

Ball \ Box	A	B	C
Red	3	2	4
White	6	3	1
Blue	1	5	5

1. If the ball is red, what is the probability that box A was selected?
2. If the ball is white, what is the probability that box A was selected?
3. If the ball is blue, what is the probability that box A was selected?
4. If the ball is white, what is the probability that box C was selected?

In a collection of 25 coins 24 are unbiased and one is biased 75 percent heads and 25 percent tails.

5. A coin is selected at random and flipped three times. The coin is heads all three times. What is the probability of this result:

   a) for an unbiased coin?   b) for the biased coin?
   c) What is the probability that the coin is the biased coin?

6. Repeat Exercise 5 if the coin is heads on each of four flips.
7. Repeat Exercise 5 if the coin is heads on each of five flips.
8. At least how many times would the coin need to be flipped and be heads every time in order to be 30 percent confident,

   $P_r(E_2 \text{ given } E) \geq 0.3,$

   that the selected coin was the biased coin?

9. A coin is selected at random, is flipped once and is tails. Repeat Exercise 5 for this event.
10. Repeat Exercise 9 if the coin is flipped three times and is tails each time.

The instructor in a certain course estimates that an average student who has read the text has a 90 percent probability of answering quiz questions correctly; an average student who has not read the text has a 20 percent probability of answering quiz questions correctly. Under these assumptions what is the probability that a student has read the text if he answers correctly:

11. The question on a one-question quiz?
12. Both questions on a two-question quiz?
13. All three questions on a three-question quiz?
14. Exactly two out of three on a three-question quiz?
15. All five questions on a five-question quiz?
16. Exactly four out of five on a five-question quiz?

Supplementary Exercises

On a certain type of multiple choice quiz there are five possible answers for each question. Suppose that an average student who has read the text will know 90 percent of the answers and a student who has not read the text will know 25 percent of the answers. If a student knows an answer, he should get the answer correct with probability 1. What is the probability that a student:

1. Who selects an answer at random will get a correct answer?
2. Who has not read the text will:
    a) know the correct answer for a given question?
    b) get the correct answer?
3. Who has read the text will:
    a) know the correct answer for a given question?
    b) get the correct answer?
4. Who has read the text will get the wrong answer for a given question?
5. Read the text if he has the correct answer on a one-question quiz?
6. Who has not read the text will get the correct answers for both questions on a two-question quiz?
7. Who has read the text will get the correct answers for both questions on a two-question quiz?
8. Read the text if he has the correct answers for both questions on a two-question quiz?
9. Who has not read the text will get the correct answers for all three questions on a three-question quiz?
10. Who has read the text will get the correct answers for all three questions on a three-question quiz?
11. Read the text if he has the correct answers for all three questions on a three-question quiz?

Suppose that a certain truth serum is 90 percent reliable for guilty people and 99 percent reliable for innocent people. From a group of ten people in which only one person is expected to be guilty, a person is selected and given the truth serum.

12. If the truth serum indicates that he's guilty:
    a) what is the probability that he's innocent?
    b) what are the odds that he's guilty?
13. If the truth serum indicates that he's innocent:
    a) what is the probability that he's guilty?
    b) what are the odds that he's innocent?
. . . .

3.4 BINOMIAL DISTRIBUTIONS

Sequences of independent events that are basically *repeated trials* of the same experiment occur frequently. For example, the experiment of flipping n coins may be considered as n repeated probability independent trials of flipping one coin. The experiment of drawing two cards from an ordinary deck of 52 cards may be considered as drawing one card and then drawing a second card without replacing the first card. In this experiment if we were seeking diamonds the probability would be $\frac{1}{4}$ for the first card and the conditional probability for the second card would be $\frac{12}{51}$. Since the probabilities for success for the two cards are different, the two trials (events) are not probability independent events.

The flipping of a coin n times has four basic properties that characterize **binomial experiments**:

1. The experiment consists of n repeated trials.
2. The repeated trials are independent events.
3. The outcome of each trial may be classified in one of *two* ways, success or failure.
4. The probability p of success is the same for all trials.

Consider the flipping of an unbiased coin three times. The probabilities of the various outcomes may be indicated on a tree diagram shown in Fig. 3.7 at the top of page 94.

The probabilities in the array are for the *permutations* of the outcomes of the individual trials. For example, *HTH* denotes heads on the first trial, tails on the second trial, and heads on the third trial. The probabilities of the *combinations* of outcomes of the trials are indicated in the next array where the variable x indicates the number of heads.

Outcome	$\{T, T, T\}$	$\{H, T, T\}$	$\{H, H, T\}$	$\{H, H, H\}$
x	0	1	2	3
Probability	$\frac{1}{8}$	$\frac{3}{8}$	$\frac{3}{8}$	$\frac{1}{8}$

Each outcome for flipping 3 unbiased coins consists of x heads and $3 - x$ tails. The x heads may be obtained in $_3C_x$ ways. Each head has probability $\frac{1}{2}$ and each tail has probability $\frac{1}{2}$. Thus the previous array may be expressed in the form:

x	0	1	2	3
$P_r(x)$	$_3C_0(\frac{1}{2})^0(\frac{1}{2})^3$	$_3C_1(\frac{1}{2})^1(\frac{1}{2})^2$	$_3C_2(\frac{1}{2})^2(\frac{1}{2})$	$_3C_3(\frac{1}{2})^3(\frac{1}{2})^0$
that is,	$1 \times (\frac{1}{8})$	$3 \times (\frac{1}{8})$	$3 \times (\frac{1}{8})$	$1 \times (\frac{1}{8})$

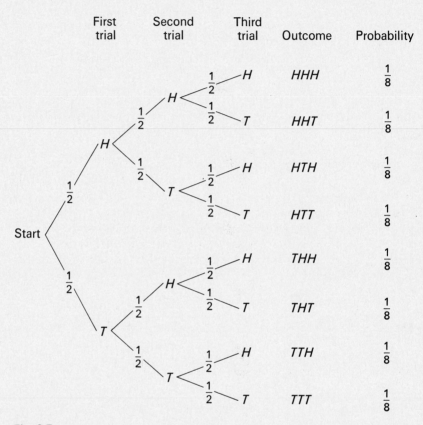

Fig. 3.7

The corresponding array for three coins biased $\frac{2}{3}$ heads, $\frac{1}{3}$ tails, has the form:

x	0	1	2	3
$P_r(x)$	${}_3C_0(\frac{2}{3})^0(\frac{1}{3})^3$	${}_3C_1(\frac{2}{3})^1(\frac{1}{3})^2$	${}_3C_2(\frac{2}{3})^2(\frac{1}{3})$	${}_3C_3(\frac{2}{3})^3(\frac{1}{3})^0$
that is,	$1 \times (\frac{1}{27})$	$3 \times (\frac{2}{27})$	$3 \times (\frac{4}{27})$	$1 \times (\frac{8}{27})$

In general, consider a trial of a binomial experiment in which a success has probability p. Then a failure has probability $1 - p$. The number x of successes is called a **binomial random variable**. The distribution of probabilities of x in n independent trials can be represented for $x = 0, 1, 2, \ldots, n$ as

$$b(x; n, p) = {}_nC_x p^x(1 - p)^{n-x}.$$

The symbol $b(x; n, p)$ represents the probability in a binomial experiment of x successes in n trials in which each success has probability p. For the probability of heads in the flipping of three unbiased coins

$$b(x; 3, \tfrac{1}{2}) = {}_3C_x(\tfrac{1}{2})^x(\tfrac{1}{2})^{3-x}.$$

For the probability of heads in the flipping of three coins biased $\tfrac{2}{3}$ heads and $\tfrac{1}{3}$ tails

$$b(x; 3, \tfrac{2}{3}) = {}_3C_x(\tfrac{2}{3})^x(\tfrac{1}{3})^{3-x}.$$

Note that each of these last two equations presents practically all the information of a complete array that had been previously developed.

We identify $b(x; n, p)$ as a **binomial probability distribution function** of x and use it for most binomial experiments instead of a tree diagram. In general, a **probability distribution function** has as its values the set of probabilities of a set of mutually exclusive and exhaustive events.

Example Find the probability of at least four heads when five unbiased coins are flipped ten times.

Solution.

$$b(4; 10, \tfrac{1}{2}) + b(5; 10, \tfrac{1}{2}) = {}_{10}C_4(\tfrac{1}{2})^4(\tfrac{1}{2})^6 + {}_{10}C_5(\tfrac{1}{2})^5(\tfrac{1}{2})^5$$

$$= \frac{10!}{4!\,6!}\,(\tfrac{1}{2})^{10} + \frac{10!}{5!\,5!}\,(\tfrac{1}{2})^{10}$$

$$= 210(\tfrac{1}{1024}) + 252(\tfrac{1}{1024})$$

$$= \tfrac{462}{1024} = \tfrac{231}{512}.$$

The adjective "random" in "binomial random variable" means that the events are mutually exclusive and exhaustive. The adverb "randomly" as in "randomly selected" means that there are no biases and each element has an equal chance of being selected.

. . . .

Exercises

1. An unbiased coin is flipped n times. Find for the given value of n the probability that there are exactly $n/2$ heads:

   a) 4;   b) 8;   c) 16.

2. Assume that the probability that a patient recovers from a certain transplant operation is $\frac{9}{10}$. Find an expression for the probability that among the next 10 patients having this operation:
   a) exactly 8 recover;   b) exactly 9 recover;
   c) all 10 recover;   d) at least 8 recover.

3. Assume that on a certain large four-engine plane the engines operate independently and each engine has probability $\frac{1}{10}$ of failing. If the plane needs at least two of its engines running for a safe landing, what is the probability of a safe landing with this unusual plane?

4. Bob considers himself a fine hunter and estimates that he brings down $\frac{4}{5}$ of the quail that he shoots at. What is the probability that among the next 5 quail that he shoots at:
   a) he will bring down exactly 3?
   b) he will bring down at least 4?

5. A certain multiple choice test has 10 questions. Each question has 4 answers with exactly one correct answer. Find an expression for the probability that completely blind guess work will result in:
   a) exactly 6 correct answers;
   b) at least 6 correct answers.

6. A certain baseball player has probability $\frac{3}{10}$ for getting a hit when he comes to bat. Assume that his hits may be considered as a binomial experiment. If he will come to bat four times in a certain game, what is the probability that he will get:
   a) no hits?   b) four hits?
   c) at least three hits?   d) at least one hit?

7. A poll is being taken on a question that is favored by only 40 percent of the students. If five students are randomly selected, what is the probability that at least three of the selected students favor the proposal?

8. An unbiased coin is flipped n times. Find for the given value of n the probability that the number x of heads satisfies the condition $n/4 \le x \le 3n/4$:
   a) 4;   b) 8;   c) 16.

9. An unbiased coin is flipped n times. For the given value of n find (by trial and error) the greatest possible value k of x such that the probability of $x \ge k$ is at least 0.9:
   a) 4;   b) 8.

Supplementary Exercises

An unbiased coin is flipped n times. Explain each statement:
   1. $b(0; n, \frac{1}{2}) = b(n; n, \frac{1}{2})$.

2. $b(1; n, \frac{1}{2}) = b(n - 1; n, \frac{1}{2})$.
3. $b(2; n, \frac{1}{2}) = b(n - 2; n, \frac{1}{2})$.

The proprietor of a store that sells milk shakes prides himself on keeping just enough shakes made up ready for his customers. Suppose that ten students come to the store and each flips a coin to decide whether to have a chocolate or a vanilla shake.

4. Find the probability that the number of shakes of one kind that will be needed is:

     a) at least 9;   b) at least 8;
     c) at least 7;   d) at least 6.

5. At least how many of each kind must the proprietor have on hand to be 90 percent sure of having the kind each student orders?

6. For any binomial experiment with n trials the number of "expected successes" may be estimated as np. For $n = 6$ and $p = \frac{1}{3}$ find $b(x; 6, \frac{1}{3})$ for $x = 0, 1, 2, 3, 4, 5, 6$ and thereby show that 2 is the most likely value of x. (In general, values near np occur with the largest probability.)

The *law of large numbers* indicates that for a binomial random variable x and n sufficiently large, $x \approx np$. Note that this condition can be stated as $x/n \approx p$. The law of large numbers can be stated for any given $\varepsilon > 0$ as

$$P_r\left(-\varepsilon \leq \frac{x}{n} - p \leq \varepsilon\right)$$

approaches 1 as n increases indefinitely. We illustrate this by considering

$$P_r\left(-0.2 \leq \frac{x}{n} - \frac{1}{2} \leq 0.2\right)$$

for flipping n unbiased coins.

7. For $n = 5$,

$$P_r\left(-0.2 \leq \frac{x}{5} - \frac{1}{2} \leq 0.2\right) = P_r(-1 \leq x - 2.5 \leq 1)$$
$$= P_r(1.5 \leq x \leq 3.5)$$
$$= P_r(x = 2 \text{ or } 3)$$
$$= P_r(x = 2) + P_r(x = 3).$$

Find $P_r(x = 2 \text{ or } 3)$ for flipping 5 unbiased coins.

8. For $n = 10$,

$$P_r\left(-0.2 \le \frac{x}{10} - \frac{1}{2} \le 0.2\right) = P_r(-2 \le x - 5 \le 2)$$
$$= P_r(3 \le x \le 7)$$
$$= P_r(x = 3, 4, 5, 6, \text{ or } 7).$$

Find this probability for flipping 10 unbiased coins.

....

3.5 OTHER PROBABILITY DISTRIBUTIONS

The binomial distribution function $b(x; n, p)$ is one of several distributions of probabilities. Some of these require special tables of values and will be left for more advanced courses in probability and/or statistics. A few others can be conveniently considered here.

A slight modification of a binomial experiment leads to repeated independent trials that can be classified as successes with constant probability p, or classified as failures with probability $1 - p$, and that are continued until a success is achieved. Flipping a coin until heads are obtained would be an example of this type of experiment. Drawing a card from a deck until an ace was obtained would fit this pattern only if each card was replaced before another was drawn (to keep the probability of success constant).

Example 1 For a coin that is biased $\frac{1}{3}$ heads and $\frac{2}{3}$ tails find the probability that the first head is obtained on (a) the first trial, (b) second trial, (c) third trial, (d) xth trial.

Solution. (a) $\frac{1}{3}$, (b) $(\frac{1}{3})(\frac{2}{3})$, (c) $(\frac{1}{3})(\frac{2}{3})^2$, (d) $(\frac{1}{3})(\frac{2}{3})^{x-1}$.

In Example 1 note for the first success on the xth trial and the sequence of values of $x = 1, 2, 3, \ldots$, that the sequence of probabilities is a *geometric sequence*,

$$\tfrac{1}{3};\ (\tfrac{1}{3})(\tfrac{2}{3}),\ (\tfrac{1}{3})(\tfrac{2}{3})^2,\ (\tfrac{1}{3})(\tfrac{2}{3})^3, \ldots, (\tfrac{1}{3})(\tfrac{2}{3})^{x-1}.$$

Accordingly the distribution of probabilities is called a **geometric distribution**. In general, suppose that repeated independent trials have probability of success p and probability of failure $1 - p$. Then the probability that the first success will be on the xth trial for $x = 1, 2, 3, \ldots$ is

$$g(x; p) = p(1 - p)^{x-1}.$$

We identify $g(x, p)$ as a **geometric probability distribution function** of the variable x.

Example 2 Find the probability that in flipping an unbiased coin the first head will occur on the 5th trial.

Solution. $x = 5, p = \frac{1}{2}, g(5, \frac{1}{2}) = \frac{1}{2}(\frac{1}{2})^4 = \frac{1}{32}$.

A second modification of a binomial experiment arises when the kth success is sought. In this case the first $k - 1$ successes may arise in $_{x-1}C_{k-1}$ ways and the kth success is assumed to arise on the xth trial. Suppose that repeated independent trials have probability of success p and probability of failure $1 - p$. Then the probability that the kth success will be on the xth trial for $x = k, k + 1, k + 2, \ldots$ is

$$b^*(x; k, p) = {}_{x-1}C_{k-1}p^k(1 - p)^{x-k}.$$

We identify $b^*(x; k, p)$ as a **negative binomial probability distribution function** of the variable x.

Example 3 Find the probability that a person flipping two coins will get two heads for the third time on the seventh flip of the coins.

Solution. $x = 7, k = 3, p = \frac{1}{4}$,

$$b^*(7; 3, \tfrac{1}{4}) = {}_6C_2(\tfrac{1}{4})^3(\tfrac{3}{4})^4$$

$$= \frac{6(5)}{2(1)} \times \frac{81}{16,384} = \frac{1215}{16,384}.$$

Still another type of experiment may be obtained from a binomial experiment by extending the outcomes to three or more possibilities rather than just success or failure. In this case the experiment is a multinomial experiment and as in the multinomial theorem (Section 2.8), an expression of the form

$$\frac{n!}{n_1!\, n_2!\, n_3! \cdots n_k!}$$

arises. Suppose that there are n independent trials. For each trial there are k possible outcomes $E_1, E_2, \ldots, E_k$ with probabilities $p_1, p_2, \ldots, p_k$, where $p_1 + p_2 + \cdots + p_k = 1$. Then the probability that the n

trials will lead, independent of order, to x_1 occurrences of E_1, x_2 occurrences of $E_2, \ldots,$ and x_k occurrences of E_k, where $x_1 + x_2 + \cdots + x_k = n$ is

$$\frac{n!}{x_1!\, x_2! \cdots x_k!}\, p_1^{x_1} p_2^{x_2} \cdots p_k^{x_k},$$

a **multinomial probability distribution function**.

Example 4 Find the probability that when two unbiased coins are flipped 10 times they are both heads 3 times, both tails twice, and fail to match 5 times.

Solution. For E_1: both heads, $p_1 = \frac{1}{4}$, $x_1 = 3$;
$\qquad\qquad E_2$: both tails, $p_2 = \frac{1}{4}$, $x_2 = 2$;
$\qquad\qquad E_3$: don't match, $p_3 = \frac{1}{2}$, $x_3 = 5$.

$$\frac{10!}{3!\, 2!\, 5!} \left(\frac{1}{4}\right)^3 \left(\frac{1}{4}\right)^2 \left(\frac{1}{2}\right)^5 = \frac{2520}{32,768} = \frac{315}{4096}.$$

The final type of probability distribution that we shall consider is concerned with the number x of successes obtained in a random sample of n elements from a set of N elements of which k are successes and $N - k$ are failures.

Example 5 Suppose that 3 light bulbs are selected from a basket of 12 bulbs of which 2 are burned out and 10 will light. What is the probability that all three bulbs in the sample will light?

Solution. The 3 bulbs can be selected from the 10 good bulbs in $_{10}C_3$ ways. The 3 bulbs can be selected from the 12 bulbs in $_{12}C_3$ ways. Thus the desired probability is

$$\frac{_{10}C_3}{_{12}C_3} = \frac{10(9)(8)}{12(11)(10)} = \frac{6}{11}.$$

We now extend the problem in Example 5 to obtain x bulbs that light when $x = 0, 1, 2,$ or 3. For $x = 0$, we need all 3 bulbs burned out which is impossible, probability 0. For $x = 1$, the one good bulb can be selected in $_{10}C_1$ ways, the two burned out bulbs can be selected in $_2C_2$ ways, and the probability is

$$\frac{_{10}C_1\,_2C_2}{_{12}C_3} = \frac{10 \times 1}{220} = \frac{1}{22}.$$

For $x = 2$, the two good bulbs can be selected in $_{10}C_2$ ways, the one burned out bulb can be selected in $_2C_1$ ways, and the probability is

$$\frac{_{10}C_2\,_2C_1}{_{12}C_3} = \frac{45 \times 2}{220} = \frac{9}{22}.$$

Then, as in Example 1, for $x = 3$ the probability is

$$\frac{_{10}C_3\,_2C_0}{_{12}C_3} = \frac{120}{220} = \frac{6}{11}.$$

Note that the sum of the probabilities for $x = 0, 1, 2, 3$, is 1;

$$0 + \tfrac{1}{22} + \tfrac{9}{22} + \tfrac{6}{11} = 1.$$

This result provides a check on our work.

In the general case the set of elements from which the sample is selected is called the **population**. If n elements are selected at random from a population of N elements, then the **sample size** is n and the **population size** is N. If a population of size N has k "successes" and $N - k$ "failures," then the probability of x successes in a sample of size n for $x = 0, 1, 2, \ldots, n$ is

$$h(x; N, n, k) = \frac{_kC_x\,_{N-k}C_{n-x}}{_NC_n},$$

where $_nC_b = 0$ if $a < b$. We identify $h(x; N, n, k)$ as a **hypergeometric probability distribution function**.

Example 6 Suppose that 900,000 men are eligible for the draft and 3000 are called up. If 200,000 of the eligible men do not qualify, write an expression for the probability that 2000 of those that are called up will qualify? (Keep the calculations as a number of thousands).

Solution. $\dfrac{_{700}C_2\,_{200}C_1}{_{900}C_3}.$

When, as in Example 6, the sample size n is small relative to the population size N, the binomial distribution with $p = k/N$ is often used as an approximation for the hypergeometric.   For Example 6, $b(2; 3, \frac{7}{9})$ is

$$_3C_2 \left(\frac{7}{9}\right)^2 \left(\frac{2}{9}\right)^1 = 3 \times \frac{98}{81 \times 9} = \frac{98}{243}.$$

In decimal form $b(2; 3, \frac{7}{9}) = 0.40329 +$ and $h(2; 900, 3, 700) = 0.40406 +$.   Thus the binomial distribution is 99.8 percent of the hypergeometric.   For most purposes the easier computations for the binomial distribution make the approximations worthwhile whenever N is very large relative to n.

. . . .

Exercises

1. For a coin that is biased $\frac{4}{10}$ heads and $\frac{6}{10}$ tails find the probability that:

    a) the first head is obtained on the second trial;

    b) the first two trials are both heads;

    c) the second head is obtained on the seventh trial.

2. A certain traffic light is green $\frac{1}{3}$ of the time and red $\frac{2}{3}$ of the time. Find the probability for random approaches of:

    a) arriving at the light when it is green on three consecutive days;

    b) arriving at the light when it is red on three consecutive days;

    c) arriving at the light on four consecutive days and finding the light green for the first time on the fourth day;

    d) arriving at the light when it is red on three days out of four.

3. In a certain roll of 100 pennies there are five biased coins. What is the probability that exactly one biased coin is selected when one randomly selects:

    a) one coin?   b) two coins?   c) five coins?

4. Use a binomial distribution to approximate each answer for Exercise 3. Note that the binomial experiment is equivalent to replacing each coin before another is selected, whereas the hypergeometric experiment involves selection without replacement.

5. At one large university 20 percent of the students are married. What is the probability that a random sample of ten students would include exactly four married students?

6. An unbiased die is rolled ten times. What is the probability of obtaining one 1, three 2's, two 3's, one 4, one 5, and two 6's?

7. Five unbiased coins are flipped. What is the probability of obtaining four heads and one tail?

8. A pair of unbiased coins are flipped and matched ten times. What is the probability of matching heads five times, matching tails once, and failing to match four times?

9. A card is drawn at random from a deck of 52 cards. If the card is replaced after each drawing and the experiment is done four times, what is the probability of obtaining exactly two clubs, one diamond, and one other card?

10. Bob has six matching grey socks and four matching black socks in a drawer. If he closes his eyes and randomly selects two socks, what is the probability that they:

   a) are both grey?   b) match?

. . . .

3.6 EXPECTATIONS

Probabilities may be interpreted as the long run expectation of the ratio of the number of successes to the number of trials. For example, a coin is considered to be unbiased (probability of heads $\frac{1}{2}$, and probability of tails $\frac{1}{2}$) if by taking a sufficiently large number of trials the ratio of the number of heads to the number of trials remains as close to $\frac{1}{2}$ as desired. For example, for a sufficiently large number of trials the ratio could be on the interval 0.5 ± 0.01 or for a still larger value of n on the interval 0.5 ± 0.0001. Thus for sufficiently large values of the number n of trials one expects for x successes that the probability of success has the value of $p \approx x/n$. Similarly, the expected number of successes has the value $x \approx pn$. This relation is often called the **law of large numbers**.

The study of expected values, and indeed of probability, originated in the study of gambling. Gamblers wanted to determine in advance what was a "good bet." Suppose that someone will pay you $10 whenever an unbiased coin is flipped and comes up heads. In the long run the coin should be heads half the time and tails half the time. If the game were played 100 times in this manner, about 50 heads would be expected and you would receive about $500. Your expected gain in the long run is $5 per game. What would you be willing to pay to play the game?

Suppose that you pay $5 to play a game in which you win $10 if the coin is heads and you get nothing if the coin is tails. Then in dollars relative to your payment of $5 to play the game, the value to you of heads is $+5$ and the value of tails is -5. If the coin is unbiased the probabilities are each $\frac{1}{2}$ and the expected value of a payment of $5 to play the game is

$$\tfrac{1}{2}(+5) + \tfrac{1}{2}(-5) = 0.$$

This zero expectation is an indication that the game is a **fair game**. If you paid $6 to play the same game, then

$$\tfrac{1}{2}(+4) + \tfrac{1}{2}(-6) = -1,$$

and your expectation is a loss of $1 per game. If you paid only $4 to play the same game, then

$$\tfrac{1}{2}(+6) + \tfrac{1}{2}(-4) = +1,$$

and your expectation is a gain of $1 per game under the assumption that the coin is unbiased. If the coin were biased $\frac{2}{3}$ tails and $\frac{1}{3}$ heads, then for this biased coin

$$\tfrac{1}{3}(+6) + \tfrac{2}{3}(-4) = -\tfrac{2}{3},$$

and your expectation is a loss of two-thirds of a dollar per game.

In any experiment in which each outcome has a value, the **expected value** of the experiment may be obtained by multiplying the value of each outcome by the probability of that outcome and adding these products. In general, if the outcomes $E_1, E_2, \ldots, E_k$ have probabilities $p_1, p_2, \ldots, p_k$ and values $v_1, v_2, \ldots, v_k$, then the expected value is E, where

$$E = v_1 p_1 + v_2 p_2 + \cdots + v_k p_k.$$

Example Two coins each biased $\frac{1}{3}$ heads and $\frac{2}{3}$ tails are flipped together. The payoff is $5 for matching heads, $3 for matching tails, and $1 if they don't match. What should a player pay to play this game if the game is to be a fair game?

Solution. The probabilities may be found using a tree diagram shown in Fig. 3.8.

$$\tfrac{4}{9}(5) + \tfrac{1}{9}(3) + \tfrac{4}{9}(1) = \tfrac{27}{9} = 3.$$

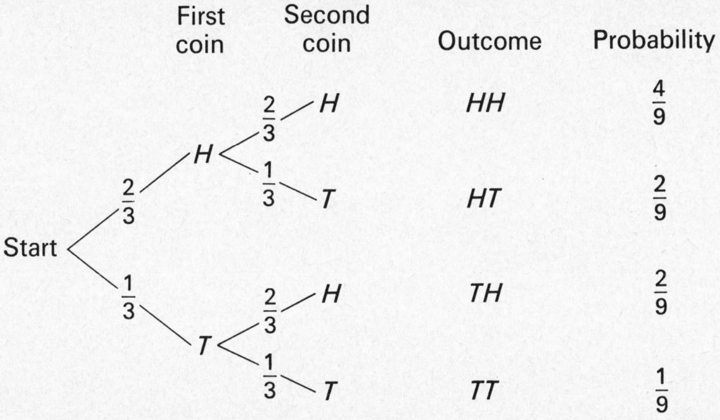

	First coin	Second coin	Outcome	Probability

Fig. 3.8

For a fair game the player should pay \$3. Then the values to him are \$2 for matching heads, \$0 for matching tails, \$(−2) for failure to match;

$$\tfrac{4}{9}(2) + \tfrac{1}{9}(0) + \tfrac{4}{9}(-2) = 0.$$

The expected values need not be monetary. For example, the expected value might be simply the number of heads when two coins are flipped. For the biased coins used in the Example the outcomes are 2 heads, 1 head, 0 heads, with values (count) 2, 1, 0 and probabilities from the Example of $\tfrac{4}{9}, \tfrac{4}{9}, \tfrac{1}{9}$. Thus the expected value, in the long run, for the number of heads is

$$2(\tfrac{4}{9}) + 1(\tfrac{4}{9}) + 0(\tfrac{1}{9}) = \tfrac{12}{9} = \tfrac{4}{3}.$$

For unbiased coins the expected number of heads would be

$$2(\tfrac{1}{4}) + 1(\tfrac{1}{2}) + 0(\tfrac{1}{4}) = 1.$$

. . . .

Exercises

1. When a certain coin was flipped 1000 times 600 heads and 400 tails were obtained.
   a) What is the expected value of the probability of heads for this particular coin?
   b) What is the expected number of heads when an unbiased coin is flipped 1000 times?

2. Bob found that his car used 150 gallons of gasoline in traveling 3600 miles.
   a) What is the expected value of the miles per gallon for Bob's car?
   b) How many gallons of gas would his car be expected to use on a 240-mile trip?

3. Two coins were flipped five hundred times and matched 251 of these times. Does this appear to be a reasonable outcome:
   a) for unbiased coins?
   b) for two coins each biased $\frac{3}{4}$ heads and $\frac{1}{4}$ tails?

4. A small lottery had four cash prizes worth $20, $10, $5, and $1 respectively. Two hundred tickets are sold at 50 cents each.
   a) What is the expected value of a single ticket?
   b) What is the expected gross profit of the operator of the lottery?

5. Repeat Exercise 4 for the case in which one thousand tickets are sold at 10 cents each.

What is the expected number of heads when:

6. Three unbiased coins are flipped?

7. Four unbiased coins are flipped?

8. Five unbiased coins are flipped?

A certain set of coins are each biased $\frac{2}{3}$ heads and $\frac{1}{3}$ tails. What is the expected number of heads when:

9. Two of these coins are flipped?

10. Three of these coins are flipped?

11. Four of these coins are flipped?

12. A player rolls an unbiased die. If the number obtained is even, the player receives that number of dollars. If the number obtained is odd, he receives nothing. How much should a player pay for playing this game, if it is to be a fair game?

13. Repeat Exercise 12 if the payoff is:
   a) the number shown of dollars when the number is odd, nothing when the number is even,
   b) a number of dollars equal to the number obtained for all numbers.

14. The game of roulette is played in Monte Carlo using a wheel with numbered slots of equal lengths around its edge. The wheel is spun and a ball stops in one of the slots. The slots are numbered 0, 1, 2, . . . , 36. If a player places a bet of $1 (his stake) on a given number and the ball stops in that slot, the player is paid $36,

thereby gaining $35. If the ball does not stop in the selected slot, the player loses his stake.

a) What is the expected value of this game?

b) If a player plays the game with $10 stakes one hundred times, what are his expected winnings or losses?

15. The roulette wheel at Las Vegas is like the one at Monte Carlo except that the slots are numbered 00, 0, 1, 2, . . . , 36. The procedure is as before. Repeat Exercise 14 for the Las Vegas version

16. Identify each statement as true or false:

a) If the value of each outcome of an experiment is doubled, then the value of the experiment is doubled.

b) If the value of each outcome of an experiment is multiplied by a constant t, then the value of the experiment is multiplied by t.

c) If the value of each outcome of an experiment is increased by a constant c, then the value of the experiment is increased by c.

. . . .

3.7 MARKOV CHAINS

In this section we extend our consideration of single events and repeated trials of an event to sequences of events in which the probability of the outcome at one stage depends upon the outcome at the immediately preceding stage.

Suppose that Tom and Jerry find a $5 bill and decide to determine who will keep the bill by flipping an unbiased coin. Since they have plenty of time, a single flip of the coin seems to lack excitement. They decide to give each other theoretical interests of $2.50 in the bill, to make the first bet for 50 cents, and thereafter to make each bet for $1 until one of them had the entire $5.

Initial state: Jerry $2.50   Tom $2.50

Suppose Tom won the first flip of the coin

First step for the $1 bets: Jerry $2.00   Tom $3.00

The betting continued. At each step $1 bets were made. To simplify the accounting they decided to record only Jerry's interest in the $5 bill, knowing that if Jerry had $x then Tom had $(5 − x)$. The betting continued and the values x of Jerry's interest rose and fell at various stages.

Let us consider the possible values of Jerry's interest in the $5 bill; x could have anyone of the values

0, 1, 2, 3, 4, 5.

If the value became 0, then the game was over and the $5 bill belonged to Tom. If the value became 5, then the game was over and the $5 bill belonged to Jerry. If $x = 1, 2, 3,$ or 4 at any step, then the value of Jerry's interest would be either $x + 1$ or $x - 1$ at the next step. If x_n is the value of x at the nth step, then $x_{n+1} = x_n + 1$ or $x_n - 1$ and the probability of each of these outcomes is $\frac{1}{2}$. The probability of any other value for x_{n+1} is 0. We assume that if $x_n = 0$, then $x_{n+1} = 0$; if $x_n = 5$, then $x_{n+1} = 5$ since in each case the game is over. This information can be easily presented in tabular form with rows for the values of x_n and columns for the values of x_{n+1}; that is, rows for the possible outcomes at the nth step and columns for the possible outcomes at the $(n + 1)$st.

The entry p_{ij} on the ith row and the jth column is the probability of the jth outcome at the $(n + 1)$st step given the ith outcome at the nth step.

		$(n + 1)$st step outcome					
		0	1	2	3	4	5
	0	1	0	0	0	0	0
	1	$\frac{1}{2}$	0	$\frac{1}{2}$	0	0	0
nth step	2	0	$\frac{1}{2}$	0	$\frac{1}{2}$	0	0
outcome	3	0	0	$\frac{1}{2}$	0	$\frac{1}{2}$	0
	4	0	0	0	$\frac{1}{2}$	0	$\frac{1}{2}$
	5	0	0	0	0	0	1

The probabilities in the array describe the transition from one step to the next and are called **transition probabilities**. The square array of entries in the table is an example of a *matrix*. Matrices will be studied in the next chapter. The matrix for the present table would be expressed as

$$\begin{pmatrix} 1 & 0 & 0 & 0 & 0 & 0 \\ \frac{1}{2} & 0 & \frac{1}{2} & 0 & 0 & 0 \\ 0 & \frac{1}{2} & 0 & \frac{1}{2} & 0 & 0 \\ 0 & 0 & \frac{1}{2} & 0 & \frac{1}{2} & 0 \\ 0 & 0 & 0 & \frac{1}{2} & 0 & \frac{1}{2} \\ 0 & 0 & 0 & 0 & 0 & 1 \end{pmatrix}.$$

Side and top headings may be used for the rows and columns of the matrix as for the table.

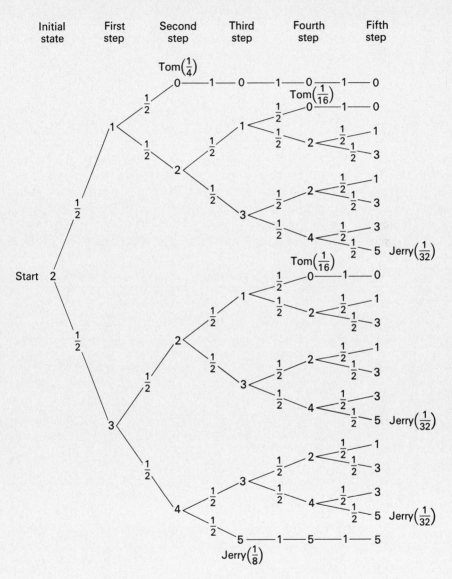

Fig. 3.9

The matrix neatly represents the game that Jerry and Tom are playing. The question of who wins the $5 bill is essentially a question as to the probabilities of the outcomes 0 and 5. The matrix indicates the probabilities one step later for each given outcome. These probabilities may be used to find probabilities any given number of steps later as indicated in the tree diagram (Fig. 3.9) starting with Jerry's $2 at the initial state. The entries in the tree diagram represent Jerry's interest in the $5 bill with probabilities shown on the branches. Winners of the $5 bill are shown in appropriate spots with probabilities.

Given the outcome 2 as the initial state, the probabilities of the various outcomes at each succeeding step can be obtained. For example, the probabilities from the tree diagram may be presented in tabular form as follows:

Outcomes	0	1	2	3	4	5
Initial state	0	0	1	0	0	0
First step	0	$\frac{1}{2}$	0	$\frac{1}{2}$	0	0
Second step	$\frac{1}{4}$	0	$\frac{1}{2}$	0	$\frac{1}{4}$	0
Third step	$\frac{1}{4}$	$\frac{1}{4}$	0	$\frac{3}{8}$	0	$\frac{1}{8}$
Fourth step	$\frac{3}{8}$	0	$\frac{5}{16}$	0	$\frac{3}{16}$	$\frac{1}{8}$
Fifth step	$\frac{3}{8}$	$\frac{5}{32}$	0	$\frac{1}{4}$	0	$\frac{7}{32}$

Note that the row for the first step is precisely the row of 2 in the previous matrix and table. At the first step neither Tom nor Jerry can win the $5 bill. By the second step Tom has a $\frac{1}{4}$ probability of winning but Jerry's probability of winning is still 0. By the third step Tom has $\frac{1}{4}$ probability of winning and Jerry has $\frac{1}{8}$. By the fourth step Tom has $\frac{3}{8}$ probability of winning and Jerry has $\frac{1}{8}$; and so forth.

The patterns in the array enable us to continue the lists of probabilities without extending the tree diagram. The probabilities of the outcomes 0, 1, 2, 3, 4, 5 respectively, at the nth step resulting from an initial state of 2 may be denoted by

$$p_{20}^{(n)}, p_{21}^{(n)}, p_{22}^{(n)}, p_{23}^{(n)}, p_{24}^{(n)}, p_{25}^{(n)}.$$

Then as may be observed from the array of probabilities for the various steps

$$p_{20}^{(n+1)} = p_{20}^{(n)} + \tfrac{1}{2}p_{21}^{(n)}$$
$$p_{21}^{(n+1)} = \tfrac{1}{2}p_{22}^{(n)}$$
$$p_{22}^{(n+1)} = \tfrac{1}{2}p_{21}^{(n)} + \tfrac{1}{2}p_{23}^{(n)}$$
$$p_{23}^{(n+1)} = \tfrac{1}{2}p_{22}^{(n)} + \tfrac{1}{2}p_{24}^{(n)}$$
$$p_{24}^{(n+1)} = \tfrac{1}{2}p_{23}^{(n)}$$
$$p_{25}^{(n+1)} = p_{25}^{(n)} + \tfrac{1}{2}p_{24}^{(n)}$$

Thus the array may be extended for as many steps as we like to determine each person's probability of winning the $5 bill in a given number of steps.

The imaginary problem that we have been considering illustrates the basic properties of a **Markov chain**:

1. There is a sequence of experiments with the outcome at each step (experiment) one of a finite set of possible outcomes.

2. The probability of each outcome for a specified experiment is either known or determined by the outcome of the immediately preceding experiment.

For any specified experiment we denote the probability of outcome x_j given the outcome x on the previous experiment as p_{ij}, a transition probability. Then for any given initial state we can use a tree diagram to determine probabilities of outcomes at future steps.

. . . .

Exercises

Suppose that you are walking in a city with streets running only north–south and east–west. Think of your possible headings as north (N), east (E), south (S), and west (W). Then the matrix of the transition probabilities has the form

$$
\begin{array}{c}
 \\
N \\
E \\
S \\
W
\end{array}
\begin{array}{cccc}
N & E & S & W \\
\left(\begin{array}{cccc}
\underline{} & \underline{} & \underline{} & \underline{} \\
\underline{} & \underline{} & \underline{} & \underline{} \\
\underline{} & \underline{} & \underline{} & \underline{} \\
\underline{} & \underline{} & \underline{} & \underline{}
\end{array}\right)
\end{array}
$$

Make a matrix of the transition probabilities for each of these types of decisions at the intersections. At each intersection:

1. Go straight ahead.

2. Flip an unbiased coin to decide whether to turn right or turn left.

3. Flip an unbiased coin to decide whether to go straight or turn right.

4. Roll an unbiased die to decide whether to turn left (1 or 2), go straight (3 or 4), or turn right (5 or 6).

Assume that you start walking north as in the previous exercises. Make a table of the probabilities of the possible headings for this initial state and the next four steps under the conditions stated in:

5. Exercise 1.

6. Exercise 2.

7. Exercise 3.

8. Exercise 4.

For the problem discussed in this section find the probability that:

9. a) Tom wins the $5 bill in at most 5 steps,
   b) Jerry wins in at most 5 steps.
10. a) Tom wins in at most 6 steps,
    b) Jerry wins in at most 6 steps.
11. a) Tom wins in at most 7 steps,
    b) Jerry wins in at most 7 steps.
12. a) Tom wins in at most 8 steps,
    b) Jerry wins in at most 8 steps.

Supplementary Exercises

Two gamblers have $200 each and decide to bet $100 each on the flip of an unbiased coin again and again until one is wiped out.

1. What are the possible outcomes at various steps for the first gambler?
2. Make a matrix of the transition probabilities for the outcomes for the first gambler.
3. Make a table of the probabilities of each outcome for the first gambler for the initial state and the first nine steps of the experiment.
4. Find the probability that the first gambler is wiped out in at most:
   a) 2 steps;   b) 5 steps;   c) 9 steps.
5. Find the probability that the game lasts at most:
   a) 1 step;   b) 2 steps;
   c) 5 steps;   d) 9 steps.

Two gamblers have $300 each and decide to bet $100 each on the flip of an unbiased coin again and again until one is wiped out.

6. What are the possible outcomes at various steps for the first gambler?
7. Make a matrix of the transition probabilities for the outcomes for the first gambler.
8. Make a table of the probabilities of each outcome for the first gambler for the initial state and the first seven steps of the experiment.
9. Find the probability that the first gambler is wiped out in at most:
   a) 2 steps;   b) 5 steps;   c) 7 steps.
10. Find the probability that the game lasts at most:
    a) 2 steps;   b) 5 steps;   c) 7 steps.

John and Dave are partners in a small business. If a letter arrives on John's desk the probability that he will answer it that day is 0.5, the probability that he'll send it to Dave's desk for the following day is 0.3, and the probability that he'll hold it on his own desk is 0.2. For Dave the corresponding probabilities are 0.7, 0.2, and 0.1, respectively. Then the possible outcomes for a letter may be indicated as:

   To John   John holds   To Dave   Dave holds   Answered.

Assume that a letter that is answered has probability 1 of remaining answered the next day. Also assume that a letter held by a person is included among the letters to that person the next day.

11. Make a table of the transition probabilities.
12. For a letter that arrives on John's desk, make a table of the probabilities for this initial state and the next three steps.
13. Find the probability that a letter that arrives on John's desk will be answered within:

   a) 1 day;   b) 2 days;   c) 3 days.

14. What is the sum of the elements on a row of a matrix of transition probabilities? Explain why the sum must always have this value.
. . . .

3.8 STOCHASTIC PROCESSES

Any finite sequence of experiments in which each experiment has a finite number of possible outcomes and each actual outcome depends upon some chance element (has a probability p, $0 \le p \le 1$) is a **stochastic process**. The sequence of experiments associated with a finite Markov chain is a stochastic process. The sequences of experiments associated with binomial and other probability distributions are stochastic processes. Sequences of experiments associated with tree diagrams are stochastic processes. The word "stochastic" comes from the Greek word "stochos" meaning "guess". The probabilities that we have studied provide a basis for estimating the outcomes of several types of stochastic processes.

. . . .

REVIEW EXERCISES FOR CHAPTER 3

Consider an ordinary deck of 52 cards.
1. What is the sample space for the suits of the cards?
2. If a single card is drawn at random, what is the probability that the card is a club?
3. If the first card drawn is replaced and then a second card is drawn, what is the probability that the two cards are both clubs?
4. If two cards are selected together, what is the probability that both cards are clubs?

Eight people are to be seated at random around a round table.

   5. In how many ways can they be seated?

   6. What is the probability that two particular people of the group will be seated together?

In a certain state Mr. Jones and Mr. Brown are the major candidates for governor. Political analysts estimate that the probability of Mr. Jones being elected is 30 percent, the probability of Mr. Brown being elected is 70 percent, the probability of a sales tax if Mr. Jones is elected is 80 percent, and the probability of a sales tax if Mr. Jones is not elected is 10 percent. According to these predications:

   7. What is the probability of a sales tax?

   8. If there is later a sales tax, what is the probability that Mr. Jones was elected?

For flipping a coin that is biased $\frac{2}{3}$ heads and $\frac{1}{3}$ tails, find the probability that:

   9. The first two trials are both heads.

 10. The first head is obtained on the third trial.

 11. The second head is obtained on the sixth trial.

An unbiased die is rolled 240 times.

 12. How many 2's are expected?

 13. How many odd numbers are expected?

A garden supply store has only five trees of a certain type. Three trees are selected at random and set out.

 14. If each tree has a probability of $\frac{4}{5}$ of surviving, find the probability that all three trees will survive.

 15. If four of the five trees are certain to survive and one has been damaged and will not survive, find the probability that all three trees will survive.

A gambler has \$2. He repeatedly bets \$1, loses with probability $\frac{2}{3}$, and gains \$1 with probability $\frac{1}{3}$. Assume that he quits when he has lost his \$2 or gained another \$2.

 16. What are the possible outcomes for the gambler?

 17. Make a matrix of the transition probabilities.

 18. Make a table of the probabilities of each outcome for the initial state and the next four steps.

 19. What is the probability that the gambler wins another \$2 in at most four steps?

 20. What is the probability that the gambler loses his \$2 in at most four steps?

vectors and matrices 4

Vectors may be considered as ordered finite sets of numbers and also as a special class of matrices, that is, rectangular arrays of numbers. Both vectors and matrices have many applications and serve as very effective new tools in our study of finite mathematics. The uses of matrices for Markov chains and in solving systems of linear equations are particularly important. Extensive use of matrices is made in the remaining two chapters of this book.

4.1 VECTORS

Vectors are often represented by directed line segments. Under this interpretation two line segments with the same length and the same direction represent the same vector. On a number line each vector may be represented by a single real number. For example, in Fig. 4.1 each vector may be represented by $+2$. The number $+2$ may be used to determine both the point P_2 and the vector $\overrightarrow{OP_2}$ from the origin to that point.

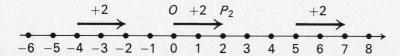

Fig. 4.1

Points on a coordinate plane are represented by ordered pairs of real numbers (x, y). See Fig. 4.2. Each ordered pair of numbers may be used to determine both a point and the vector from the origin to that point. Points in coordinate space are represented by ordered triples of real numbers (x, y, z). See Fig. 4.3. Each ordered triple of numbers may be used to determine both a point and the vector from the origin to that point.

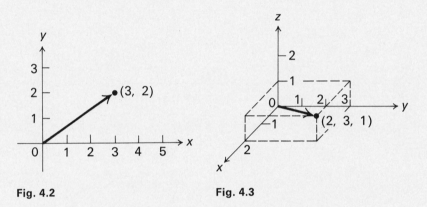

Fig. 4.2   **Fig. 4.3**

Geometric representations on a line (one dimension), on a plane (two dimensions), and in space (three dimensions) help us to recognize that ordered sets of 1, 2, or 3 numbers may represent vectors. These concepts may be extended for all finite ordered sets of numbers. Accordingly, a **row vector** with n **components** is an ordered set of n numbers written in a row. These are examples of row vectors:

$$(2), \quad (3, 2), \quad (2, 3, 1), \quad (1, 2, 3, \ldots, 99).$$

A **column vector** with n components is an ordered set of n numbers written in a column. These are examples of column vectors:

$$(2), \quad \begin{pmatrix} 3 \\ 2 \end{pmatrix}, \quad \begin{pmatrix} 2 \\ 3 \\ 1 \end{pmatrix}, \quad \begin{pmatrix} 1 \\ -2 \\ 3 \\ -4 \end{pmatrix}, \quad \begin{pmatrix} 1 \\ 2 \\ 3 \\ \vdots \\ 99 \end{pmatrix}.$$

Vectors are often indicated by single letters such as

$$x = (x_1, x_2, x_3, \ldots, x_n)$$

for a row vector x with components x_i, $1 \leq i \leq n$. The corresponding column vector is

$$x^t = \begin{pmatrix} x_1 \\ x_2 \\ x_3 \\ \vdots \\ x_n \end{pmatrix}.$$

Each of the vectors x and x^t is called the **transpose** of the other.

Any rectangular array with m rows and n columns is called an $m \times n$ **matrix** (read as "m by n matrix"). The plural of "matrix" is "matrices." A row vector is a $1 \times n$ matrix and a column vector is an $n \times 1$ matrix. The properties that we now consider for vectors will be considered for all finite matrices in Section 4.3.

Two vectors are **equal vectors** if and only if they have the same number of rows, the same number of columns, and their corresponding components are equal. For example, the vector equation

$$(2, 3x, t) = (r, 6, 7)$$

is equivalent to the three equations

$$\begin{aligned} 2 &= r, \\ 3x &= 6, \\ t &= 7. \end{aligned}$$

This property is important in numerous applications. For example, the transition probabilities (Section 3.7) from an outcome x_2 to the set of possible outcomes $\{x_1, x_2, x_3, x_4, x_5\}$ can be represented as a **transition vector** $(p_{21}, p_{22}, p_{23}, p_{24}, p_{25})$. Then values can be assigned to all five of the transition probabilities by the single vector equation

$$(p_{21}, p_{22}, p_{23}, p_{24}, p_{25}) = (\tfrac{1}{2}, 0, \tfrac{1}{2}, 0, 0).$$

Example 1 Phyllis is a cashier who uses a vector (H, Q, D, N, P) to keep track of the coins in her cashier's drawer. H is the number of half-dollars, Q is the number of quarters, D is the number of dimes, N is the number of nickels, and P is the number of pennies. How many coins of each type does she have if $(H, Q, D, N, P) = (6, 18, 24, 16, 31)$?

Solution. 6 half-dollars, 18 quarters, 24 dimes, 16 nickels, and 31 pennies.

In Example 1 if the number of coins of each type was doubled, we would expect $2(6, 18, 24, 16, 31) = (12, 36, 48, 32, 62)$. In general, we define the **product of a number** b **and a vector** v to be a vector with each of its components b times the corresponding component of v; that is,

$$b(v_1, v_2, \ldots, v_n) = (bv_1, bv_2, \ldots, bv_n),$$

and

$$b\begin{pmatrix} v_1 \\ v_2 \\ \vdots \\ v_n \end{pmatrix} = \begin{pmatrix} bv_1 \\ bv_2 \\ \vdots \\ bv_n \end{pmatrix}.$$

Again using the situation in Example 1, suppose that the contents of the cash drawer on two days were combined. For example, suppose

$$(H, Q, D, N, P) = (6, 18, 24, 16, 31)$$

and these coins were set aside. Then on the second day suppose

$$(H, Q, D, N, P) = (3, 21, 28, 18, 27).$$

If the coins from these two days were combined we would have

$$(6, 18, 24, 16, 31) + (3, 21, 28, 18, 27) = (9, 39, 52, 34, 58).$$

In general, if two row vectors have the same number of columns, then the vectors are **conformable for addition**. Similarly, if two column vectors have the same number of rows, then they are conformable for addition. We define the **sum of two vectors** that are conformable for addition to be a vector with each of its components the sum of the corresponding components of the given vectors; that is,

$$(u_1, u_2, \ldots, u_k) + (v_1, v_2, \ldots, v_k)$$
$$= (u_1 + v_1, u_2 + v_2, \ldots, u_k + v_k),$$

and

$$\begin{pmatrix} u_1 \\ u_2 \\ \vdots \\ u_k \end{pmatrix} + \begin{pmatrix} v_1 \\ v_2 \\ \vdots \\ v_k \end{pmatrix} = \begin{pmatrix} u_1 + v_1 \\ u_2 + v_2 \\ \vdots \\ u_k + v_k \end{pmatrix}.$$

Vectors are subtracted in the same manner as signed numbers, that is,

$$-v = (-1)v,$$

and

$$u - v = u + (-v).$$

For example,

$$\begin{pmatrix} 2 \\ 5 \\ 0 \end{pmatrix} - \begin{pmatrix} 1 \\ 7 \\ 3 \end{pmatrix} = \begin{pmatrix} 1 \\ -2 \\ -3 \end{pmatrix}.$$

Example 2 Solve the vector equation for each variable:

$$\begin{pmatrix} x \\ y \\ z \end{pmatrix} + \begin{pmatrix} 1 \\ -2 \\ 3 \end{pmatrix} = \begin{pmatrix} 4 \\ 1 \\ 0 \end{pmatrix}.$$

Solution.

$$\begin{pmatrix} x + 1 \\ y - 2 \\ z + 3 \end{pmatrix} = \begin{pmatrix} 4 \\ 1 \\ 0 \end{pmatrix}; \qquad \begin{cases} x + 1 = 4, \\ y - 2 = 1, \\ z + 3 = 0; \end{cases}$$

$$x = 3, y = 3, z = -3.$$

. . . .

Exercises

1. Identify the matrices that are row vectors:

   a) $(1, 2)$;   b) (-5);   c) $\begin{pmatrix} 3 \\ 4 \end{pmatrix}$;   d) $\begin{pmatrix} 2 & 5 \\ 1 & 6 \end{pmatrix}$.

2. Identify the matrices in Exercise 1 that are column vectors.

3. Identify the vectors that are conformable for addition with $(1, 0, 2)$:

   a) $(1, 0, 2)$;   b) $(1, 2)$;   c) $\begin{pmatrix} 1 \\ 0 \\ 2 \end{pmatrix}$;   d) $(4, 1, 3, 2)$.

Let $u = (1, -2, 3)$ and $v = (2, 0, -1)$. Find:

4. a) $2u$; b) $3v$; c) $u + v$.

5. a) $u + 2v$; b) $u - v$; c) $2u - 3v$.

Let $w = \begin{pmatrix} 5 \\ -1 \\ 0 \\ 3 \end{pmatrix}$, $x = \begin{pmatrix} -2 \\ 3 \\ 4 \\ 1 \end{pmatrix}$, and find:

6. a) $2w$; b) $-x$; c) $w + x$.

7. a) $x + 2w$; b) $x - w$; c) $2w - 3x$.

Solve the vector equation for each variable:

8. $(x, -y, 2z) = (1, 2, 4)$.

9. $\begin{pmatrix} u \\ v \\ w \end{pmatrix} + \begin{pmatrix} 1 \\ 0 \\ 3 \end{pmatrix} = \begin{pmatrix} 2 \\ 4 \\ 1 \end{pmatrix}$.

10. $2\begin{pmatrix} x \\ y \\ z \end{pmatrix} - \begin{pmatrix} 1 \\ 3 \\ 4 \end{pmatrix} = \begin{pmatrix} 5 \\ 1 \\ 2 \end{pmatrix}$.

11. $3\begin{pmatrix} a \\ b \\ c \end{pmatrix} + \begin{pmatrix} 2 \\ 5 \\ 7 \end{pmatrix} = \begin{pmatrix} 5 \\ 11 \\ 1 \end{pmatrix}$.

12. $(x_1, x_2, x_3, \dots, x_9) = (10, 20, 30, \dots, 90)$.

13. $(u_1, u_2, u_3) + (0, 0, 0) = (4, 5, 6)$.

Express as a single row, or column, vector:

14. a) $(1, 0, 3)^t$; b) $(2, 4, 6, 8)^t$; c) $\begin{pmatrix} 1 \\ 5 \\ 9 \end{pmatrix}^t$

15. $(2, 4, 6, 8)^t + (1, 3, 5, 0)^t$.

16. $\begin{pmatrix} 1 \\ 2 \\ 3 \end{pmatrix} + (4, 0, 2)^t$.

17. $2(1, 2, 0)^t$.

Sums of vectors have many of the properties of sums of numbers. Assume that all components are numbers with these properties:

Commutative, $+: a + b = b + a$.

Associative, $+: (a + b) + c = a + (b + c)$.

Identity, $+:$ There is a number 0 such that $a + 0 = 0 + a = a$.

Inverse, $+$: For each number a there is a number $-a$ such that

$a + (-a) = 0.$

We summarize these properties by saying that the numbers form a commutative group under addition. Select numerical values for the variables, give an example, and check that the example holds:

18. Commutative, $+$;

$$\begin{pmatrix} u_1 \\ u_2 \\ u_3 \end{pmatrix} + \begin{pmatrix} v_1 \\ v_2 \\ v_3 \end{pmatrix} = \begin{pmatrix} v_1 \\ v_2 \\ v_3 \end{pmatrix} + \begin{pmatrix} u_1 \\ u_2 \\ u_3 \end{pmatrix}.$$

19. Associative, $+$;

$$\left[\begin{pmatrix} u_1 \\ u_2 \\ u_3 \end{pmatrix} + \begin{pmatrix} v_1 \\ v_2 \\ v_3 \end{pmatrix}\right] + \begin{pmatrix} w_1 \\ w_2 \\ w_3 \end{pmatrix} = \begin{pmatrix} u_1 \\ u_2 \\ u_3 \end{pmatrix} + \left[\begin{pmatrix} v_1 \\ v_2 \\ v_3 \end{pmatrix} + \begin{pmatrix} w_1 \\ w_2 \\ w_3 \end{pmatrix}\right].$$

20. Identity, $+$;

$$\begin{pmatrix} u_1 \\ u_2 \\ u_3 \end{pmatrix} + \begin{pmatrix} 0 \\ 0 \\ 0 \end{pmatrix} = \begin{pmatrix} 0 \\ 0 \\ 0 \end{pmatrix} + \begin{pmatrix} u_1 \\ u_2 \\ u_3 \end{pmatrix} = \begin{pmatrix} u_1 \\ u_2 \\ u_3 \end{pmatrix}.$$

21. Inverse, $+$;

$$\begin{pmatrix} u_1 \\ u_2 \\ u_3 \end{pmatrix} + \begin{pmatrix} -u_1 \\ -u_2 \\ -u_3 \end{pmatrix} = \begin{pmatrix} 0 \\ 0 \\ 0 \end{pmatrix}.$$

. . . .

4.2 SCALAR PRODUCT OF TWO VECTORS

Given two vectors u and v, it is often possible to define a sort of multiplication of the two vectors and obtain a so-called *scalar product*, written $u \cdot v$. What one obtains from the scalar product is not another vector but an ordinary number (*scalar*). It is also sometimes possible to define a product that is a vector, called a *vector product* and written $u \times v$.

    In Example 1 of Section 4.1 a cashier used a vector (H, Q, D, N, P) to help her keep track of the number of each type of coins that she had. The specific case of $(6, 18, 24, 16, 31)$ was considered. There is a related vector of the values of these coins $(50, 25, 10, 5, 1)$. Clearly the value in cents of the coins indicated by the vector $(6, 18, 24, 16, 31)$ is

$$6 \times 50 + 18 \times 25 + 24 \times 10 + 16 \times 5 + 31 \times 1.$$

We denote this number by the scalar product of the two vectors

$$(6, 18, 24, 16, 31) \cdot (50, 25, 10, 5, 1).$$

In general, two row vectors u and v are **conformable for the scalar product** $u \cdot v$ if u and v have the same number of columns. Similarly, two column vectors are conformable for the scalar product if they have the same number of rows. Also for any positive integer n a row vector with n columns and a column vector with n rows are conformable for the scalar product. For example,

$$\begin{pmatrix} u_1 \\ u_2 \\ u_3 \end{pmatrix} \cdot \begin{pmatrix} v_1 \\ v_2 \\ v_3 \end{pmatrix} = u_1 v_1 + u_2 v_2 + u_3 v_3,$$

$$(u_1, u_2, \ldots, u_n) \cdot \begin{pmatrix} v_1 \\ v_2 \\ \vdots \\ v_n \end{pmatrix} = u_1 v_1 + u_2 v_2 + \cdots + u_n v_n.$$

Note that the scalar product is always a scalar, that is, a number rather than a vector. Also note that for two row vectors or two column vectors $u \cdot v = v \cdot u$.

Example Mrs. Smith thinks of her food price index as the cost of three quarts of milk, one dozen eggs, one pound loaf of white bread, and one pound of ground hamburg. Although other items are purchased, the costs of these four items seems to provide a reliable indication of the costs of all foods. Use a vector (M, E, B, H) in the form $(3, 1, 1, 1)$ to indicate the items to be priced. Then use a vector of the form (m, e, b, h) for the prices of one quart of milk, one dozen eggs, one loaf of bread, and one pound of hamburg.

   a) Express Mrs. Smith's food price index as the scalar product of two vectors.
   b) Find the price index if $(m, e, b, h) = (30, 75, 32, 80)$.

Solution.

   a) $(3, 1, 1, 1) \cdot (m, e, b, h)$,
   b) $(3, 1, 1, 1) \cdot (30, 75, 32, 80) = 277$, that is, \$2.77.

Scalar products of vectors are used in many ways. Some of these are considered in the exercises.

. . . .

Exercises

In Exercises 1 through 4 express as a single number:

1. a) $(1, 0) \cdot (5, 2)$;   b) $(2, 0, 5) \cdot (4, 1, -1)$.

2. a) $\begin{pmatrix} 1 \\ 3 \end{pmatrix} \cdot \begin{pmatrix} 2 \\ -1 \end{pmatrix}$;   b) $\begin{pmatrix} 2 \\ 5 \\ 1 \end{pmatrix} \cdot \begin{pmatrix} 3 \\ -1 \\ 0 \end{pmatrix}$.

3. a) $(2, 5) \cdot \begin{pmatrix} 1 \\ -1 \end{pmatrix}$;   b) $(-1, 3) \cdot \begin{pmatrix} 2 \\ 4 \end{pmatrix}$.

4. a) $(2, 4, 5) \cdot (1, -2, 3)$;

    b) $(1, -1, 0, 3) \cdot (2, 4, 6, 0)$.

5. Find:

    a) $(a, b, c, d) \cdot (4, 3, 2, 1)$;

    b) $(a, b, c, d) \cdot (1, 1, 1, 1)$;

    c) $(1, 1, 1, 1) \cdot (x, y, z, w)$.

6. Write the sum of the components of the vector (v_1, v_2, v_3, v_4) in two ways as a scalar product.

    Hint: See Exercise 5.

Any line $ax + by + c = 0$ can be represented by the equation

$$(a, b, c) \cdot (x, y, 1) = 0,$$

where (a, b, c) is the **line vector** and $(x, y, 1)$ is the **point vector.** This form of the point vector is used so that the row vectors will be conformable for the scalar product. Write each equation as a scalar product of vectors equal to zero:

7. a) $x + 2y - 3 = 0$;

    b) $2x - y + 5 = 0$;

    c) $x + 3 = 0$.

8. a) $x - 2y = 5$;   b) $2x - y = 3$;   c) $y = 2$.

Use the given point vector for $(x, y, 1)$ and find the scalar product to determine whether or not each point is on the line represented by the equation $(3, 4, -12) \cdot (x, y, 1) = 0$:

9. a) $(4, 0, 1)$;   b) $(0, 3, 1)$;   c) $(2, \frac{3}{2}, 1)$.

10. a) $(-4, 6, 1)$;   b) $(4, -3, 1)$;   c) $(5, -\frac{3}{4}, 1)$.

Any plane $ax + by + cz + d = 0$ can be represented by the equation

$$(a, b, c, d) \cdot (x, y, z, 1) = 0,$$

where (a, b, c, d) is the **plane vector** and $(x, y, z, 1)$ is the **point vector**. Write each equation as a scalar product of vectors equal to zero:

11. a) $x - y + 2z + 3 = 0$;   b) $2x + y - 3z + 5 = 0$.

12. a) $x - 2y = 3z + 4$;   b) $y + z = x + 1$.

13. a) $x - 2y = 5$;   b) $3y = 5z$.

Use the given point vector for $(x, y, z, 1)$ and find the scalar product to determine whether or not each point is on the plane represented by the equation $(2, -1, 3, -6) \cdot (x, y, z, 1) = 0$:

14. a) $(1, -1, 1, 1)$;   b) $(3, 0, 0, 1)$;   c) $(0, -6, 0, 1)$.

15. a) $(1, 1, 1, 1)$;   b) $(4, 2, 0, 1)$;   c) $(5, -1, 1, 1)$.

For Exercises 16 through 18 let (a, b, c, d, f) be a grade vector for college courses where a represents the number of semester hours of courses with a grade of A, b represents the number of semester hours of courses with a grade of B, etc.

16. a) Write the grade vector for Paul who had

Course	Semester hours	Grade
English	4	B
Sociology	3	A
Mathematics	3	B
Biology	4	D
Physical Education	1	B

b) Express the total number of semester hours that Paul took as a scalar product of his grade vector and another vector.

c) Assume that each semester hour of A work is worth 4 points, each semester hour of B is worth 3 points, each semester hour of C is worth 2 points, each semester hour of D is worth 1 point, and each semester hour of F is worth 0 points. Express Paul's total number of points as a scalar product of his grade vector and another vector.

d) Express Paul's grade point average as a quotient of scalar products of vectors.

17. Repeat Exercise 16 for John with grades:

Course	Semester hours	Grade
English	4	D
Sociology	3	C
Mathematics	3	C
Biology	4	B
Physical Education	1	A

18. As in Exercise 16 Joan had a grade vector (4, 7, 1, 4, 0) her first semester and a grade vector (6, 4, 3, 3, 0) her second semester. Express in terms of these two vectors and others as needed:

a) her grade vector for the year;

b) her grade point average for the first semester;

c) her grade point average for the year.

19. Mary works part time typing. She charges \$2.50 per hour plus \$0.02 per sheet of paper for original copy and \$0.01 per sheet of paper for carbon copies. Thus her production vector for a report with p pages is $p(1/n, 1, c)$, where n is the number of pages typed each hour and c is the number of carbon copies of each page. Her corresponding cost vector is (250, 2, 1). She is asked to specify the expected charge of an original and two carbon copies of a 42-page report. She estimates that she can type six pages of this report each hour.

a) Find her production vector for this report.

b) Use a product of vectors to find the expected charge.

20. Repeat Exercise 19 for a 40-page report to be typed four pages per hour with five carbon copies.

21. Bob supplies Christmas trees for sale at four locations. Considering both the kinds of trees and heights desired, there are six different types that are needed. The numbers of each type are represented as an inventory vector (A, B, C, D, E, F). The corresponding price vector is $(3, 2, 1, 2, 1, \frac{1}{2})$ in dollars. The inventory vectors for the trees to be supplied the four locations are:

$u_1 = (10, 25, 40, 35, 50, 15),$
$u_2 = (8, 20, 30, 30, 40, 20),$
$u_3 = (20, 40, 50, 55, 70, 30),$
$u_4 = (5, 12, 20, 25, 50, 10).$

Express in terms of vectors:

a) the total number of trees in the inventory at each location;

b) the cost of the trees supplied to the operator at each location;

c) the total number of trees of each kind needed to supply the four locations.

Verify that:

22.
$$(x_1, x_2, x_3) \cdot b \begin{pmatrix} y_1 \\ y_2 \\ y_3 \end{pmatrix} = b \left[(x_1, x_2, x_3) \cdot \begin{pmatrix} y_1 \\ y_2 \\ y_3 \end{pmatrix} \right].$$

23.

$$(x_1, x_2, x_3) \cdot \left[\begin{pmatrix} y_1 \\ y_2 \\ y_3 \end{pmatrix} + \begin{pmatrix} z_1 \\ z_2 \\ z_3 \end{pmatrix} \right] = (x_1, x_2, x_3) \cdot \begin{pmatrix} y_1 \\ y_2 \\ y_3 \end{pmatrix}$$

$$+ (x_1, x_2, x_3) \cdot \begin{pmatrix} z_1 \\ z_2 \\ z_3 \end{pmatrix}.$$

....

4.3 MATRICES

A rectangular array of m rows and n columns of numbers is an $m \times n$ *matrix*. The plural of *matrix* is *matrices*. The numbers are the **elements** of the matrix. As mentioned in Section 4.1, a row vector with n components is a $1 \times n$ matrix; a column vector with m components is an $m \times 1$ matrix. The use of commas to set off the components of a row vector is conventional. In general, commas are not used to set off the elements of a matrix.

An $m \times n$ matrix may be formed using m row vectors, using n column vectors, or in other ways. For example, the rows of a transition matrix (Section 3.7) are transition vectors. Here is a specific example of the development of such a matrix.

Jim has his own theory on summer weather. He estimates that if it is a fair day, then the probability that the next day will be fair is $\frac{3}{4}$ and the probability that it will rain the next day is $\frac{1}{4}$. Given a rainy day he estimates that the probability that the next day will be fair is $\frac{2}{3}$ and the probability that it will rain the next day is $\frac{1}{3}$. Thus there are two outcomes:

o_1: a fair day,
o_2: a rainy day.

The transition probabilities given a fair day are the components of the transition vector

$$p_1 = (\tfrac{3}{4}, \tfrac{1}{4}).$$

The transition probabilities given a rainy day are the components of the transition vector

$$p_2 = (\tfrac{2}{3}, \tfrac{1}{3}).$$

The transition matrix is

$$\begin{pmatrix} \frac{3}{4} & \frac{1}{4} \\ \frac{2}{3} & \frac{1}{3} \end{pmatrix}$$

with the components of p_1 as the elements of its first row and the components of p_2 as the elements of its second row. In the general notation of Section 3.7 using p_{ij} for the probability of outcome j given outcome i,

$$p_1 = (p_{11}, p_{12}), \qquad p_2 = (p_{21}, p_{22}),$$

and the transition matrix is

$$\begin{pmatrix} p_{11} & p_{12} \\ p_{21} & p_{22} \end{pmatrix}.$$

For any $m \times n$ matrix the element on the ith row and the jth column may be denoted by a_{ij}. Then the entire matrix may be denoted as the matrix A with elements a_{ij}.

Example 1   For the matrix

$$= \begin{pmatrix} 1 & 0 & 2 & 5 \\ 3 & 4 & 7 & 11 \\ 15 & 21 & 17 & 12 \\ -1 & 13 & -2 & 20 \end{pmatrix}$$

find a) a_{23};   b) a_{32};   c) a_{44};   d) a_{42}.

Solution.   a) 7;   b) 21;   c) 20;   d) 13.

Two matrices A and B are **equal matrices** if and only if they have the same number of rows, have the same number of columns, and have $a_{ij} = b_{ij}$ for all corresponding elements. Thus

$$\begin{pmatrix} 1 & 0 \\ 2 & 3 \end{pmatrix} = \begin{pmatrix} 1 & 0 \\ 2 & 3 \end{pmatrix},$$

$$(1, 5) \neq \begin{pmatrix} 1 \\ 5 \end{pmatrix},$$

and the single matrix equation

$$\begin{pmatrix} a & b \\ c & d \end{pmatrix} = \begin{pmatrix} 2 & 0 \\ 5 & 4 \end{pmatrix}$$

is equivalent to the system of four equations

$$\begin{cases} a = 2, \\ b = 0, \\ c = 5, \\ d = 4. \end{cases}$$

The easy identification of the position of each element a_{ij} of a matrix makes matrices very useful for recording data such as inventory, costs, probabilities, and so forth. Frequently, as in Example 2, the rows and columns are labeled to aid the identification.

Example 2 Represent the Christmas tree inventories at the four locations described in Section 4.2 Exercise 21 by a matrix with four rows.

Solution.

	A	B	C	D	E	F
u_1	10	25	40	35	50	15
u_2	8	20	30	30	40	20
u_3	20	40	50	55	70	30
u_4	5	12	20	25	50	10

The **product of a number b and a matrix A** with elements a_{ij} is defined to be the matrix with elements ba_{ij}; that is, as for vectors, each element of the matrix is multiplied by b. Also as for vectors, two matrices are **conformable for addition** if and only if they have the same number of rows and the same number of columns. Then for matrices A with elements a_{ij} and B with elements b_{ij}

$$A + B = C, \qquad \text{where} \qquad c_{ij} = a_{ij} + b_{ij};$$

that is, the sum of two $m \times n$ matrices with elements a_{ij} and b_{ij} respectively is the $m \times n$ matrix with elements $a_{ij} + b_{ij}$. Similarly, $A - B = A + (-1)B = D$, where $d_{ij} = a_{ij} - b_{ij}$.

Example 3   Find

$$\begin{pmatrix} 1 & 0 & 2 \\ 3 & 5 & -1 \\ 4 & -2 & 6 \end{pmatrix} + \begin{pmatrix} 2 & 8 & -1 \\ 4 & 1 & 5 \\ -4 & 7 & -3 \end{pmatrix}.$$

Solution.

$$\begin{pmatrix} 3 & 8 & 1 \\ 7 & 6 & 4 \\ 0 & 5 & 3 \end{pmatrix}.$$

The matrices in Example 3 each have 3 rows and 3 columns; that is, they are 3×3 matrices.   All $n \times n$ matrices are often called **square matrices**.

. . . .

Exercises

1. Identify the values of m and n for each $m \times n$ matrix:

   a) $\begin{pmatrix} 1 & 0 & 3 \\ 5 & 1 & 0 \end{pmatrix}$;   b) $\begin{pmatrix} 2 & -2 & 0 & 5 \\ 4 & 1 & 3 & 6 \\ 7 & -5 & -3 & -1 \end{pmatrix}$;

   c) $\begin{pmatrix} 1 & 1 \\ 2 & 4 \\ 3 & 9 \\ 4 & 16 \end{pmatrix}$;   d) (5).

2. For the matrix A in Exercise 1(b) identify:

   a) a_{12};   b) a_{21};   c) a_{32};   d) a_{31}.

3. Repeat Exercise 2 for the matrix in Exercise 1(c).

4. Let $A = \begin{pmatrix} 2 & -1 & 3 \\ 0 & 5 & 7 \end{pmatrix}$, $B = \begin{pmatrix} 1 & 2 & 9 \\ 4 & 16 & -5 \end{pmatrix}$ and find:

   a) $2A$;   b) $-B$;   c) $A + B$;   d) $3A - 2B$.

5. See the data in Exercises 16, 17, and 18 of Section 4.2.   Then represent the grade vectors for Paul, John, Joan's first semester, and Joan's second semester as successive rows of a 4×5 matrix.

6. See the Example in Section 4.2 and assume that Mrs. Smith's price vector (m, e, b, h) at three different stores is $(30, 75, 32, 80)$, $(28, 70, 30, 90)$, and $(31, 65, 28, 75)$.

   a) Represent this data on a 3×4 matrix and label each row and each column.

   b) Represent this data on a 4×3 matrix and label each row and each column.

Solve each matrix equation:

7. $(x, y, 1) = (3, -5, 1)$.

8. $(x + 1, y - 2, 1) = (2, 1, 1)$.

9. $(3x, -2y, 1) = (6, 8, 1)$.

10. $\begin{pmatrix} x_1 & y_1 & 1 \\ x_2 & y_2 & 1 \end{pmatrix} = \begin{pmatrix} 5 & 3 & 1 \\ -4 & -2 & 1 \end{pmatrix}$.

11. $\begin{pmatrix} x_1 & y_1 & z_1 & 1 \\ x_2 & y_2 & z_2 & 1 \\ x_3 & y_3 & z_3 & 1 \end{pmatrix} = \begin{pmatrix} -1 & 0 & 1 & 1 \\ 0 & 3 & 2 & 1 \\ 5 & -1 & 3 & 1 \end{pmatrix}$.

12. $\begin{pmatrix} x_1 & x_2 & x_3 & x_4 \\ y_1 & y_2 & y_3 & y_4 \\ 1 & 1 & 1 & 1 \end{pmatrix} = \begin{pmatrix} 2 & -1 & 5 & -2 \\ -1 & 3 & 7 & 4 \\ 1 & 1 & 1 & 1 \end{pmatrix}$.

13. $\begin{pmatrix} a & b & c \\ d & e & f \end{pmatrix} + \begin{pmatrix} 2 & -1 & 3 \\ 4 & 5 & -2 \end{pmatrix} = \begin{pmatrix} 6 & 1 & 2 \\ 7 & 3 & 5 \end{pmatrix}$.

14. $2 \begin{pmatrix} x & y \\ z & w \end{pmatrix} - 3 \begin{pmatrix} 1 & 0 \\ 0 & 1 \end{pmatrix} = \begin{pmatrix} 5 & 0 \\ 6 & 7 \end{pmatrix}$.

15. $3 \begin{pmatrix} a & b \\ c & d \end{pmatrix} + 2 \begin{pmatrix} 1 & 4 \\ 2 & 5 \end{pmatrix} = \begin{pmatrix} 9 & 21 \\ 15 & -12 \end{pmatrix}$.

16. $\begin{pmatrix} x + 1 & y \\ z - 4 & 2w \end{pmatrix} + \begin{pmatrix} x & 4 \\ 7 & -w \end{pmatrix} = \begin{pmatrix} 6 & 0 \\ 11 & 2 \end{pmatrix}$.

Supplementary Exercises

See Section 4.1 Exercises 18 through 21 and explain why each property should be so defined or expected for matrices A, B, and C with elements that are numbers.

1. $bA = Ab$ for any number b.

2. Commutative, $+: A + B = B + A$.

3. Associative, $+: (A + B) + C = A + (B + C)$.

4. $A + (-1)A = 0$.

Form a transition matrix for each Markov chain (Section 3.7):

5. Jim and Don are playing pass. Each throws the ball to the other. There are two states: Either Jim has the ball or Don has the ball.

6. Jack, Bob, and Joe are playing pass.

   a) Jack throws to Bob, Bob throws to Joe, and Joe throws to Jack.

   b) Jack throws to Bob, Bob throws to Joe, and Joe flips a coin to decide whether to throw it to Jack or Bob.

   c) Each person throws to each of the others with probability $\frac{1}{2}$.

7. As in Exercise 6:

   a) Jack always throws to Bob, Bob throws to Jack with probability $\frac{1}{3}$ and to Joe with probability $\frac{2}{3}$, Joe throws to Bob with probability $\frac{3}{4}$ and to Jack with probability $\frac{1}{4}$.

   b) Jack throws to Bob or Joe with probability $\frac{1}{2}$, Bob throws to Jack with probability $\frac{1}{4}$ and to Joe with probability $\frac{3}{4}$, Joe throws to Jack with probability $\frac{1}{3}$ and to Bob with probability $\frac{2}{3}$.

8. Four people are playing pass with:

   a) each throwing to the next person as in Exercise 6(a);

   b) each throws to each of the other three with probability $\frac{1}{3}$.

9. Bill wears sneakers, loafers, or boots to class. Each day he wears a different type of shoes from the preceding day.

   a) Each day he flips a coin to see which type to wear.

   b) He never wears boots the day after wearing sneakers. The probability of his wearing sneakers after wearing boots is $\frac{3}{4}$; the probability of his wearing sneakers after wearing loafers is $\frac{1}{2}$.

. . . .

4.4 MATRIX MULTIPLICATION

Scalar products of vectors in the form

$$(a, b, c, d) \cdot \begin{pmatrix} 1 \\ 2 \\ 3 \\ 4 \end{pmatrix} = a + 2b + 3c + 4d$$

provide the model for products of matrices. There is only one product for matrices and the symbol $\cdot$ is usually omitted in matrix multiplication. Then for the following 3×4 matrix and 4×1 matrix we have

$$\begin{pmatrix} a & b & c & d \\ e & f & g & h \\ i & j & k & m \end{pmatrix} \begin{pmatrix} 1 \\ 2 \\ 3 \\ 4 \end{pmatrix} = \begin{pmatrix} a + 2b + 3c + 4d \\ e + 2f + 3g + 4h \\ i + 2j + 3k + 4m \end{pmatrix}$$

Similarly,

$$(1 \quad 0 \quad -1) \begin{pmatrix} a & b & c & d \\ e & f & g & h \\ i & j & k & m \end{pmatrix} = (a - i, b - j, c - k, d - m).$$

Suppose that A with elements a_{ij} is an $m \times n$ matrix and B with elements b_{ij} is an $r \times s$ matrix. The matrices A and B are *conformable* for the product AB if and only if $n = r$; that is, if and only if the second matrix has just as many rows as the first matrix has columns. The matrices A and B are conformable for the product BA if and only if $m = s$.

In the first of the three previous examples of this section the product of a 1×4 matrix and a 4×1 matrix is a number and may be considered as a 1×1 matrix. In the second example the product of a 3×4 and a 4×1 matrix is a 3×1 matrix. In the third example the product of a 1×3 matrix and a 3×4 matrix is a 1×4 matrix. In general, the product of an $m \times r$ matrix and an $r \times s$ matrix is an $m \times s$ matrix. The element c_{ij} on the ith row and the jth column of the product matrix AB is the scalar product of the row vector formed by the elements on the ith row of A and the column vector formed by the elements on the jth column of B. In other words,

$$c_{ij} = (a_{i1} \quad a_{i2} \quad \cdots \quad a_{ir}) \cdot \begin{pmatrix} b_{ij} \\ b_{2j} \\ \vdots \\ b_{rj} \end{pmatrix}.$$

For example,

$$\begin{pmatrix} 1 & 0 & 2 \\ 0 & 3 & -1 \\ 5 & -1 & 1 \end{pmatrix} \begin{pmatrix} a & b \\ c & d \\ e & f \end{pmatrix} = \begin{pmatrix} a + 2e & b + 2f \\ 3c - e & 3d - f \\ 5a - c + e & 5b - d + f \end{pmatrix}.$$

We assume that multiplication of matrices is associative. For square matrices M we define $M^{n+1} = MM^n$ for all positive integers n. Since matrix multiplication is not necessarily commutative (Exercises 16 and 17), MM^n may not be the same as M^nM.

Each of the vectors

$$(3, 0, 1), \qquad \begin{pmatrix} 3 \\ 0 \\ 1 \end{pmatrix}$$

is the transpose of the other. Similarly, for matrices

$$(3 \quad 0 \quad 1)^t = \begin{pmatrix} 3 \\ 0 \\ 1 \end{pmatrix},$$

$$\begin{pmatrix} 1 & 2 \\ 3 & 4 \end{pmatrix}^t = \begin{pmatrix} 1 & 3 \\ 2 & 4 \end{pmatrix},$$

$$\begin{pmatrix} 1 & a \\ 2 & b \\ 3 & c \end{pmatrix}^t = \begin{pmatrix} 1 & 2 & 3 \\ a & b & c \end{pmatrix}.$$

In general, the **transpose of a matrix** A with elements a_{ij} is a matrix B with elements b_{ij}, where $b_{ij} = a_{ji}$. Then for all values of i the ith row of A is the ith column of B and for all values of j the jth column of A is the jth row of B. In this sense the forming of the transpose of a matrix may be thought of as interchanging the rows and the columns of the matrix.

. . . .

Exercises

Perform the indicated operations. In Exercises 1 through 6 note the consequence of various matrices as factors in a product. In Exercises 9 through 11 note that a product of matrices with elements different from zero may be a matrix with only zero elements.

1.
$$(1 \quad 1 \quad 1) \begin{pmatrix} a & b & c \\ d & e & f \\ g & h & i \end{pmatrix}.$$

2.
$$\begin{pmatrix} r & s & t \\ u & v & w \\ x & y & z \end{pmatrix} \begin{pmatrix} 1 \\ 1 \\ 1 \end{pmatrix}.$$

3.
$$\begin{pmatrix} 1 & 2 \\ 0 & 1 \\ 1 & 0 \end{pmatrix} \begin{pmatrix} a & b & c & d \\ e & f & g & h \end{pmatrix}.$$

4.
$$\begin{pmatrix} 1 & 0 & 0 \\ 0 & 1 & 0 \\ 0 & 0 & 1 \end{pmatrix} \begin{pmatrix} a & b & c \\ d & e & f \\ g & h & i \end{pmatrix}.$$

5.
$$\begin{pmatrix} z & y & x \\ w & v & u \\ t & s & r \end{pmatrix} \begin{pmatrix} 1 & 0 & 0 \\ 0 & 1 & 0 \\ 0 & 0 & 1 \end{pmatrix}.$$

6. $\begin{pmatrix} z & y & x \\ w & v & u \\ t & s & r \end{pmatrix} \begin{pmatrix} 0 & 0 & 1 \\ 0 & 1 & 0 \\ 1 & 0 & 0 \end{pmatrix}$.

7. $3 \begin{pmatrix} a & b \\ c & d \end{pmatrix} + \begin{pmatrix} -3 & 2 \\ 0 & 1 \end{pmatrix} \begin{pmatrix} a & b \\ c & d \end{pmatrix}$.

8. $(2 \quad -1) \begin{pmatrix} a & b \\ c & d \end{pmatrix} + (-2 \quad 1) \begin{pmatrix} a & b \\ c & d \end{pmatrix}$.

9. $\begin{pmatrix} 2 & 4 \\ 3 & 6 \end{pmatrix} \begin{pmatrix} 2 \\ -1 \end{pmatrix}$.

10. $(2 \quad 3) \begin{pmatrix} 3 & 9 \\ -2 & -6 \end{pmatrix}$.

11. $(1 \quad -2 \quad 1) \begin{pmatrix} 1 & 2 & 1 \\ 1 & 3 & 4 \\ 1 & 4 & 7 \end{pmatrix}$.

In Exercises 12 through 15 write as systems of equations:

12. $\begin{pmatrix} 1 & 1 \\ 1 & -1 \end{pmatrix} \begin{pmatrix} x \\ y \end{pmatrix} = \begin{pmatrix} 5 \\ -1 \end{pmatrix}$.

13. $\begin{pmatrix} 2 & 3 \\ 4 & -1 \end{pmatrix} \begin{pmatrix} x \\ y \end{pmatrix} = \begin{pmatrix} 7 \\ 7 \end{pmatrix}$.

14. $\begin{pmatrix} 2 & 3 & 0 \\ 0 & 1 & -2 \\ 1 & 2 & 3 \end{pmatrix} \begin{pmatrix} x \\ y \\ z \end{pmatrix} = \begin{pmatrix} -1 \\ -7 \\ 8 \end{pmatrix}$.

15. $\begin{pmatrix} 1 & 0 & 2 \\ 3 & -1 & 1 \\ 2 & 5 & 7 \end{pmatrix} \begin{pmatrix} x \\ y \\ z \end{pmatrix} = \begin{pmatrix} 1 \\ 1 \\ 12 \end{pmatrix}$.

Use the given matrices A and B to show that it is not necessary for AB to equal BA.

16. $A = \begin{pmatrix} 1 & 2 \\ 0 & 1 \end{pmatrix}$, $B = \begin{pmatrix} 0 & 1 \\ 2 & 3 \end{pmatrix}$.

17. $A = \begin{pmatrix} 1 & 0 & 1 \\ 0 & 1 & 1 \\ 1 & 0 & 1 \end{pmatrix}$, $B = \begin{pmatrix} a & b & c \\ d & e & f \\ g & h & i \end{pmatrix}$.

Consider the transition matrix M for Jim's prediction of clear and rainy days described in Section 4.3:

$$\begin{array}{c} \\ \text{clear} \\ \text{rainy} \end{array} \begin{array}{cc} \text{clear} & \text{rainy} \\ \begin{pmatrix} \frac{3}{4} & \frac{1}{4} \\ \frac{2}{3} & \frac{1}{3} \end{pmatrix} \end{array}.$$

Let $p_1 = (1, 0)$ be the probability vector of the first stage on an assumed clear day.

18. Express the probability vector p_2 for the second day in terms of p_1 and M.

19. Express the probability vector p_3 for the third day in terms of:
    a) p_2 and M;   b) p_1 and M.

20. Express the probability vector p_k for the kth day in terms of p_1 and M.

Supplementary Exercises

For the given matrix M find (a) M^2; (b) M^3, where $M^3 = MM^2$:

1. $\begin{pmatrix} 1 & 1 \\ 0 & 1 \end{pmatrix}$.

2. $\begin{pmatrix} 1 & 0 & 0 \\ 0 & 1 & 0 \\ 0 & 0 & 1 \end{pmatrix}$.

3. $\begin{pmatrix} 0 & 0 & 1 \\ 0 & 1 & 0 \\ 1 & 0 & 0 \end{pmatrix}$.

4. $\begin{pmatrix} 1 & 2 \\ -1 & 0 \end{pmatrix}$.

5. $\begin{pmatrix} 1 & 0 & 1 \\ 0 & 1 & -1 \\ 0 & 0 & 1 \end{pmatrix}$.

6. $\begin{pmatrix} 2 & 0 & 2 \\ 0 & 2 & 0 \\ 0 & 0 & 2 \end{pmatrix}$.

In Exercises 7 through 9 show that:

7. For any number b and any 2×2 matrix M we have

$$bM = BM = MB, \text{ where } B = \begin{pmatrix} b & 0 \\ 0 & b \end{pmatrix}.$$

8. For any number b and any 3×3 matrix M we have

$$bM = BM = MB, \text{ where } B = \begin{pmatrix} b & 0 & 0 \\ 0 & b & 0 \\ 0 & 0 & b \end{pmatrix}.$$

9. The multiplication of 2×2 matrices is associative by verifying that

$$\left[\begin{pmatrix} a & b \\ c & d \end{pmatrix} \begin{pmatrix} e & f \\ g & h \end{pmatrix} \right] \begin{pmatrix} i & j \\ k & m \end{pmatrix} = \begin{pmatrix} a & b \\ c & d \end{pmatrix} \left[\begin{pmatrix} e & f \\ g & h \end{pmatrix} \begin{pmatrix} i & j \\ k & m \end{pmatrix} \right].$$

A small contractor charges \$10 per hour per man, \$5 per hour per truck without a driver, and \$15 per hour per tractor without a driver. He uses a matrix M for the requirements for various common types of work:

	A	B	C	D	E	F
men	1	1	1	2	3	3
trucks	1	0	1	1	1	2
tractors	0	1	1	1	2	1

10. Use a price vector $p = (10, 5, 15)$. Find and interpret the elements of pM.

11. For one small project he used 30 hours of type A and 40 hours of type B. Use a supply vector $s = (30, 40, 0, 0, 0)$. Find and interpret the elements of Ms^t.

12. For the data in Exercises 10 and 11 compute and interpret $p(Ms^t)$.

Four types of newspapers N_1, N_2, N_3, and N_4 are available at a certain store. The price vector is $p = (5, 10, 15, 10)$. The sales for the various days of the week are recorded as elements of a matrix M:

$$
\begin{array}{c c c c c c c}
 & M & Tu & W & Th & F & S \\
N_1 & 21 & 20 & 23 & 21 & 24 & 16 \\
N_2 & 70 & 68 & 75 & 72 & 80 & 60 \\
N_3 & 45 & 42 & 40 & 43 & 47 & 35 \\
N_4 & 12 & 10 & 13 & 11 & 15 & 8
\end{array}.
$$

13. Let $n = (1, 1, 1, 1)$. Find and interpret the elements of nM.

14. Find and interpret the elements of pM.

15. Let $s = (1, 1, 1, 1, 1, 1)$. Find and interpret the elements of Ms^t.

16. Find and interpret the elements of $p(Ms^t)$.

For the given matrix M find M^2, M^3, M^4, M^5, and general expressions for M^n, or M^{2n} and M^{2n+1}, for any positive integer n.

17. $\begin{pmatrix} 1 & 0 \\ 0 & 1 \end{pmatrix}$.

18. $\begin{pmatrix} 0 & 1 \\ 1 & 0 \end{pmatrix}$.

19. $\begin{pmatrix} \frac{1}{2} & \frac{1}{2} \\ \frac{1}{2} & \frac{1}{2} \end{pmatrix}$.

20. $\begin{pmatrix} 1 & 0 \\ \frac{1}{2} & \frac{1}{2} \end{pmatrix}$.

21. $\begin{pmatrix} 1 & 0 \\ \frac{1}{3} & \frac{2}{3} \end{pmatrix}$.

22. $\begin{pmatrix} \frac{1}{3} & \frac{2}{3} \\ \frac{1}{3} & \frac{2}{3} \end{pmatrix}$.

23. $\begin{pmatrix} 1/k & (k-1)/k \\ 1/k & (k-1)/k \end{pmatrix}$.

24. $\begin{pmatrix} 1 & 0 & 0 \\ 0 & 0 & 1 \\ 0 & 1 & 0 \end{pmatrix}$.

For the given matrix M and any positive integer n find the general expressions for M^{3n}, M^{3n+1}, and M^{3n+2}.

25. $\begin{pmatrix} 0 & 1 & 0 \\ 0 & 0 & 1 \\ 1 & 0 & 0 \end{pmatrix}$.

26. $\begin{pmatrix} 0 & 0 & 1 \\ 1 & 0 & 0 \\ 0 & 1 & 0 \end{pmatrix}$.

....

4.5 MATRICES AND MARKOV CHAINS

Consider a game of pass in which Dick always throws the ball to Tom, Tom throws to Dick or John each with probability $\frac{1}{2}$, and John always throws to Tom. The matrix of the transitional probabilities is:

$$
\begin{array}{c c c c}
 & Dick & Tom & John \\
Dick & 0 & 1 & 0 \\
Tom & \frac{1}{2} & 0 & \frac{1}{2} \\
John & 0 & 1 & 0
\end{array}.
$$

This sequence of experiments (passing the ball) has the property that the probabilities of each outcome for an experiment are known when the outcome (who has the ball) of the immediately previous experiment is known. In other words, any finite sequence of such experiments is a Markov chain (Section 3.7).

Now consider a game of pass among the three boys in which Dick throws to Tom or John each with probability $\frac{1}{2}$, Tom throws to Dick or John each with probability $\frac{1}{2}$, and John throws the ball back to the person that threw the ball to him. We try to form the transition matrix:

$$
\begin{array}{cc}
& \begin{array}{ccc} \text{Dick} & \text{Tom} & \text{John} \end{array} \\
\begin{array}{c} \text{Dick} \\ \text{Tom} \\ \text{John} \end{array} &
\begin{pmatrix}
0 & \frac{1}{2} & \frac{1}{2} \\
\frac{1}{2} & 0 & \frac{1}{2} \\
? & ? & 0
\end{pmatrix}.
\end{array}
$$

We can not complete the third row of the transition matrix because the *outcome* (who has the ball) of the immediately previous experiment is not enough to determine the probabilities of the outcomes when John has the ball. Therefore this game (sequence of experiments) does not form a Markov chain.

Consider the first game and suppose that we start with Tom having the ball. Then the probability vector for this initial state is

$$p_1 = (0 \quad 1 \quad 0).$$

The probability vector p_2 for the next outcome (second state) is

$$(0 \quad 1 \quad 0) \begin{pmatrix} 0 & 1 & 0 \\ \frac{1}{2} & 0 & \frac{1}{2} \\ 0 & 1 & 0 \end{pmatrix},$$

and $p_2 = (\frac{1}{2}, 0, \frac{1}{2}) = p_1 M$, where M is the transition matrix. In other words, if Tom has the ball $(0, 1, 0)$, then at the next step the probability is $\frac{1}{2}$ that Dick has the ball and $\frac{1}{2}$ that John has the ball, that is, $(\frac{1}{2}, 0, \frac{1}{2})$.

Can we find the probability vector p_3 for the next step? At the second step either Dick or John has the ball, each with probability $\frac{1}{2}$. If Dick has the ball, he throws it to Tom. If John has the ball, he throws it to Tom. In either case Tom will have the ball for the third state; $p_3 = (0, 1, 0)$. Note that

$$p_3 = p_2 M = (\frac{1}{2} \quad 0 \quad \frac{1}{2}) \begin{pmatrix} 0 & 1 & 0 \\ \frac{1}{2} & 0 & \frac{1}{2} \\ 0 & 1 & 0 \end{pmatrix}.$$

The pattern for this game can now be established. Tom will either start with the ball or have it at the next step. After Tom has the ball, the other two each have probability $\frac{1}{2}$ of getting the ball. Then Tom gets the ball again and another cycle starts; that is, if $p_1 = (0, 1, 0)$, then

$$p_1 = p_3 = p_5 = \cdots = (0, 1, 0),$$
$$p_2 = p_4 = p_6 = \cdots = (\tfrac{1}{2}, 0, \tfrac{1}{2}).$$

Suppose that two gamblers each have $1 and bet $1 on the flip of an unbiased coin. The possible outcomes (*states*) for the first gambler are $0, $1, and $2. We designate these as s_0, s_1, and s_2. The transition matrix is:

$$
\begin{array}{c}
\\
s_0 \\
s_1 \\
s_2
\end{array}
\begin{array}{ccc}
s_0 & s_1 & s_2 \\
\begin{pmatrix}
1 & 0 & 0 \\
\frac{1}{2} & 0 & \frac{1}{2} \\
0 & 0 & 1
\end{pmatrix}
\end{array}.
$$

The probability vector for the initial stage is $p_1 = (0, 1, 0)$ since the gambler's initial state is having $1, that is, s_1. After the first flip of the coin his probability vector p_2 is given by the equation

$$
p_2 = (0 \quad 1 \quad 0)
\begin{pmatrix}
1 & 0 & 0 \\
\frac{1}{2} & 0 & \frac{1}{2} \\
0 & 0 & 1
\end{pmatrix}
= (\tfrac{1}{2} \quad 0 \quad \tfrac{1}{2}).
$$

In practice we know that the game is over and he has won or lost, each with probability $\frac{1}{2}$. However, suppose that we try to find a probability vector p_3 for the next flip of the coin. We obtain

$$
p_3 = (\tfrac{1}{2} \quad 0 \quad \tfrac{1}{2})
\begin{pmatrix}
1 & 0 & 0 \\
\frac{1}{2} & 0 & \frac{1}{2} \\
0 & 0 & 1
\end{pmatrix}
= (\tfrac{1}{2} \quad 0 \quad \tfrac{1}{2}) = p_2.
$$

Similarly, $p_4 = p_2$, $p_5 = p_2$, and so forth. All probability vectors p_i, where $i \geq 2$ are the same. We describe this situation by saying that the probability vector $(\tfrac{1}{2}, 0, \tfrac{1}{2})$ remains *fixed* and the game has reached a *steady state* of **equilibrium**.

In order for a probability vector p to remain fixed for a Markov chain with transition matrix M we need $pM = p$, as in the case of $(\tfrac{1}{2}, 0, \tfrac{1}{2})$. In general, a probability vector p is called a **fixed vector** of a matrix M if $pM = p$. The particular matrix M that was used for the two gamblers with \$1 each has three fixed vectors; namely, $(1, 0, 0)$, $(\frac{1}{2}, 0, \frac{1}{2})$, and $(0, 0, 1)$:

$$(1 \quad 0 \quad 0) \begin{pmatrix} 1 & 0 & 0 \\ \frac{1}{2} & 0 & \frac{1}{2} \\ 0 & 0 & 1 \end{pmatrix} = (1 \quad 0 \quad 0),$$

$$(\tfrac{1}{2} \quad 0 \quad \tfrac{1}{2}) \begin{pmatrix} 1 & 0 & 0 \\ \frac{1}{2} & 0 & \frac{1}{2} \\ 0 & 0 & 1 \end{pmatrix} = (\tfrac{1}{2} \quad 0 \quad \tfrac{1}{2}),$$

$$(0 \quad 0 \quad 1) \begin{pmatrix} 1 & 0 & 0 \\ \frac{1}{2} & 0 & \frac{1}{2} \\ 0 & 0 & 1 \end{pmatrix} = (0 \quad 0 \quad 1).$$

The fixed vectors $(1, 0, 0)$ and $(0, 0, 1)$ correspond to the states s_0 and s_2. Thus it is impossible to leave either of these states. One might say that if you have won, your status can not change; if you have lost, your status can not change. The fixed vector $(\frac{1}{2}, 0, \frac{1}{2})$ does not correspond to a state. However, the remaining state, s_1, is such that it is possible to get from s_1 into at least one (actually both) of the fixed states s_0 and s_2. Thus from any given state one eventually gets *absorbed* in one of the fixed states s_0, s_2.

Next suppose that the gamblers each have \$2 and bet \$1 as before. The transition matrix M for outcomes of \$0, \$1, \$2, \$3, and \$4 is:

$$
\begin{array}{c}
\begin{array}{ccccc} s_0 & s_1 & s_2 & s_3 & s_4 \end{array} \\
\begin{array}{c} s_0 \\ s_1 \\ s_2 \\ s_3 \\ s_4 \end{array}
\begin{pmatrix}
1 & 0 & 0 & 0 & 0 \\
\frac{1}{2} & 0 & \frac{1}{2} & 0 & 0 \\
0 & \frac{1}{2} & 0 & \frac{1}{2} & 0 \\
0 & 0 & \frac{1}{2} & 0 & \frac{1}{2} \\
0 & 0 & 0 & 0 & 1
\end{pmatrix}.
\end{array}
$$

The probability vector p_1 is $(0, 0, 1, 0, 0)$ for the initial state of having \$2. Then

$$
\begin{aligned}
p_2 &= p_1 M = (0, \quad \tfrac{1}{2}, \quad 0, \quad \tfrac{1}{2}, \quad 0), \\
p_3 &= p_2 M = (\tfrac{1}{4}, \quad 0, \quad \tfrac{1}{2}, \quad 0, \quad \tfrac{1}{4}), \\
p_4 &= p_3 M = (\tfrac{1}{4}, \quad \tfrac{1}{4}, \quad 0, \quad \tfrac{1}{4}, \quad \tfrac{1}{4}), \\
p_5 &= p_4 M = (\tfrac{3}{8}, \quad 0, \quad \tfrac{1}{4}, \quad 0, \quad \tfrac{3}{8}), \\
p_6 &= p_5 M = (\tfrac{3}{8}, \quad \tfrac{1}{8}, \quad 0, \quad \tfrac{1}{8}, \quad \tfrac{3}{8}), \\
p_7 &= p_6 M = (\tfrac{7}{16}, \quad 0, \quad \tfrac{1}{8}, \quad 0, \quad \tfrac{7}{16}),
\end{aligned}
$$

and so forth. The states s_0 and s_4 appear to be *absorbing* the probabilities. This occurs because it is possible to get into at least one of these states from each of the others and it is not possible to leave either the state s_0 or the state s_4. The impossibility of leaving each state can be seen from the fact that each state is represented by a fixed vector of the transition matrix

$$(1\ \ 0\ \ 0\ \ 0\ \ 0)M = (1\ \ 0\ \ 0\ \ 0\ \ 0),$$
$$(0\ \ 0\ \ 0\ \ 0\ \ 1)M = (0\ \ 0\ \ 0\ \ 0\ \ 1).$$

In any Markov chain a state that it is impossible to leave is an **absorbing state**. If also it is possible to go from each state to at least one absorbing state, then the Markov chain is an **absorbing chain**. The Markov chain for the two gamblers with \$2 each is an absorbing chain with s_0 and s_4 as absorbing states.

The same matrix may be useful for several Markov chains. For example, the matrix for the Markov chain for the two gamblers with \$2 each can also be used for a **random walk** along a number line. See Fig. 4.4.

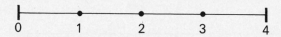

Fig. 4.4

Suppose that one starts at the point with coordinate 2, steps right or left one unit each with probability $\frac{1}{2}$, and stops completely whenever one of the barriers at points with coordinates 0 and 4 are reached. The possible outcomes are 0, 1, 2, 3, 4. The transition matrix is:

$$
\begin{array}{c}
 \\
0 \\
1 \\
2 \\
3 \\
4
\end{array}
\begin{array}{ccccc}
0 & 1 & 2 & 3 & 4 \\
\begin{pmatrix}
1 & 0 & 0 & 0 & 0 \\
\frac{1}{2} & 0 & \frac{1}{2} & 0 & 0 \\
0 & \frac{1}{2} & 0 & \frac{1}{2} & 0 \\
0 & 0 & \frac{1}{2} & 0 & \frac{1}{2} \\
0 & 0 & 0 & 0 & 1
\end{pmatrix}
\end{array}.
$$

Thus the mathematical model for this Markov chain is the same as for the gamblers with \$2 each.

Exercises

1. Consider the transition matrix:

$$\begin{array}{cc} & \begin{array}{cc} s_1 & s_2 \end{array} \\ \begin{array}{c} s_1 \\ s_2 \end{array} & \begin{pmatrix} 1 & 0 \\ 0 & 1 \end{pmatrix} \end{array}.$$

   a) Is $(\frac{1}{2}, \frac{1}{2})$ a fixed vector?
   b) Is (a, b) a fixed vector for any numbers a and b?
   c) Is s_1 an absorbing state?
   d) Is any associated Markov chain an absorbing chain?

2. Repeat Exercise 1 for the matrix:

$$\begin{pmatrix} 0 & 1 \\ 1 & 0 \end{pmatrix}.$$

3. Consider the transition matrix:

$$\begin{pmatrix} 1 & 0 \\ \frac{1}{2} & \frac{1}{2} \end{pmatrix}.$$

   a) Is $(1, 0)$ a fixed vector?
   b) Is the state s_1 corresponding to $(1, 0)$ an absorbing state?
   c) For $p_1 = (0, 1)$, find $p_2, p_3, p_4,$ and p_5.
   d) Is any associated Markov chain an absorbing chain?

4. Repeat Exercise 3 for the matrix:

$$\begin{pmatrix} 1 & 0 \\ \frac{1}{4} & \frac{3}{4} \end{pmatrix}.$$

5. For a given probability vector p_1 and transition matrix M we know that for $k \geq 1$ the probability vector $p_{k+1} = p_k M$. Express in terms of p_1 and powers of M: $p_2, p_3, p_4, p_5,$ and p_{k+1}.

6. Assume that states s_1, s_2, s_3 have transition matrix M where

$$\begin{array}{cc} & \begin{array}{ccc} s_1 & s_2 & s_3 \end{array} \\ \begin{array}{c} s_1 \\ s_2 \\ s_3 \end{array} & \begin{pmatrix} 0 & 1 & 0 \\ 0 & 0 & 1 \\ 1 & 0 & 0 \end{pmatrix} \end{array}.$$

   a) Find $M^2, M^3,$ and M^4.
   b) For $p_{11} = (1, 0, 0)$ find $p_{12}, p_{13}, p_{14},$ and p_{15}.
   c) For $p_{21} = (0, 1, 0)$ find $p_{22}, p_{23}, p_{24},$ and p_{25}.
   d) For $p_{31} = (0, 0, 1)$ find $p_{32}, p_{33}, p_{34},$ and p_{35}.
   e) Interpret the row vectors of $M, M^2, M^3,$ and M^4 in terms of the answers for parts (b), (c), and (d).

7. Repeat parts (a) and (b) of Exercise 6 for the matrix

$$\begin{pmatrix} \frac{1}{2} & 0 & \frac{1}{2} \\ 0 & 1 & 0 \\ \frac{1}{2} & \frac{1}{2} & 0 \end{pmatrix}.$$

Bill and Bob are shooting at a can on a fence post with a 22 rifle. Bill hits the can 4 out of 10 times. Bob hits the can 5 out of 10 times. Each boy shoots until he fails to hit the can, then it becomes the other boy's turn. Think of the states

s_1: Bill shoots at the can.
s_2: Bob shoots at the can.

8. a) Find the transition matrix M.

   b) Suppose that Bill starts; that is, $p_{11} = (1, 0)$. Find and interpret p_{12}.

9. a) Find M^2.

   b) If $p_{11} = (1, 0)$, what is the probability that Bill takes the third shot at the can?

   c) If $p_{21} = (0, 1)$, what is the probability that Bill takes the third shot at the can?

10. a) Find M^3 and M^4 to two decimal places.

    b) Note that as n increases M^n approaches a matrix with the same row vector p on each row. Verify that this vector p is a fixed vector (actually the unique fixed vector) of M. Give an interpretation of p.

Supplementary Exercises

For each of these Markov chains repeat (a) Exercise 8(a); (b) Exercise 8(b); (c) Exercise 9(a); (d) Exercise 9(b); and (e) Exercise 9(c) of the previous set of exercises.

1. Bill hits 2 out of 3 and Bob misses 2 out of 3.
2. Bill never misses and Bob hits 2 out of 3.
3. Bill hits only 1 out of 10 and Bob misses only 1 out of 10.
4. Bill hits 4 out of 10 and Bob hits 4 out of 10.
5. Bill hits 6 out of 10 and Bob hits 6 out of 10.

Determine whether or not each transition matrix is for an absorbing chain:

6. $\begin{pmatrix} 1 & 0 \\ 0 & 1 \end{pmatrix}.$ 7. $\begin{pmatrix} 1 & 0 \\ \frac{1}{2} & \frac{1}{2} \end{pmatrix}.$

8. $\begin{pmatrix} 1 & 0 & 0 \\ 0 & 0 & 1 \\ 0 & 1 & 0 \end{pmatrix}.$ 9. $\begin{pmatrix} 1 & 0 & 0 \\ \frac{1}{3} & \frac{1}{3} & \frac{1}{3} \\ 0 & 0 & 1 \end{pmatrix}.$

10. $\begin{pmatrix} \frac{1}{3} & \frac{1}{3} & \frac{1}{3} \\ \frac{1}{2} & 0 & \frac{1}{2} \\ 0 & 0 & 1 \end{pmatrix}.$ 11. $\begin{pmatrix} \frac{1}{2} & \frac{1}{4} & \frac{1}{4} \\ \frac{1}{4} & \frac{1}{2} & \frac{1}{4} \\ \frac{1}{3} & \frac{1}{3} & \frac{1}{3} \end{pmatrix}.$

Make a flowchart of steps that can be used to determine whether or not a square matrix:

12. Can be used as a transition matrix.

13. That is a transition matrix has an absorbing state.

14. That is a transition matrix with at least one absorbing state is the matrix of an absorbing chain.

. . . .

4.6 MATRICES AND SYSTEMS OF LINEAR EQUATIONS

An equation such as

$$2x + 3 = 11$$

in one variable may be solved by finding an equivalent (same solution) equation of the form

$$x = r.$$

An equivalent equation is obtained whenever:

1. the same number is added to (or subtracted from) both sides of an equation; or

2. both sides of an equation are multiplied (or divided) by the same nonzero number.

For the equation $2x + 3 = 11$, we subtract 3 from both sides of the equation and obtain

$$2x = 8.$$

Then we divide both sides by 2 and obtain

$$x = 4.$$

An equation such as

$$x + 2y = 7$$

in two variables may be solved for either variable in terms of the other;

$$x = 7 - 2y, \qquad y = \tfrac{1}{2}(7 - x).$$

However, a *system* of two equations is needed to obtain a solution of the form

$$x = r, \qquad y = s,$$

where r and s are numbers. We first express each equation in the form

$$ax + by = c, \tag{1}$$

where a and b are not both zero. Any equation of the form (1) has the numbers a and b as **coefficients**, has c as its **constant term**, has a straight line as its **graph** on a coordinate plane, and is a **linear equation** in x and y.

Consider the system of equations

$$\begin{cases} x + 2y = 7, \\ x - y = 4. \end{cases} \tag{2}$$

This system of equations has as its solution the coordinates of the point of intersection of the graphs of the two equations (Fig. 4.5). To solve the system we find an equivalent (same solution) system of the form

$$\begin{cases} x = r, \\ y = s. \end{cases}$$

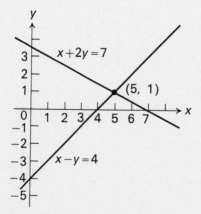

Fig. 4.5

An equivalent system may be obtained in the same ways that an equivalent equation may be found for equations in one variable. The solution of the system (2) requires several steps. Also any one of several sequences of steps could be used. We first note that the second equation of the system (2) is a statement that "$x - y$" and "4" are names for the same number. We subtract this number from both sides of the first equation to obtain the equivalent system

$$\begin{cases} 3y = 3, \\ x - y = 4. \end{cases} \tag{3}$$

This first step is usually described as "replacing the first equation by itself minus the second equation." Next we divide (both members of) the first equation of the new system by 3 and obtain the system

$$\begin{cases} y = 1, \\ x - y = 4. \end{cases} \tag{4}$$

Then we replace the second equation by itself plus the first

$$\begin{cases} y = 1, \\ x = 5, \end{cases} \tag{5}$$

and interchange equations to obtain the solution in its preferred form

$$\begin{cases} x = 5, \\ y = 1. \end{cases} \tag{6}$$

The amount of writing needed to solve the system (2) can be substantially reduced using matrices. We first detach the coefficients and the constants (as the right members of the equations) to obtain the matrix

$$\begin{pmatrix} 1 & 2 & 7 \\ 1 & -1 & 4 \end{pmatrix}. \tag{2'}$$

Then we perform the same sequence of operations on the rows of the matrix (2') that we used on the equations of the system (2). Specifically, we replace the first row by itself minus the second row and obtain

$$\begin{pmatrix} 0 & 3 & 3 \\ 1 & -1 & 4 \end{pmatrix}. \tag{3'}$$

We divide the (members of the) first row by 3 and obtain

$$\begin{pmatrix} 0 & 1 & 1 \\ 1 & -1 & 4 \end{pmatrix}. \tag{4'}$$

We replace the second row by itself plus the first and obtain

$$\begin{pmatrix} 0 & 1 & 1 \\ 1 & 0 & 5 \end{pmatrix}. \tag{5'}$$

We interchange rows

$$\begin{pmatrix} 1 & 0 & 5 \\ 0 & 1 & 1 \end{pmatrix} \tag{6'}$$

and we *translate* the matrix (6') as the system of equations (6).

The following operations upon the rows of a matrix are called **row transformations**:

1. The elements of any row may be multiplied (or divided) by any nonzero number.
2. Any row may be replaced by itself plus (or minus) any fixed multiple of another row.
3. Any two rows may be interchanged.

We assume from the corresponding treatment of the equations that when row transformations are used on a matrix such as (2') for a system of linear equations, a matrix for an equivalent system (same solutions) of equations is obtained.

We consider a special form of matrix before solving additional systems of equations. The elements $a_{11}, a_{22}, a_{33}, \ldots$ on the first row and first column, the second row and second column, the third row and third column, and so forth are the **diagonal elements** of the matrix. A square matrix with all elements 0 except possibly its diagonal elements is a **diagonal matrix**. For example, these are diagonal matrices:

$$\begin{pmatrix} 1 & 0 \\ 0 & 2 \end{pmatrix}, \quad \begin{pmatrix} 3 & 0 & 0 \\ 0 & 2 & 0 \\ 0 & 0 & 5 \end{pmatrix}, \quad \begin{pmatrix} 1 & 0 & 0 \\ 0 & 2 & 0 \\ 0 & 0 & 0 \end{pmatrix}.$$

Row transformations may be used to transform any square matrix into a diagonal matrix. Indeed, this may be done so that all nonzero diagonal elements are ones.

Example 1 Use row transformations and transform the given matrix into a diagonal matrix:

$$\begin{pmatrix} 2 & 1 & -1 \\ 1 & 4 & 5 \\ 3 & -1 & 2 \end{pmatrix}.$$

Solution. One very effective general approach is to:

1. select a number, preferably 1, in a column.
2. make all other elements in that column 0.
3. proceed with another number in a different row and column.
4. reorder the rows.

In the following solution the selected numbers are circled and at each stage the row vectors r_1, r_2, r_3 refer to the rows of the matrix at the immediately preceding stage. Note that arrows are used to show the sequence of matrices since the matrices are *not* equal matrices. Other sequences of steps could be used.

$$\begin{pmatrix} 2 & ① & -1 \\ 1 & 4 & 5 \\ 3 & -1 & 2 \end{pmatrix} \rightarrow \begin{pmatrix} 2 & 1 & -1 \\ -7 & 0 & 9 \\ 5 & 0 & ① \end{pmatrix} \quad \begin{array}{l} r_1 \\ r_2 - 4r_1 \\ r_3 + r_1 \end{array}$$

$$\rightarrow \begin{pmatrix} 7 & 1 & 0 \\ \boxed{-52} & 0 & 0 \\ 5 & 0 & 1 \end{pmatrix} \quad \begin{array}{l} r_1 + r_3 \\ r_2 - 9r_3 \\ r_3 \end{array}$$

$$\rightarrow \begin{pmatrix} 0 & 1 & 0 \\ 1 & 0 & 0 \\ 0 & 0 & 1 \end{pmatrix} \quad \begin{array}{l} r_1 + (\frac{7}{52})r_2 \\ (-\frac{1}{52})r_2 \\ r_1 + (\frac{5}{52})r_2 \end{array}$$

$$\rightarrow \begin{pmatrix} 1 & 0 & 0 \\ 0 & 1 & 0 \\ 0 & 0 & 1 \end{pmatrix} \quad \begin{array}{l} r_2 \\ r_1 \\ r_3 \end{array}$$

Example 2 Use a matrix and row transformations to solve the system

$$\begin{cases} 3y + x = 1, \\ 2x + y = 7. \end{cases}$$

Solution. A matrix is formed with a row for each equation, a column for the coefficients of each variable, and a column for the constant terms as the right members of the equations. Row transformations are used to make the first two rows and two columns into a diagonal matrix with ones as diagonal elements. Note that the system is considered first in the form

$$\begin{cases} x + 3y = 1, \\ 2x + y = 7. \end{cases}$$

$$\begin{pmatrix} \textcircled{1} & 3 & 1 \\ 2 & 1 & 7 \end{pmatrix} \rightarrow \begin{pmatrix} 1 & 3 & 1 \\ 0 & -5 & 5 \end{pmatrix} \quad \begin{matrix} r_1 \\ r_2 - 2r_1 \end{matrix}$$

$$\rightarrow \begin{pmatrix} 1 & 3 & 1 \\ 0 & \textcircled{1} & -1 \end{pmatrix} \quad \begin{matrix} r_1 \\ r_2/(-5) \end{matrix}$$

$$\rightarrow \begin{pmatrix} 1 & 0 & 4 \\ 0 & 1 & -1 \end{pmatrix} \quad \begin{matrix} r_1 - 3r_2 \\ r_2 \end{matrix}$$

Note that the last two steps could have been combined. Translate the last matrix as

$$\begin{cases} x = 4, \\ y = -1. \end{cases}$$

Check by substitution in the original system of equations:

$$4 + 3(-1) = 1,$$
$$2(4) + (-1) = 7.$$

Example 3 Solve by matrices

$$\begin{cases} x + y + z = 2, \\ x - 2y = 0, \\ 2x - 2y + z = 1. \end{cases}$$

First solution.

$$\begin{pmatrix} 1 & 1 & ① & 2 \\ 1 & -2 & 0 & 0 \\ 2 & -2 & 1 & 1 \end{pmatrix} \to \begin{pmatrix} 1 & 1 & 1 & 2 \\ ① & -2 & 0 & 0 \\ 1 & -3 & 0 & -1 \end{pmatrix} \begin{matrix} r_1 \\ r_2 \\ r_3 - r_1 \end{matrix}$$

$$\to \begin{pmatrix} 0 & 3 & 1 & 2 \\ 1 & -2 & 0 & 0 \\ 0 & ⊖① & 0 & -1 \end{pmatrix} \begin{matrix} r_1 - r_2 \\ r_2 \\ r_3 - r_2 \end{matrix}$$

$$\to \begin{pmatrix} 0 & 0 & 1 & -1 \\ 1 & 0 & 0 & 2 \\ 0 & 1 & 0 & 1 \end{pmatrix} \begin{matrix} r_1 + 3r_3 \\ r_2 - 2r_3 \\ r_3 \end{matrix}$$

$$\to \begin{pmatrix} 1 & 0 & 0 & 2 \\ 0 & 1 & 0 & 1 \\ 0 & 0 & 1 & -1 \end{pmatrix} \begin{matrix} r_2 \\ r_3 \\ r_1 \end{matrix}$$

$$\begin{cases} x = 2, \\ y = 1, \\ z = -1. \end{cases}$$

Check.

$$2 + 1 + (-1) = 2,$$
$$2 - 2(1) = 0,$$
$$2(2) - 2(1) + (-1) = 1.$$

Second solution.

$$\begin{pmatrix} ① & 1 & 1 & 2 \\ 1 & -2 & 0 & 0 \\ 2 & -2 & 1 & 1 \end{pmatrix} \to \begin{pmatrix} 1 & 1 & 1 & 2 \\ 0 & -3 & -1 & -2 \\ 0 & -4 & -1 & -3 \end{pmatrix} \begin{matrix} r_1 \\ r_2 - r_1 \\ r_3 - 2r_1 \end{matrix}$$

$$\to \begin{pmatrix} 1 & 1 & 1 & 2 \\ 0 & ① & 0 & 1 \\ 0 & -4 & -1 & -3 \end{pmatrix} \begin{matrix} r_1 \\ r_2 - r_3 \\ r_3 \end{matrix}$$

$$\to \begin{pmatrix} 1 & 0 & 1 & 1 \\ 0 & 1 & 0 & 1 \\ 0 & 0 & ⊖① & 1 \end{pmatrix} \begin{matrix} r_1 - r_2 \\ r_2 \\ r_3 + 4r_2 \end{matrix}$$

$$\to \begin{pmatrix} 1 & 0 & 0 & 2 \\ 0 & 1 & 0 & 1 \\ 0 & 0 & 1 & -1 \end{pmatrix} \begin{matrix} r_1 + r_3 \\ r_2 \\ -r_3 \end{matrix}$$

The rest of the solution is the same as for the first solution. The second step of the second solution illustrates the use of a combination of rows to obtain a 1 or other convenient element.

Example 4   Solve by matrices

$$\begin{cases} x + y = 1, \\ 2x + 2y = 5. \end{cases}$$

Solution.

$$\begin{pmatrix} \text{①} & 1 & 1 \\ 2 & 2 & 5 \end{pmatrix} \rightarrow \begin{pmatrix} 1 & 1 & 1 \\ 0 & 0 & 3 \end{pmatrix} \begin{matrix} r_1 \\ r_2 - 2r_1 \end{matrix}$$

The second row can be translated as $0x + 0y = 3$; that is, $0 = 3$, which is impossible. Thus the given system does not have a solution and the solution set is $\varnothing$.

In general, if a system such as the one in Example 4 does not have a solution, the equations of the system are said to be **inconsistent equations**.

Example 5   Solve by matrices

$$\begin{cases} x + y = 1, \\ 2x + 2y = 2. \end{cases}$$

Solution.

$$\begin{pmatrix} \text{①} & 1 & 1 \\ 2 & 2 & 2 \end{pmatrix} \rightarrow \begin{pmatrix} 1 & 1 & 1 \\ 0 & 0 & 0 \end{pmatrix} \begin{matrix} r_1 \\ r_2 - 2r_1 \end{matrix}$$

The second row can be translated as $0x + 0y = 0$; that is, $0 = 0$, which is always true. Thus the second equation does not add any additional restriction upon the values of x and y. The system is equivalent to the single equation $x + y = 1$; that is, $y = 1 - x$. For every real number x the ordered pair $(x, 1 - x)$ is a solution. Thus the system has infinitely many solutions $\{(x, 1 - x)\}$.

In general, an equation such as the second equation in Example 5 that can be expressed in terms of the other equations of a system (in this case $r_2 = 2r_1$) is said to be *linearly dependent* upon the other equations. An equation is **linearly dependent** upon the others in a system if and only if its row can be transformed into a row of zeros by row transformations. Similarly, a row of a matrix is said to be linearly dependent upon the other rows if and only if it can be transformed into a row of zeros by row transformations.

Any equation in which each variable that occurs is to the first power and there is at least one such variable is a **linear equation**. For example,

$$x = 2,$$
$$x + y - 2z + 7 = 0,$$
$$u + v - w + 2x + 5y - 3z = 13$$

are linear equations. Row transformations and matrices may be used to solve any system of a finite number of linear equations in a finite number of variables. If the system has a unique solution, that solution can be found. If the system has no solution, that fact can be established. If the system has infinitely many solutions, representatives of them can be found. Linear equations are used extensively in linear programming (Chapter 5).

. . . .

Exercises

Identify each row of the new matrix in terms of the row vectors r_1, r_2, r_3 of the previous matrix:

1. $\begin{pmatrix} 2 & 3 & 5 & 4 \\ 1 & 2 & 0 & -1 \\ 3 & 4 & 5 & 6 \end{pmatrix} \rightarrow \begin{pmatrix} 0 & -1 & 5 & 6 \\ 1 & 2 & 0 & -1 \\ 0 & -2 & 5 & 9 \end{pmatrix}.$

2. $\begin{pmatrix} 2 & 3 & 5 & 4 \\ 1 & 2 & 0 & -1 \\ 3 & 4 & 5 & 6 \end{pmatrix} \rightarrow \begin{pmatrix} 3 & 5 & 5 & 3 \\ 1 & 2 & 0 & -1 \\ 1 & 1 & 0 & 2 \end{pmatrix}.$

3. $\begin{pmatrix} 2 & 3 & 4 \\ 5 & 2 & 7 \\ -2 & -3 & 1 \\ 4 & 6 & 8 \end{pmatrix} \overset{(a)}{\rightarrow} \begin{pmatrix} 0 & 0 & 5 \\ 1 & -4 & 9 \\ -2 & -3 & 1 \\ 0 & 0 & 10 \end{pmatrix} \overset{(b)}{\rightarrow} \begin{pmatrix} 0 & 0 & 1 \\ 1 & -4 & 0 \\ 0 & -11 & 19 \\ 0 & 0 & 0 \end{pmatrix}.$

4. $\begin{pmatrix} -2 & 0 & -3 \\ 2 & 1 & -2 \\ 4 & 7 & 9 \\ -6 & 2 & 5 \end{pmatrix} \rightarrow \begin{pmatrix} 2 & 0 & 3 \\ 0 & 1 & -5 \\ 0 & 7 & 3 \\ 0 & 2 & 14 \end{pmatrix}.$

Use row transformations and transform the given matrix into a diagonal matrix. Indicate the transformations used as in Exercises 1 through 4.

5. $\begin{pmatrix} 1 & 2 \\ 4 & -3 \end{pmatrix}.$ 6. $\begin{pmatrix} 2 & 1 \\ -1 & 2 \end{pmatrix}.$

7. $\begin{pmatrix} 1 & 5 & -3 \\ 2 & 12 & 1 \\ 3 & 2 & 4 \end{pmatrix}$.

8. $\begin{pmatrix} 5 & 3 & 1 \\ 2 & 4 & 6 \\ -3 & 0 & -1 \end{pmatrix}$.

Solve by matrices:

9. $\begin{cases} x - y = 3, \\ 2x + y = 0. \end{cases}$

10. $\begin{cases} 2x - y = 5, \\ 3x + 4y = 2. \end{cases}$

11. $\begin{cases} 2y = 1 - x, \\ x = y + 7. \end{cases}$

12. $\begin{cases} x = y - 1, \\ y = x + 1. \end{cases}$

13. $\begin{cases} x - y = 5, \\ 2x - 2y = 7. \end{cases}$

14. $\begin{cases} 2x + 3y = 1, \\ 3x + 2y = 4. \end{cases}$

Supplementary Exercises

Solve by matrices:

1. $\begin{cases} x - y + z = 4, \\ 2x + y - z = 2, \\ y + z = 4. \end{cases}$

2. $\begin{cases} x + 2y - z = 6, \\ 3x + y + 2z = -7, \\ 3x - 2y + 3z = -16. \end{cases}$

3. $\begin{cases} x - y - z = 3, \\ 4x + 3y + 4z = 4, \\ y + 2z = -2. \end{cases}$

4. $\begin{cases} x + y - z = 5, \\ x + z = 7. \end{cases}$

5. $\begin{cases} x - y - 2z - 3w = -2, \\ 3x + 2y + w = 1, \\ 3x - 3z - 5w = -3, \\ 2x + 2z + 7w = 6. \end{cases}$

6. $\begin{cases} x + y - w = 5, \\ 2y + z + 3w = 8, \\ 3x - y - z - 2w = 3, \\ 2x + y + 2z + w = 3. \end{cases}$

Show that the first equation is linearly dependent upon the others in the given system:

7. $\begin{cases} 4x + 8y = 2, \\ 2x + 4y = 1. \end{cases}$

8. $\begin{cases} x + 2z = 3, \\ x + y = -2, \\ - y + 2z = 5. \end{cases}$

· ·

REVIEW EXERCISES FOR CHAPTER 4

1. Identify the vectors that are conformable for addition with $(2, 1)$:
   a) $(1, 2)$;   b) $(1, 2)^t$;   c) $(1, 0, 2)$.

2. Identify the vectors in Exercise 1 that are conformable for scalar multiplication with $(2, 1)$.

For Exercises 3 through 5 let $u = (2, 0, 3)$ and $v = (1, 2, -1)$. Find:

3. a) $2u$;   b) $3v$.

4. a) $u + v$;   b) $u - v$.

5. a) $2u + 3v$;   b) $2u - 2v$.

6. Solve the vector equation for each variable

$$3 \begin{pmatrix} x \\ y \\ z - 1 \end{pmatrix} + \begin{pmatrix} 1 \\ 4 \\ -2 \end{pmatrix} = \begin{pmatrix} 7 \\ 1 \\ 4 \end{pmatrix}.$$

7. Ruth works on work scholarship at \$1.75, baby sitting at \$1 an hour, and typing at \$2.50 an hour. If she works 8 hours on work scholarship, 3 hours baby sitting, and 5 hours typing in one week, express in dollars her earnings for the week as a scalar product of row vectors.

For Exercises 8 through 10 let

$$A = \begin{pmatrix} 1 & -2 & 3 \\ 2 & 0 & 1 \end{pmatrix} \quad \text{and} \quad B = \begin{pmatrix} 2 & 1 & -1 \\ 1 & 2 & -2 \end{pmatrix}.$$

Find:

8. a) $2A$;   b) $-B$.

9. a) $A + B$;   b) $A - B$.

10. a) $A + 2B$;   b) $2A + 3B$.

11. Form a transition matrix for this Markov chain. Judy sticks a pin in a 6-inch ruler at the 3-inch mark and moves the pin one inch to the left or right according to the flip of an unbiased coin as heads or tails. When the pin reaches the 0- or 6-inch end of the ruler, the pin stays there and the game is over.

12. Find: $\begin{pmatrix} 0 & 1 & 1 \\ 1 & -1 & 0 \\ -1 & 0 & 1 \end{pmatrix} \begin{pmatrix} a & b & c \\ d & e & f \\ g & h & i \end{pmatrix}.$

13. Find M^2 and M^3 for the given matrix M:

$$\begin{pmatrix} 0 & 1 & 0 \\ 1 & 0 & -1 \\ 0 & -1 & 1 \end{pmatrix}.$$

14. The elements of the matrix M indicate the numbers of hours that Ruth worked at each type of work for each of four weeks. See Exercise 7 for earnings per hour.

week	1	2	3	4
scholarship	8	8	8	8
baby sitting	3	5	0	1
typing	5	2	7	6

a) Let p be her earnings vector. Find and interpret the elements of pM.

b) Find a matrix product that will have as its elements the total number of hours that she worked each week.

c) Find a product of three matrices that will have as its element her total earnings for the four weeks.

15. Consider the transition matrix:

$$\begin{pmatrix} 1 & 0 & 0 \\ \frac{1}{3} & \frac{1}{3} & \frac{1}{3} \\ 0 & 0 & 1 \end{pmatrix}.$$

a) Is $(1, 0, 0)$ a fixed vector?

b) Is the state s_1 corresponding to $(1, 0, 0)$ an absorbing state?

c) Is any associated Markov chain an absorbing chain?

d) Is $(\frac{1}{3}, \frac{1}{3}, \frac{1}{3})$ a fixed vector?

e) Is $(\frac{1}{2}, 0, \frac{1}{2})$ a fixed vector?

f) Is s_2 an absorbing state?

16. Consider the transition matrix:

$$\begin{pmatrix} 1 & 0 \\ \frac{1}{5} & \frac{4}{5} \end{pmatrix}.$$

a) Is $(1, 0)$ a fixed vector?

b) Is s_1 an absorbing state?

c) If $p_{21} = (0, 1)$, find p_{22}, p_{23}, and p_{24}.

d) Is any associated Markov chain an absorbing chain?

17. Use row transformations and transform the given matrix into a diagonal matrix:

$$\begin{pmatrix} 4 & -1 & 3 \\ 2 & 3 & 1 \\ 0 & 2 & -1 \end{pmatrix}.$$

Solve by matrices:

18. $\begin{cases} 3x + 2y = 7, \\ 2x - y = 0. \end{cases}$

19. $\begin{cases} 4x - 3y = 12, \\ 8x - 6y = 6. \end{cases}$

20. $\begin{cases} x + 2y - z = 6, \\ 3x + y - 2z = 5, \\ 2x + 3y + z = 1. \end{cases}$

linear programming 5

Linear programming is an important and widely used area of mathematics. Consider for example:

1. the distribution of a manufactured product, raw material, or mail from several sources to several destinations in such a manner as to minimize cost or time.
2. the routing of telephone calls, electrical energy, automobile traffic, delivery trucks, service men, or sales men to minimize delays.
3. the assignment of tasks to employees and machines to maximize productivity or profits.
4. the use of raw materials to minimize waste.
5. the use of available materials (vitamins, building materials, etc.) to meet minimum standards and minimize cost.

Unfortunately detailed discussions of most significant applications require a specialized knowledge of the field in which the application is made. Also most significant problems can be solved only by very detailed computations for which electronic computers are practically essential.

The present introduction of linear programming includes only the simplified forms of basic procedures. Both the techniques used and the types of problems that can be solved are illustrated but the presentation and the problems are restricted to computations that can reasonably be done by hand.

This introduction of linear programming completes the second major stage of our introduction to finite mathematics. The final chapter, game theory, includes a significant application of the simplex algorithm and duality used in solving linear programming problems.

5.1 LINEAR STATEMENTS IN ONE VARIABLE

Any linear equation in one variable x may be expressed in the form

$$ax + b = 0, \quad a \neq 0. \tag{1}$$

Then $x = -b/a$ and the graph of the equation (1) is the point $P_{-b/a}$ on a number line. For example, the equation $2x - 6 = 0$ has P_3 as its graph that is shown in Fig. 5.1.

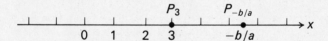

Fig. 5.1

On the number line the points on the right of P_3 form a **half-line** $\{P_x : x > 3\}$. This half-line is the graph of $2x - 6 > 0$ since $2x - 6 > 0$ if and only if $x > 3$. We emphasize that P_3 is not a member of the half-line by calling the half-line an **open half-line**. A hollow dot is used to show that P_3 is not a point of the graph of $x > 3$.

The set of points $\{P_x : x \geq 3\}$ including P_3 is called a **closed half-line** or **ray**. A solid dot is used to show that P_3 is a point of the graph of $x \geq 3$. These and other related graphs in Fig. 5.2 illustrate the various common forms of linear statements.

The solution sets and graphs for any linear statements

$$ax + b = 0, \quad ax + b < 0, \quad ax + b > 0,$$
$$ax + b \neq 0, \quad ax + b \geq 0, \quad ax + b \leq 0$$

are similar to those considered for $ax + b = 2x - 6$.

On a number line each linear statement $ax + b = 0$ has a point as its graph; $ax + b \neq 0$ has the rest of the line (the complement, Section

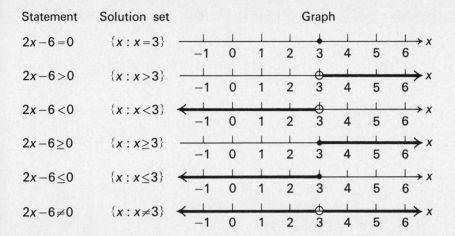

Statement	Solution set	Graph

$2x-6=0$ $\{x : x=3\}$

$2x-6>0$ $\{x : x>3\}$

$2x-6<0$ $\{x : x<3\}$

$2x-6\geq0$ $\{x : x\geq3\}$

$2x-6\leq0$ $\{x : x\leq3\}$

$2x-6\neq0$ $\{x : x\neq3\}$

Fig. 5.2

2.3) as its graph. Each statement $ax + b < 0$ has an open half-line as its graph; $ax + b \geq 0$ (also written as $ax + b \not< 0$) has the rest of the line, a closed half-line as its graph. Similarly, the open half-line that is the graph of $ax + b > 0$ is the complement of the closed half-line that is the graph of $ax + b \leq 0$ (also written $ax + b \not> 0$).

Each of the graphs of linear statements involving $<$, $\leq$, $>$, or $\geq$ has the property that if A and B are points of the graph, then the line segment $\overline{AB}$ is a subset of the graph. This property is described by saying that the graph is a **convex set**.

The **solution set** of a system of statements is the set of all values of the variable(s) that satisfy each and every one of the statements of the system.

Example   Graph the system

$$\begin{cases} x \geq 0, \\ 2x \leq 6. \end{cases}$$

Solution. The graph of the given system is $\{P_x : 0 \leq x \leq 3\}$, the line segment that is the graph of the solution set of the system. See Fig. 5.3.

We may use systems of linear statements to solve problems.

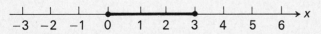

Fig. 5.3

Suppose that John has three cords of wood that he could sell as fireplace wood or he could saw and split it into stove wood before selling it. He estimates that it will cost him $4 a cord to deliver the fireplace wood and $30 a cord to prepare and deliver the stove wood. He can sell the fireplace wood for $25 a cord and the stove wood for $50 a cord. How much of the wood should he sell as fireplace wood and how much as stove wood?

Let x be the number of cords of fireplace wood sold. Then $3 - x$ is the number of cords of stove wood sold. The system of linear statements restricting the value of x is

$$\begin{cases} 0 \leq x, \\ x \leq 3. \end{cases}$$

His profit p is $25x - 4x$ for the fireplace wood and $50(3 - x) - 30(3 - x)$ for the stove wood. Thus

$$\begin{aligned} p &= (25x - 4x) + [50(3 - x) - 30(3 - x)] \\ &= 25x - 4x + 20(3 - x) \\ &= 21x + 60 - 20x \\ &= x + 60. \end{aligned}$$

We now have a very elementary **linear programming problem**. Specifically, we wish to maximize a linear expression, called the **objective function**,

$$p = x + 60$$

subject to the **constraints**

$$\begin{cases} 0 \leq x, \\ x \leq 3. \end{cases}$$

The points of the solution set of the system of inequalities are the **feasible points** corresponding to the **constraint set** of values of the variable. In other words, each of the feasible points represents a value of x that satisfies all of the constraints of the problem. At each of the feasible points the objective function has a value, called the **program value** at that point. For our particular linear programming problem the profit is $60 for $x = 0$ and $63 for $x = 3$. In other words, the profit selling all of the wood as stove wood is $60 and the profit selling all of the wood as fireplace wood is \$63. Since $0 \leq x \leq 3$ implies $60 \leq x + 60 \leq 63$, the maximum profit is \$63 and John should sell all of the wood as fireplace wood.

. . . .

Exercises

Graph each linear statement on a number line:

1. $3x - 12 \leq 0$.   2. $3 - x \leq 0$.
3. $2 + x \leq 0$.   4. $x + 3 \geq 0$.

Graph each system on a number line:

5. $\begin{cases} 0 \leq x, \\ 3x - 12 \leq 0. \end{cases}$ 6. $\begin{cases} x + 2 \geq 0, \\ x - 5 \leq 0. \end{cases}$

7. $\begin{cases} 3x + 6 \geq 0, \\ 5x - 10 \leq 0. \end{cases}$ 8. $\begin{cases} 6x - 4 < 0, \\ 2x + 3 > 0. \end{cases}$

Find the value of x for a maximum value of the function p subject to the given constraints:

9. $p: 25 - 2x,$ $\begin{cases} 0 \leq x, \\ 3x - 15 \leq 0. \end{cases}$

10. $p: 12 - 3x,$ $\begin{cases} 0 \leq x, \\ 2x - 10 \leq 0. \end{cases}$

11. $p: 100 - 20(3 - x),$ $\begin{cases} 0 \leq x, \\ 50 - 2x \geq 0. \end{cases}$

12. $p: 80 - 16(4 - x),$ $\begin{cases} 0 \leq x, \\ 35 - 7x \geq 0. \end{cases}$

Formulate and solve as a linear programming problem:

13. Bill picked six quarts of blueberries. He can sell them to a local grocery store for 50 cents a quart. He can also sell them from door to door around town for 70 cents a quart. He estimates the additional expense to him of going from door to door as 15 cents a quart. Let x be the number of quarts sold to the grocery store. Find an expression for:

   a) the number of quarts sold door to door,
   b) the profit from the blueberries sold to the grocery store,
   c) the profit from the blueberries sold door to door,
   d) the total profit,
   e) the constraints on x,
   f) the number of quarts that Bill should sell to the grocery store to maximize his net earnings.

14. Don has 800 pounds of newspapers. At a cost of 10 cents per hundred pounds he can sell as many as he wants to a local salvage company for 50 cents per hundred pounds. Bob offered to buy the papers for 35 cents a hundred pounds and pick them up himself. Let x be the number of hundreds of pounds of papers sold to Bob. Find an expression for:

    a) the number of hundreds of pounds sold to the salvage company,

    b) the total profit,

    c) the constraints on x,

    d) the number of hundreds of pounds of papers that Don should sell to Bob to maximize Don's profit.

15. The Acme Junk Yard has 150 junk cars. A metal salvage company offered to buy the cars at $15 each. The owner of the junk yard estimates that on an average junk car he receives $35 for the sale of parts and has an overhead expense of $21. Let x be the number of cars sold to the salvage company.

    a) Find an expression for the total profit.

    b) How many of the 150 junk cars should be sold to the salvage company to maximize the junk yard owner's profit?

16. A store chain has 500 pounds of peanuts and 300 pounds of walnuts. Suppose that peanuts can be sold for 25 cents per pound; a mixture by weight of two parts peanuts and one part walnuts can be sold at 40 cents per pound; and walnuts can be sold at 50 cents per pound. Let m be the number of pounds of the mixed nuts that are sold. Find:

    a) the number of pounds of nuts sold as peanuts,

    b) the number of pounds of nuts sold as walnuts,

    c) an expression for the profit,

    d) the constraints on m,

    e) for a maximum income to the stores the number of pounds of nuts that should be packaged in each of the three ways (peanuts, mixed nuts, walnuts).

. . . .

5.2 LINEAR STATEMENTS IN TWO VARIABLES

Any linear statement in two variables x and y may be expressed in the form

$$ax + by + c = 0,$$

where *a* and *b* are not both zero. On a coordinate plane each such equation has a line as its graph. If *a*, *b*, and *c* are all different from zero, the points at which the line crosses the coordinate axes can be used to determine the line. For example, if

$$2x + 3y - 6 = 0,$$

then $x = 3$ when $y = 0$, and $y = 2$ when $x = 0$. Thus, as in Fig. 5.4, the graph of $2x + 3y - 6 = 0$ contains the points $(3, 0)$ and $(0, 2)$. Usually a third point is obtained by selecting a value for one variable and solving for the corresponding value of the other variable. The third point serves as a check that the line has been graphed correctly.

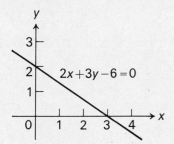

Fig. 5.4

      On the coordinate plane the points above the graph of $2x + 3y - 6 = 0$ form a **half-plane** $\{P_{(x, y)}: 2x + 3y - 6 > 0\}$. We emphasize that the line is not a subset of the half-plane by calling the half-plane an **open half-plane** (Fig. 5.5). The set of points below the line is the open half-plane that is the graph of $2x + 3y - 6 < 0$. For any given values of *x* and *y* exactly one of the relations

$$2x + 3y - 6 = 0, \quad 2x + 3y - 6 > 0, \quad 2x + 3y - 6 < 0$$

must hold. Similarly, any point (x, y) of the coordinate plane is on the line, above the line, or below the line. To identify which half-plane is the graph of an inequality such as $2x + 3y - 6 > 0$, we try the coordinates of any point that is not on the line. For example, at $(0, 0)$ we have $2x + 3y - 6 = -6 < 0$. Accordingly, the origin $(0, 0)$ is a point of the half-plane that is the graph of $2x + 3y - 6 < 0$ and the half-plane that does not contain the origin is the graph of the inequality $2x + 3y - 6 > 0$.

The set of points $\{P_{(x,y)}: 2x + 3y - 6 \geq 0\}$ including the points of the line is a **closed half-plane**. Similarly, the graph of $2x + 3y - 6 \leq 0$ is a closed half-plane (Fig. 5.6). We use a dashed line for the **edge** of an open half-plane (Fig. 5.5) to show that the line is not a subset of the open half-plane. We use a solid line (Fig. 5.6) for the edge of a closed half-plane to show that the line is a subset of the closed half-plane. Note that an open half-plane and a closed half-plane are each convex sets.

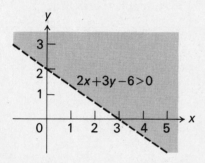

Fig. 5.5

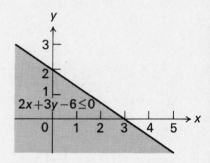

Fig. 5.6

Example   Graph the system

$$\begin{cases} x \geq 0, \\ y \geq 0, \\ 2x + 3y - 6 \leq 0. \end{cases}$$

Solution.

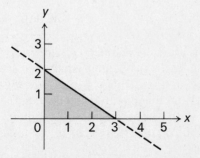

. . . .

Exercises

Graph each linear statement on a coordinate plane:
1. $3x + 4y - 12 \leq 0$.
2. $5x - 2y + 10 \geq 0$.
3. $x - 2y - 5 \geq 0$.
4. $3x + y - 4 \leq 0$.

Graph each system on a coordinate plane:

5. $\begin{cases} 0 \leq x, \\ 0 \leq y, \\ 2x + 4y - 8 \leq 0. \end{cases}$

6. $\begin{cases} x + y - 1 \leq 0, \\ x + 2 \geq 0, \\ y \geq 0. \end{cases}$

7. $\begin{cases} x - y + 4 \geq 0, \\ x - y - 4 \leq 0, \\ x + y + 4 \geq 0, \\ x + y - 4 \leq 0. \end{cases}$

8. $\begin{cases} x + 2y + 6 \geq 0, \\ x + 2y - 6 \leq 0, \\ x - 2y + 6 \geq 0, \\ x - 2y - 6 \leq 0. \end{cases}$

On the same coordinate axes graph the given equation for k equal to 0, 1, 2, and 4. Then label each graph with its equation.
9. $y = 2x + k$.
10. $x + y - k = 0$.
11. $\frac{1}{2}x + \frac{2}{3}y - k = 0$.
12. $\frac{1}{2}x - \frac{1}{3}y - k = 0$.

. . . .

5.3 LINEAR PROGRAMS WITH TWO VARIABLES

Suppose that Bill makes jig saw puzzles, carves wooden boats, and canes chair seats. The materials for a puzzle cost $1.00, the materials for a boat cost 70 cents, and the materials for a chair seat cost 80 cents. The time required for making a jig saw puzzle is about the same as for carving a boat or making a chair seat. He can do a total of any 20 items in his spare time in a month but wants to do at least two of each and at most five boats. He sells his puzzles for $5.25, his boats for $5.00, and his chair seats for $5.00. How many of each should he make each month to maximize his net earnings?

Let x be the number of jig saw puzzles made and y the number of boats carved. Then $20 - x - y$ is the number of chair seats made; $x(5.25 - 1.00)$ is his profit on puzzles; $y(5.00 - 0.70)$ is his profit on boats; and $(20 - x - y)(5.00 - 0.80)$ is his profit on chair seats. His total profit in cents is

$$p = 425x + 430y + (20 - x - y)(420)$$
$$= 5x + 10y + 8400.$$

We have a linear programming problem to maximize the function

$$p = 5x + 10y + 8400$$

subject to the constraints

$$\begin{cases} 2 \leq x, \\ 2 \leq y, \\ 2 \leq 20 - x - y, \\ y \leq 5. \end{cases}$$

The constraint $2 \leq 20 - x - y$ can also be expressed in the form $x + y \leq 18$. The graphs of the individual constraints are shown in Fig. 5.7.

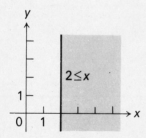
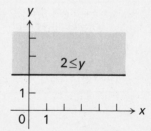
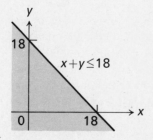
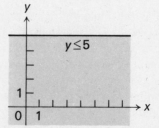

Fig. 5.7

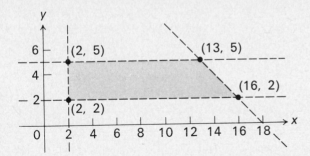

Fig. 5.8

Then the graph of the set of constraints, called the **constraint set**, is shown in Fig. 5.8.

The constraint set is a convex set and may be identified as a **polygonal region** with vertices at (2, 2), (16, 2), (13, 5), and (2, 5). These vertices are called the **extreme points**. Adjacent vertices such as (2, 2) and (16, 2) are called **adjacent extreme points**.

Our task is to find a point of the constraint set for which $5x + 10y + 8400$ has its greatest value. Since $p = 5x + 10y + 8400$, we know that

$$y = -\tfrac{1}{2}x + \tfrac{1}{10}p - 840.$$

For each value of p this equation has the form

$$y = -\tfrac{1}{2}x + k$$

for some value of k. The graphs of such equations with $k = 1, 2, 3,$ and 4 are shown in Fig. 5.9.

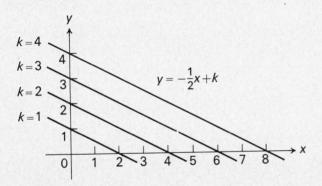

Fig. 5.9

The lines $y = -\frac{1}{2}x + k$ for various values of k are parallel lines and the further the line is above the origin, the larger the value of k. The objective function has a constant value ($\frac{1}{10}p - 840 = k$; $p = 10k + 8400$) for the points on each line. To maximize p we want to find the largest possible value of k such that a line $y = -\frac{1}{2}x + k$ contains a feasible point. Thus to solve our linear programming problem we may sketch several of these lines on a coordinate plane with the constraint set and find the largest possible value of k. See Fig. 5.10.

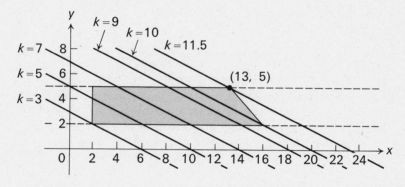

Fig. 5.10

The value of k for the line that contains the extreme point $(2, 2)$ is 3 and this is clearly the *least* possible value of k for any extreme point. In other words, the *worst* that Bill can do if he makes 20 items is to make 2 puzzles, 2 boats and 16 chair seats. In this case $x = 2$, $y = 2$, and $p = 5x + 10y + 8400 = 8430$, that is, his net earnings are $84.30.

The value of k for the line that contains the extreme point $(2, 5)$ is 6 since $5 = (-\frac{1}{2})2 + 6$. The value of k for the line that contains $(13, 5)$ is 11.5 since $5 = (-\frac{1}{2})13 + 11.5$. The value of k for the line that contains $(16, 2)$ is 10 since $2 = (-\frac{1}{2})16 + 10$. This concentration on the values at extreme points is typical of linear programming problems. Think of a line that remains parallel to $y = (-\frac{1}{2})x$ but is slid away from the origin. Since the constraint set is bounded (finite in area) and the sides of the polygonal region are line segments, our sliding line cannot have its last contact with the constraint set at an interior point of a side. Rather the largest possible value of k must occur at an extreme point or at all points of a line segment with two adjacent extreme points as endpoints. In the case of our specific problem the largest possible value of k is 11.5 at (13, 5) and the maximum value of p is \$85.15 since

$$p = 5x + 10y + 8400 = 65 + 50 + 8400 = 8515,$$

when Bill makes 13 puzzles, 5 boats, and 2 chair seats.

. . . .

Exercises

Find the values of x and y for (a) the maximum value, and (b) the minimum value, of the given function p subject to the constraints:

$$\begin{cases} 2 \leq x, \\ 0 \leq y, \\ y \leq 7, \\ y + y - 10 \leq 0. \end{cases}$$

1. $p: x - y$.
2. $p: 5x - 5y + 5280$.
3. $p: x + 2y$.
4. $p: 2x + y$.
5. $p: x + y$.

6–10. Repeat Exercises 1 through 5, respectively, for the constraints:

$$\begin{cases} x - y - 5 \leq 0, \\ x + 2y - 11 \leq 0, \\ y - 4 \leq 0, \\ 0 \leq x, \\ 0 \leq y. \end{cases}$$

11. The illustrative problem in Section 5.1 may be treated as a linear programming problem in two variables by letting x be the number of cords of fireplace wood sold and y the number of cords of stove wood sold. Then the constraints are:

$$\begin{cases} 0 \leq x, \\ 0 \leq y, \\ x + y \leq 3. \end{cases}$$

Find p and complete the problem in two variables.

Repeat the problem in this section regarding things made by Bill with a change of the cost of materials for a boat from 70 cents to:

12. 75 cents.
13. 10 cents.

14. A toy company makes three kinds of toys—cars, trucks, and buses. They can make 500 toys in a week including at most 300 of any one kind. The cost of manufacture is $20 per hundred for cars, $40 per hundred for trucks, and $60 per hundred for buses. Cars are sold at $1.00 each, trucks at $1.25 each, and buses at $1.35 each. How many of each should be made for a maximum profit?

15. A manufacturer of dietetic foods uses two basic types of food. Suppose that a unit of type I costs 20 cents and contains 20 grams of protein and 30 grams of carbohydrates; a unit of type II costs 30 cents and has 25 grams of protein and 30 grams of carbo-hydrates. Let x be the number of units of type I and y be the number of units of type II. For an order that must contain at least 1000 grams of protein and at least 1260 grams of carbohydrates find:

    a) the set of constraints;

    b) the constraint set;

    c) the finite extreme points;

    d) the least expensive mixture for the order;

    e) the cost of the least expensive mixture;

    f) the number of grams of protein and the number of grams of carbohydrates for the cheapest mixture for the order.

16. In Exercise 15 find the least expensive mixture for the specified order if:

    a) type II costs 18 cents per unit;

    b) type II costs 22 cents per unit.

. . . .

5.4 SLACK VARIABLES

Any linear inequality in n variables $x_1, x_2, x_3, \ldots, x_n$ involving either $\leq$ or $\geq$ may be written in the form

$$a_1 x_1 + a_2 x_2 + \cdots + a_n x_n \leq b. \tag{1}$$

For example,

if $x + 2y - 5 \leq 0$, then $x + 2y \leq 5$;
if $2x - 6y + 10 \geq 0$, then $2x - 6y \geq -10$,
and $-2x + 6y \leq 10$.

In the last example note that if $a \geq b$, then $-a \leq -b$. For example, $5 \geq -1$ but $-5 \leq 1$; $20 \geq 10$ but $-20 \leq -10$.

The inequality $x \leq 5$ is satisfied when $x = 3$ as well as when $x = 5$. In the case $x = 3$ where $3 \leq 5$, we may think of $x + x_1 = 5$, where $0 \leq x_1$ and the **slack variable** x_1 "takes up the slack" between x and its upper bound 5. Slack variables with nonnegative values are used in this way in linear programming to convert systems of linear inequalities to systems of linear equations.

Consider the illustrative example in Section 5.1 to determine whether John should sell his wood as fireplace wood or as stove wood. In one variable he sold

x cords of fireplace wood at a profit of $21x$, and
$3 - x$ cords of stove wood at a profit of $60 - 20x$.

The problem was to maximize the function $60 + x$ subject to the constraints

$$\begin{cases} x \geq 0, \\ 3 - x \geq 0; \end{cases}$$

that is,

$$\begin{cases} x \geq 0, \\ x \leq 3. \end{cases}$$

We now introduce a slack variable y and have the equivalent system

$$\begin{cases} x \geq 0, y \geq 0, \\ x + y = 3. \end{cases}$$

The graph is a line segment, as shown in Fig. 5.11.

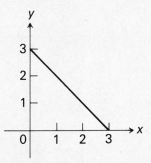

Fig. 5.11

The maximum value of $60 + x$ occurs at an extreme point. Each extreme point is a point of intersection of two of the lines with equations from the system

$$\begin{cases} x = 0, & y = 0, \\ x + y = 3. \end{cases}$$

This set of three equations has $_3C_2$, that is, 3, subsets of two equations:

$$\begin{cases} x = 0, \\ y = 0, \end{cases}$$

with intersection $(0, 0)$, which is not feasible for $x + y = 3$;

$$\begin{cases} x = 0, \\ x + y = 3, \end{cases}$$

with intersection $(0, 3)$, which is feasible, since $y \geq 0$ is allowed and thus is an extreme point; and

$$\begin{cases} y = 0, \\ x + y = 3, \end{cases}$$

with intersection $(3, 0)$, which is an extreme point. The objective function $60 + x$ has value 60 at $(0, 3)$ and 63 at $(3, 0)$. Thus, as in Section 5.1, the maximum is \$63.

The methods of Section 5.3 may also be used for the previous problem. The objective function $60 + x$ takes on values $60 + k$ on lines $x = k$ parallel to the y-axis. The largest value of k for a line that contains a feasible point is 3 at $(3, 0)$ with value \$63 for the objective function. See Fig. 5.12.

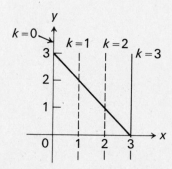

Fig. 5.12

We next consider a modification of the illustrative example in Section 5.3 to determine how many puzzles, boats, and chair seats Bill should make each month. Suppose that Bill makes at most 18 puzzles and boats, at most 5 boats, and 20 items in all with a profit

$$p = 5x_1 + 10x_2 + 8400,$$

where x_1 is the number of puzzles made and x_2 is the number of boats made. For our new problem the constraints are as follows:

$$\begin{cases} 0 \le x_1, \quad 0 \le x_2, \\ x_1 + x_2 \le 18, \\ x_2 \le 5. \end{cases}$$

The graph of the constraints is shown in Fig. 5.13.

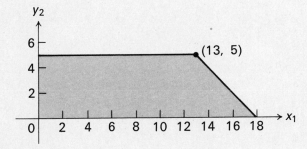

Fig. 5.13

Slack variables x_3 and x_4 are introduced to obtain the equivalent system

$$\begin{cases} 0 \le x_1, \quad 0 \le x_2, \quad 0 \le x_3, \quad 0 \le x_4, \\ x_1 + x_2 + x_3 = 18, \\ x_2 + x_4 = 5. \end{cases}$$

This problem in four variables may be considered geometrically in a manner analogous to that for two variables on a plane. For $n \ge 4$ the graph of each linear equation

$$a_1x_1 + a_2x_2 + \cdots + a_nx_n = b$$

is called a **hyperplane**. The system of linear statements has a convex region as its graph. The maximum or minimum of any linear function must occur at an extreme point.   Each extreme point is a point of intersection of n hyperplanes.

For our particular problem we consider the hyperplanes with equations from the system

$$\begin{cases} A: x_1 = 0, \\ B: x_2 = 0, \\ C: x_3 = 0, \\ D: x_4 = 0, \\ E: x_1 + x_2 + x_3 = 18, \\ F: x_2 + x_4 = 5, \end{cases}$$

where the equations have been identified by letters.   This set of six equations has $_6C_4$, that is, 15, subsets of four equations each that may be identified as

ABCD,   ABCE,   ABCF,   ABDE,   ABDF,
ABEF,   ACDE,   ACDF,   ACEF,   ADEF,
BCDE,   BCDF,   BCEF,   BDEF,   CDEF.

The equations A, B, C, and D may be replaced by inequalities $x_i \geq 0$.   The equations E and F must be satisfied in order to obtain a feasible extreme point.   The status of the intersection, if any, of each set of four equations is shown in the following array.

Equations	(x_1, x_2, x_3, x_4)	Status
ABCD	(0, 0, 0, 0)	Not feasible for E or F
ABCE	——	Inconsistent
ABCF	(0, 0, 0, 5)	Not feasible for E
ABDE	(0, 0, 18, 0)	Not feasible for F
ABDF	——	Inconsistent
ABEF	(0, 0, 18, 5)	An extreme point
ACDE	(0, 18, 0, 0)	Not feasible for F
ACDF	(0, 5, 0, 0)	Not feasible for E
ACEF	(0, 18, 0, −13)	Not feasible for $0 \leq x_4$
ADEF	(0, 5, 13, 0)	An extreme point
BCDE	(18, 0, 0, 0)	Not feasible for F
BCDF	——	Inconsistent
BCEF	(18, 0, 0, 5)	An extreme point
BDEF	——	Inconsistent
CDEF	(13, 5, 0, 0)	An extreme point

The four extreme points $(0, 0, 18, 5)$, $(0, 5, 13, 0)$, $(18, 0, 0, 5)$, and $(13, 5, 0, 0)$ correspond to the extreme points $(0, 0)$, $(0, 5)$, $(18, 0)$, $(13, 5)$ on the xy-plane. The values of $5x_1 + 10x_2 + 8400$ at these four points are respectively 8400, 8450, 8490, and 8515. Thus the maximum value is $85.15 for $x = 13$ and $y = 5$, that is, under the conditions that Bill makes 13 puzzles, 5 boats, and 2 chair seats.

The principal ideas in this section may be summarized as follows:

1. Any inequality $a \geq b$ may be expressed as an inequality $-a \leq -b$.

2. Any inequality

$$a_1x_1 + a_2x_2 + \cdots + a_nx_n \leq b$$

may be expressed as an equality

$$a_1x_1 + a_2x_2 + \cdots + a_nx_n + x_{n+1} = b,$$

where $0 \leq x_{n+1}$.

3. As in the case of systems of linear statements in one or two variables, the maximum for a linear programming problem in any finite number of variables occurs at an extreme point.

4. The set of extreme points for a system of linear statements in n variables is a subset of the set of intersections of the hyperplanes taken n at a time.

5. Since the slack variables do not occur in the objective function, each slack variable may be taken as zero when the objective function is evaluated.

. . . .

Exercises

Write in the form $a \leq b$:

1. $x \geq -1$.
2. $x - y \geq 2$.
3. $-2x_1 + x_2 + 3x_3 - 4x_4 \geq -75$.
4. $5x_1 - 2x_2 - 7x_3 + x_4 \geq 0$.

Write as a system consisting of an equation and an inequality of the form $x_j \geq 0$, where x_j is a slack variable:

5. $x_1 + x_2 \leq 5$.

6. $2x_1 - x_2 \leq 7$.

7. $x_1 - x_2 \geq -1$.

8. $-3x_1 + 5x_2 - x_3 \geq -17$.

Graph and find the extreme points as in Section 5.1 or Section 5.3. Then introduce slack variables and find extreme points as the feasible points that are intersections of the graphs of n equations:

9. $\begin{cases} x_1 \geq 0, \\ x_1 \leq 5. \end{cases}$

10. $\begin{cases} x_1 \geq 0, x_2 \geq 0, \\ x_1 + x_2 \leq 5. \end{cases}$

11. $\begin{cases} x_1 \geq 0, x_2 \geq 0. \\ x_1 + x_2 \leq 5, \\ x_2 \leq 3. \end{cases}$

12. $\begin{cases} x_1 \geq 0, x_2 \geq 0. \\ 2x_1 - x_2 \leq 1, \\ x_1 + x_2 \leq 4. \end{cases}$

The polyhedral region for the set of constraints

$$\begin{cases} 0 \leq x, 0 \leq y, 0 \leq z, \\ x + z \leq 4, \\ y \leq 3, \\ z \leq 2 \end{cases}$$

is shown in Fig. 5.14. The extreme points are $(0, 0, 0)$, $(4, 0, 0)$, $(2, 0, 2)$, $(0, 0, 2)$, $(0, 3, 0)$, $(4, 3, 0)$, $(2, 3, 2)$, and $(0, 3, 2)$.

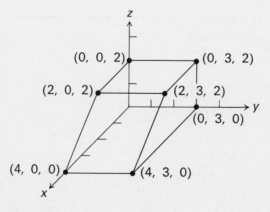

Fig. 5.14

a) Copy the figure and add the graphs of the objective function (planes) for the indicated values of k.

b) Find the maximum value k of the objective function subject to the above constraints. Note that the maximum occurs at at least one extreme point.

13. $x + y + z = k$ for $k = 4, 7, 10$.

14. $x + 2y = k$ for $k = 6, 8, 10$.

....

5.5 ROW TRANSFORMATIONS FOR EVALUATION

The row transformations that were used in Section 4.6 to solve systems of linear equations may also be used to find the value of a linear objective function for the unique solution of a system of linear equations. In this case the modified matrix is often called a **tableau**.

Consider the linear objective function $3x - y + 5$ subject to the constraints

$$\begin{cases} x + 2y = 1, \\ x - y = 4, \\ 2x + 3y = 3. \end{cases} \qquad (2)$$

We form a matrix with a row E_i for each equation, a column C_j for the coefficients of each variable, a column for the constant terms (assumed to be the right members of the equations), and a last row for the objective function. In this last row we enter (-1) times the coefficient of x in the x-column, (-1) times the coefficient of y in the y-column, and the constant term (or 0) in the last column.

	C_1	C_2	
E_1	1	2	1
E_2	1	-1	4
E_3	2	3	3
	-3	1	5

$$(3)$$

The procedures for the elements on the last row of the tableau (3) will be explained using this illustrative example. If we solved the system (1) as in Section 4.6, we would start with the matrix

$$\begin{pmatrix} \textcircled{1} & 2 & 1 \\ 1 & -1 & 4 \\ 2 & 3 & 3 \end{pmatrix}. \qquad (4)$$

Then we might select a nonzero element in the first column and use row transformations [as indicated in terms of the row vectors of (4)] to make the selected element one and all other elements of the first column zero.

$$
\begin{pmatrix} 1 & 2 & 1 \\ 0 & \text{\textcircled{-3}} & 3 \\ 0 & -1 & 1 \end{pmatrix} \begin{array}{l} r_1 \\ r_2 - r_1 \\ r_3 - 2r_1 \end{array} \tag{5}
$$

Next we would select a nonzero element in the second column but not on the first row of (5) and proceed as before [indicated in terms of the row vectors of (5)].

$$
\begin{pmatrix} 1 & 0 & 3 \\ 0 & 1 & -1 \\ 0 & 0 & 0 \end{pmatrix} \begin{array}{l} r_1 + (\frac{2}{3})r_2 \\ (-\frac{1}{3})r_2 \\ r_3 - (\frac{1}{3})r_2 \end{array} \tag{6}
$$

From the matrix (6) we know that the third equation is superfluous, the system is consistent, and the solution is $x = 3, y = -1$. If we use the matrix (6) for the first three rows of the tableau (3), we have:

$$
\begin{array}{rrr}
1 & 0 & 3 \\
0 & 1 & -1 \\
0 & 0 & 0 \\
\hline
-3 & 1 & 5
\end{array}
$$

Then substituting $x = 3$ in the objective function is accomplished by adding three times the first row to the last, thereby making the first entry in the last row zero:

$$
\begin{array}{rrr}
1 & 0 & 3 \\
0 & 1 & -1 \\
0 & 0 & 0 \\
\hline
0 & 1 & 14
\end{array}
$$

Similarly, to make the second element of the last row zero we substitute $y = -1$ by subtracting the second row from the last row:

$$
\begin{array}{ccc}
1 & 0 & 3 \\
0 & 1 & -1 \\
0 & 0 & 0
\end{array}
\tag{7}
$$

$$
\begin{array}{ccc}
\hline
0 & 0 & 15
\end{array}
$$

From the tableau (7) we may read that the objective function has value 15 at the solution $x = 3$, $y = -1$ of the system of linear equations. This value checks since at $(3, -1)$ we have:

$$3x - y + 5 = 3(3) - (-1) + 5 = 9 + 1 + 5 = 15.$$

From this example observe that the last row of the tableau (3) is formed using the *negatives* of the coefficients of the variables in the objective function so that we may substitute into that function by using row transformations to make those elements on the last row zero.

The tableau (7) may be obtained directly from the tableau (3). The procedure is basically as before:

1. We select (circle) a nonzero element in one of the columns of coefficients, call this element the **pivot element**, call its column the **pivotal column**, and call its row the **pivotal row**.

2. If the pivot element is different from 1, we divide each element of the pivotal row by the pivot element to obtain the elements for that row in the new tableau. If the pivot element is 1, we use the pivotal row in the new tableau. In either case, we label the new row with the heading of the pivotal column. All other rows retain their present labels in the new tableau.

3. We use row transformations to make all of the other elements of the pivotal column zero (including the element in the last row).

4. We repeat this process for as many of the columns of coefficients as possible.

5. If there remain columns of coefficients of variables that have not been considered, the system of linear equations does not have a unique solution.

6. If there remain rows that are not equivalent to $0 = 0$, then the system is inconsistent.

7. If the system is consistent and has a unique solution, then that solution is given on the rows labeled with the C_j's and the value of the objective function for that solution is given by the last element of the last row.

For the tableau (3) we have:

$$
\begin{array}{c c c c}
 & C_1 & C_2 & \\
E_1 & \text{①} & 2 & 1 \\
E_2 & 1 & -1 & 4 \\
E_3 & 2 & 3 & 3 \\
\hline
 & -3 & 1 & 5 \\
\end{array}
$$

$$
\begin{array}{c c c c l}
 & C_1 & C_2 & & \\
C_1 & 1 & 2 & 1 & r_1 \\
E_2 & 0 & \text{⊝3} & 3 & r_2 - r_1 \\
E_3 & 0 & -1 & 1 & r_3 - 2r_1 \\
\hline
 & 0 & 7 & 8 & r_4 + 3r_1 \\
\end{array}
$$

$$
\begin{array}{c c c c l}
 & C_1 & C_2 & & \\
C_1 & 1 & 0 & 3 & r_1 + (\tfrac{2}{3})r_2 \\
C_2 & 0 & 1 & -1 & (-\tfrac{1}{3})r_2 \\
E_3 & 0 & 0 & 0 & r_3 - (\tfrac{1}{3})r_2 \\
\hline
 & 0 & 0 & 15 & r_4 + (\tfrac{7}{3})r_2 \\
\end{array}
$$

. . . .

Exercises

Use a tableau to find for the system of constraints (2) of this section, the value of:

1. $4x - y$.
2. $3x - 2y$.
3. $3x + 2y$.
4. $2x + y + 2$.

For the system of constraints

$$
\begin{cases}
x + y + z = 4, \\
2x - y - z = 2, \\
x + 2y = 0,
\end{cases}
$$

use a tableau to find the value of:

5. $3x + 2y$.
6. $x + 3y + 2z$.
7. $2x - 5y$.
8. $3y + 4z$.

For the system of constraints

$$\begin{cases} x - y + z - w = 2, \\ y + z + w = 6, \\ x + 2y - 3z = 0, \\ 2x - 3z + w = 5, \end{cases}$$

use a tableau to find the value of:

9. $x + y + z + w$.

10. $2x - 3y + 7$.

11. $x + 2y - 3z + w$.

12. $3x - 7y - 5z + 2w$.

....

5.6 THE SIMPLEX ALGORITHM FOR MAXIMIZATION

The procedure for evaluation in Section 5.5 can be used to evaluate objective functions at extreme points of the constraint set. The necessary modifications of our previous procedures to select an extreme point at which the objective function will have a maximum value are part of the **simplex algorithm**. Detailed proofs of the procedures of the algorithm may be found in textbooks on linear programming. We shall recognize but not prove these procedures.

Consider the problem of finding the maximum value of $x + 3y$ subject to the constraints:

$$\begin{cases} 0 \le x, \quad 0 \le y, \\ x + 2y \le 7, \\ y \le 2. \end{cases} \tag{8}$$

As in Section 5.3 the *constraint set* is the graph (Fig. 5.15) of the constraints. From the graph the extreme points are $(0, 0)$, $(7, 0)$,

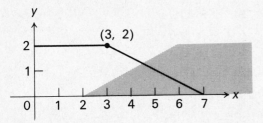

Fig. 5.15

(3, 2), and (0, 2). The values of $x + 3y$ at these extreme points are respectively 0, 7, 9, and 6. Thus the maximum value is 9 at (3, 2). However, our task is to find a routine algebraic procedure that can also be used when there are several variables.

The **simplex tableau** is based upon the use of nonnegative variables ($0 \leq x, 0 \leq y$) and the replacement of the remaining constraints as in Section 5.4 using slack variables (also nonnegative). Then for slack variables u and v the system (8) becomes

$$\begin{cases} x + 2y + u = 7, \\ y + w = 2, \end{cases} \tag{9}$$

where $0 \leq x, 0 \leq y, 0 \leq u, 0 \leq w$. The simplex tableau for the system (9) and the objective function $x + 3y$ is

	C_1	C_2	E_1	E_2	
E_1	1	2	1	0	7
E_2	0	1	0	1	2
	−1	−3	0	0	0

$$\tag{10}$$

Indicators

The column heading E_1 is used for the column of the slack variable in the first equation; E_2 for the column of the slack variable in the second equation. In addition to providing coefficients for the slack variables, the elements of these columns indicate the use that is made of the corresponding equations. On the last row all elements except the last are called **indicators**. One of the aims of our procedures will be to remove all negative indicators.

For the particular simplex tableau (10) it happens that we may proceed exactly as in Section 5.5:

	C_1	C_2	E_1	E_2	
C_1	1	2	1	0	7
E_2	0	①	0	1	2
	0	−1	1	0	7

	C_1	C_2	E_1	E_2	
C_1	1	0	1	−2	3
C_2	0	1	0	1	2
	0	0	1	1	9

Then, as before, the maximum value of the indicator function $x + 3y$ is 9 at $(3, 2)$.

The use of slack variables can be observed in the next example where the maximum value of the objective function occurs at an extreme point at which one of the original variables is zero. The problem is to maximize the objective function $x + y$ subject to the constraints (8). The simplex tableau is then

	C_1	C_2	E_1	E_2	
E_1	1	2	1	0	7
E_2	0	1	0	1	2
	-1	-1	0	0	0

(11)

If we select the first column, the next tableau is

	C_1	C_2	E_1	E_2	
C_1	1	2	1	0	7
E_2	0	1	0	1	2
	0	1	1	0	7

(12)

Now the simplex procedure is quite different from the one used in Section 5.5.

1. We have reached a final tableau since all indicators are non-negative.

2. Only the rows labeled with a C_j are used to obtain values of variables, all other variables are taken as zero. If a row is labeled C_j, then the last element of that row is the value of the variable associated with the column C_j. These values of the variables identify an extreme point at which the objective function has a maximum value.

3. The last element of the last row is the maximum value of the objective function subject to the given constraints.

For the tableau (12) the objective function $x + y$ has its maximum value 7, when $x = 7$ and $y = 0$. This result checks since $x + y$ has the value 0 at $(0, 0)$, 7 at $(7, 0)$, 5 at $(3, 2)$, and 2 at $(0, 2)$.

The need for still another procedure for the simplex algorithm can be observed if we start with the second column of (11) and select the element on the first row of the second column as our pivot element. In this case our next tableau is

	C_1	C_2	E_1	E_2	
C_2	$\frac{1}{2}$	1	$\frac{1}{2}$	0	$\frac{7}{2}$
E_2	$-\frac{1}{2}$	0	$-\frac{1}{2}$	1	$-\frac{3}{2}$
	$-\frac{1}{2}$	0	$\frac{1}{2}$	0	$\frac{7}{2}$

Then we must select E_2, a different row from C_2, for the first column

	C_1	C_2	E_1	E_2	
C_2	0	1	0	1	2
C_1	1	0	1	-2	3
	0	0	1	1	5

This tableau would appear to indicate that $x + y$ has its maximum value of 5 at (3, 2). The point (3, 2) is an extreme point at which the objective function $x + y$ has the value 5. However, this is not the extreme point at which the objective function has its maximum value.

Here are the simplex algorithm procedures that enable us to find the extreme point at which the given objective function has its maximum value:

4. At the start select a pivotal column in which the indicator is negative (preferably, but not necessarily, the negative indicator with the largest absolute value).

5. In the pivotal column C_j identify the elements a_{ij} (the element on the ith row and the jth column) that are positive. Divide each positive a_{ij} into the last element of its row. Select as the pivotal row the row in which this quotient is nonnegative and as small as possible.

If we use the procedure (5) and select the second column of the simplex tableau (11), we note that $\frac{2}{1} < \frac{7}{2}$ and select the second row as the pivotal row. Then the next tableau is

	C_1	C_2	E_1	E_2	
E_1	1	0	1	-2	3
C_2	0	1	0	1	2
	-1	0	0	1	2

Then we have

	C_1	C_2	E_1	E_2	
C_1	1	0	1	-2	3
C_2	0	1	0	1	2
	0	0	1	-1	5

This tableau indicates that $x + y$ has the value 5 at (3, 2) but since the E_2 column has a negative indicator, this value 5 is not the maximum value of the objective function. Thus we proceed using the fourth column as the pivotal column, the second row as pivotal row (since a positive a_{ij} is needed), and labeling the new second row with the heading E_2 of the pivotal column.

	C_1	C_2	E_1	E_2	
C_1	1	2	1	0	7
E_2	0	1	0	1	2
	0	1	1	0	7

This tableau is a final tableau since all the indicators are nonnegative. As before the objective function $x + y$ has its maximum value of 7 at $x = 7$ and $y = 0$ (since the label on the second row is an E_i instead of a C_j).

The simplex algorithm can always be used when the following three conditions are satisfied. Frequently the algorithm can be used when one or more of the conditions are not satisfied. Details of such applications are considered in some texts on linear programming.

1. **Assumption of nonnegative constant terms:** When the constraints are expressed in the usual form for the simplex algorithm, all the constant terms are nonnegative.

2. **Assumption of the independence of the objective function:** Let A be the matrix of the coefficients of the original variables (exclude the slack variables) in the linear constraints. Also suppose that row transformations can not be used to obtain a row of zeros for any r rows of the matrix A but if there exist $r + 1$ rows, then for any $r + 1$ rows at least one row is linearly dependent (can be replaced by a row of zeros, Section 4.6) upon the others. It is then assumed that the analogous row for the objective function is not linearly dependent upon any $r - 1$ rows of the matrix A.

3. **Assumption of the independence of the constant terms:**
   Define r as for the assumption of the independence of the objective
   function.   Relative to the columns of the simplex tableau it is
   assumed that the column of the constant terms is not linearly
   dependent upon any $r - 1$ columns of the matrix A. (Either each
   matrix may be transposed (Section 4.1) to interchange rows and
   columns or column transformations analogous to row transformations may be used.)

Geometric interpretations of these assumptions are considered in
the Supplementary Exercises.
   The main advantage of the simplex algorithm is that it can be used
for systems with several variables without the graph of the constraints.

Example Find the maximum value of $x - 2y + 3z - w$ subject to
the constraints:

$$\begin{cases} 0 \le x, \quad 0 \le y, \quad 0 \le z, \quad 0 \le w, \\ x + y + z + 2w \le 10, \\ x - 2y \qquad\qquad \le 5, \\ 3x \qquad + z - w \le 3, \\ \qquad y - z + 2w \le 2. \end{cases} \tag{13}$$

Solution.

	C_1	C_2	C_3	C_4	E_1	E_2	E_3	E_4	
E_1	1	1	1	2	1	0	0	0	10
E_2	1	-2	0	0	0	1	0	0	5
E_3	3	0	1	-1	0	0	1	0	3
E_4	0	1	-1	2	0	0	0	1	2
	-1	2	-3	1	0	0	0	0	0

Since the negative indicator with the largest absolute value is in the
C_3 column, we chose C_3 as the pivotal column. Since $\frac{3}{1} < \frac{10}{1}$, the pivotal
row is E_3.

	C_1	C_2	C_3	C_4	E_1	E_2	E_3	E_4		
E_1	-2	1	0	3	1	0	-1	0	7	$r_1 - r_3$
E_2	1	-2	0	0	0	1	0	0	5	r_2
C_3	3	0	1	-1	0	0	1	0	3	r_3
E_4	3	1	0	1	0	0	1	1	5	$r_4 + r_3$
	8	2	0	-2	0	0	3	0	9	$r_5 + 3r_3$

The next pivotal column is C_4. Since $\frac{7}{3} < \frac{5}{1}$, the pivotal row is E_1.

	C_1	C_2	C_3	C_4	E_1	E_2	E_3	E_4		
C_1	$-\frac{2}{3}$	$\frac{1}{3}$	0	1	$\frac{1}{3}$	0	$-\frac{1}{3}$	0	$\frac{7}{3}$	$r_1/3$
E_2	1	-2	0	0	0	1	0	0	5	r_2
C_3	$\frac{7}{3}$	$\frac{1}{3}$	1	0	$\frac{1}{3}$	0	$\frac{2}{3}$	0	$\frac{16}{3}$	$r_3 + r_1/3$
E_4	$\frac{11}{3}$	$\frac{2}{3}$	0	0	$-\frac{1}{3}$	0	$\frac{4}{3}$	1	$\frac{8}{3}$	$r_4 - r_1/3$
	$\frac{20}{3}$	$\frac{8}{3}$	0	0	$\frac{2}{3}$	0	$\frac{7}{3}$	0	$\frac{32}{3}$	$r_5 + 2r_1/3$

This is a final tableau since it has no negative indicators. The maximum value of the objective function is $\frac{32}{3}$ at $(\frac{7}{3}, 0, \frac{16}{3}, 0)$.

. . . .

Exercises

Use the simplex tableau to find the maximum of the given function subject to the set of constraints (8) of this section:

1. $x + 4y$.
2. $3x + y$.
3. $3x - y + 2$.
4. $2x - y + 5$.

In Exercises 5 through 8 use the simplex algorithm to find the maximum of the given function subject to the set of constraints (13) of the example of this section:

5. $3x + y + w$.
6. $3x - y + z - w$.
7. $2y + 3z + w$.
8. $x + 2y + 3z + 4w$.
9. Linda's father gave her $1000 to invest in the stocks of the four companies specified in the array:

Company	Cost per share	Annual dividend per share
Able Accounts	$15	$1.00
Handy Holders	40	3.00
Normal Nuts	25	1.50
Telephone Tapes	50	4.00

The conditions of the gift are that she buy no more than $600 worth of any one kind of stock. Linda decided to purchase stock for as large an annual income from dividends as possible.

a) Let w be the number of shares of Able Accounts purchased,
   x be the number of shares of Handy Holder purchased,
   y be the number of shares of Normal Nuts purchased, and
   z be the number of shares of Telephone Tapes purchased.

   Find the set of constraints.
b) State the objective function.
c) Set up a simplex tableau.
d) Solve the problem to determine how many shares of each kind of stock Linda should purchase to maximize her annual income from dividends.

Note: There is a simpler way of solving this particular problem which can provide a check on the application of the simplex method and also provide insight as to the basis for some of the procedures used. The simplex method is particularly appropriate for more complex problems and solution by electronic computer.

10. A toy company has facilities for making five types of toys—buses, farm trucks, panel trucks, race cars, and passenger cars. The data in the array includes the manufacturing time in hours, the cost (overhead and materials), and the manufacturer's selling price for each toy.

Type	Manufacturing time	Cost	Selling price
Bus	$\frac{1}{10}$	$0.03	$1.25
Farm truck	$\frac{1}{15}$	0.02	1.00
Panel truck	$\frac{1}{10}$	0.03	1.00
Race car	$\frac{1}{20}$	0.01	0.75
Passenger car	$\frac{1}{20}$	0.01	0.50

The company has 50 hours of manufacturing time available each day. Unfortunately sales opportunities are limited. The company estimates that they can expect to sell in any one day not more than 200 buses, 300 trucks (farm or panel), 300 race cars, and 400 cars (race or passenger).

a) Let v be the number of buses, w the number of farm trucks, x the number of panel trucks, y the number of race cars, and z the number of passenger cars manufactured. Find the set of constraints.

b) The objective is to maximize profits (selling price less costs). Find the objective function in cents.

c) Set up a simplex tableau for this problem.

d) Find the maximum profit per day and the number of each type of toy that should be made to realize this profit.

e) Check that all 50 hours, and no more than 50 hours, of the available manufacturing time is used for your solution in part (d).

Supplementary Exercises

1. On a coordinate plane, graph the constraints:

a) $\begin{cases} 0 \le x, & 0 \le y, \\ 2x + y \le 0; \end{cases}$

b) $\begin{cases} 0 \le x, & 0 \le y, \\ x - y \le 0, \\ -3x + y \le 0; \end{cases}$

c) $\begin{cases} 0 \le x, & 0 \le y, \\ x + y \le -1; \end{cases}$

d) $\begin{cases} 0 \le x, & 0 \le y, \\ -x - 2y \le -4. \end{cases}$

2. Draw additional graphs as needed and observe that for two non-negative variables and constraints in the usual form with constant terms b_i:

a) If the constant terms b_i are nonnegative, then $(0, 0)$ is a feasible point and an extreme point.

b) If all the constant terms b_i are zero, then the constraint set may consist of only the point $(0, 0)$ or may be an angular region with $(0, 0)$ as its only extreme point.

c) If any constant term b_i is negative, then $(0, 0)$ is not a feasible point and thus not an extreme point.

d) For any number of variables the assumption of nonnegative constant terms is equivalent to an assumption that the origin (all variables zero) is an extreme point.   Also note that this assumption is not satisfied for the example used in Section 5.3 even though the simplex algorithm can be used for this particular problem.

3. Consider the problem of maximizing the function $2x + y$ subject to the constraints:

$$\begin{cases} 0 \le, & 0 \le y, \\ x + y \le 7, \\ x + y \le 5, \\ y \le 3. \end{cases}$$

a) Graph each constraint and note that $x + y \le 5$ implies $x + y \le 7$; that is, the constraint $x + y \le 7$ is superfluous and should not be used in the determination of extreme points.

b) Solve the problem using the simplex algorithm and identify the particular procedure that requires the use of $x + y \leq 5$ instead of $x + y \leq 7$.

4. Consider the objective function $x + y$ and the constraints

$$\begin{cases} x + y \leq 5, \\ y \leq 3. \end{cases}$$

Note that the assumption of the independence of the objective function is not satisfied and the maximum occurs along a side of the constraint set instead of at a unique extreme point. For the set of constraints (8) consider the applicability of the previous observation for the objective function:

a) y; b) x; c) $x + 2y$;
d) k^2y; e) $k^2(x + 2y)$; f) $k^2y + m$;
g) $k^2(x + 2y) + t$.

5. State whether or not the assumption of the independence of the constant terms is satisfied for a linear programming problem with a system of constraints

a) with all constant terms zero;

b) $\begin{cases} x + y \leq 2, \\ y \leq 0; \end{cases}$ c) $\begin{cases} x + y \leq 2, \\ y \leq 2; \end{cases}$

d) $\begin{cases} x \leq 2, \\ x - y \leq 0; \end{cases}$ e) $\begin{cases} x + y \leq 2, \\ x - y \leq 2. \end{cases}$

Note that in each case in which the assumption of the independence of the constant terms is not satisfied, two of the graphs of constraints intersect on a coordinate axis without using the constraints $0 \leq x, 0 \leq y$; in other words, an extreme point arose in two or more different ways.

6. a) Explain why the assumption of the independence of the constant terms includes an assumption that the constant terms are not all zero.

b) Explain why there must be at least one positive constant term if all three assumptions for the simplex algorithm are satisfied.

. . . .

5.7 THE SIMPLEX ALGORITHM FOR MINIMIZATION

Minimization problems may be solved by considering a related maximization problem and thus by using a simplex tableau. For a maximization problem the simplex tableau (Section 5.6) consists of:

1. a row E_i for each constraint,

2. a row for the negatives of the coefficients of the objective function.

3. a column C_j for each original variable,

4. a column for the slack variable for each equation, and

5. a column for the constant terms of the constraints.

Maximization problems are stated with constraints in the form $\leq b$ for nonnegative variables. Furthermore, if the assumption of nonnegative constant terms is satisfied, then the origin is always an extreme point (Section 5.6, Supplementary Exercise 2). Thus the minimum is zero or a negative number for any objective function with constant term zero and constraints stated in the form $\leq b$ with nonnegative constant terms.

The constraints for a minimization problem are stated in the form $\geq b$ to provide a basis for keeping the feasible points away from the origin. The $\geq b$ form is always possible since if $c \leq d$, then $-c \geq -d$. For a minimization problem the simplex tableau consists of:

1. a row for each original variable,

2. a row for the negatives of the constant terms of the constraints,

3. a column C_j for each constraint,

4. a column E_j for the nonnegative nature of each of the original variables, and

5. a column for the coefficients (signs unchanged) of the objective function.

The labels for the rows and columns are the same as for the maximization problem so that the same procedures may be used.

Consider the problem of minimizing the objective function

$$5u + 4v + 6w$$

subject to the constraints:

$$\begin{cases} u + w \geq 5, \\ v \geq 1, \\ v + w \geq 3. \end{cases} \tag{14}$$

We add the constraints that the variables are nonnegative

$$u \geq 0, \quad v \geq 0, \quad w \geq 0. \tag{15}$$

Then the simplex tableau for the minimization problem is

	C_1	C_2	C_3	E_1	E_2	E_3	
E_1	1	0	0	1	0	0	5
E_2	0	1	1	0	1	0	4
E_3	1	0	1	0	0	1	6
	-5	-1	-3	0	0	0	0

(16)

Note that in the simplex tableau (16) for a minimization problem the row E_1 is for the variable u, the row E_2 is for the variable v, the row E_3 is for the variable w, and the last row is for the negatives of the constant terms. Similarly, the columns of the tableau (16) are for the coefficients of the constraints (14), the coefficients of the constraints (15), and the coefficients of the objective function.

The tableau (16) could also be used to maximize the objective function

$$5x + y + 3z$$

subject to the constraints:

$$\begin{cases} 0 \le x, \quad 0 \le y, \quad 0 \le z, \\ x \qquad\qquad \le 5, \\ \quad\; y + z \le 4, \\ x \qquad + z \le 6. \end{cases}$$

(17)

Since they have the same simplex tableau, the linear programming problem of minimizing $5u + 4v + 6w$ subject to the constraints (14) and the problem of maximizing $5x + y + 3z$ subject to the constraints (17) are called **dual problems**.

The problem of maximizing $x + 3y$ subject to the constraints

$$\begin{cases} x + 2y \le 7, \\ \quad\; y \le 2 \end{cases}$$

(18)

was considered in Section 5.6 with simplex tableau

	C_1	C_2	E_1	E_2	
E_1	1	2	1	0	7
E_2	0	1	0	1	2
	-1	-3	0	0	0

(19)

The dual problem is to minimize $7u + 2v$ subject to the constraints

$$\begin{cases} u \geq 1, \\ 2u + v \geq 3. \end{cases} \tag{20}$$

We use the same row transformations on the simplex tableau (19) for both problems. As in Section 5.6 we obtain

	C_1	C_2	E_1	E_2	
C_1	1	0	1	-2	3⎫ Coordinates of point for
C_2	0	1	0	1	2⎭ maximum using rows C_j
	0	0	1	1	9 ← Maximum or minimum

Coordinates of point for
minimum using all columns E_i

Then as indicated on the tableau $x + 3y$ has its maximum of 9 at $(3, 2)$ and $7u + 2v$ has its minimum of 9 at $(1, 1)$.

The graphical methods of Section 5.3 may be used for either maximization or minimization problems. To maximize $x + 3y$ subject to the constraints (18), we graph the constraints (Fig. 5.16); identify the extreme points $(0, 0)$, $(7, 0)$, $(3, 2)$, and $(0, 2)$; and evaluate $x + 3y$ at each point. To minimize $7u + 2v$ subject to the constraints (20), we graph the constraints (Fig. 5.17); identify the finite extreme points $(\frac{3}{2}. 0)$ and $(1, 1)$; and evaluate $7u + 2v$ at each finite extreme point. Since $7(1) + 2(1) = 9$ and $7(\frac{3}{2}) + 2(0) = 10.5$, the minimum value is 9 at $(1, 1)$.

The assumptions for the use of the simplex algorithm for minimization problems may be interpreted directly from those for maximization problems using the same tableaux. Specifically the assumption of nonnegative constant terms for maximization problems becomes an *assumption of nonnegative coefficients on the objective function* for

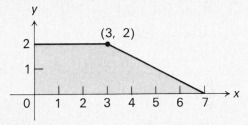

Fig. 5.16

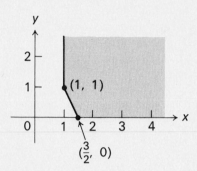

Fig. 5.17

minimization problems; the assumptions of the independence of the objective function and of the constant terms interchange but both remain for minimization problems.

The basic relationship between dual problems is very effectively illustrated in Section 6.5 where the dual problems are the solutions of a two person game from the points of view of the two players.

. . . .

Exercises

For each simplex tableau (a) state the maximization problem in terms of variables x and y and (b) state the dual minimization problem in terms of variables u and v.

1.

	C_1	C_2	E_1	E_2	
E_1	1	2	1	0	5
E_2	1	0	0	1	3
	-3	-2	0	0	0

2.

	C_1	C_2	E_1	E_2	
E_1	2	-1	1	0	4
E_2	1	1	0	1	5
	-1	-3	0	0	0

For the simplex tableau in the specified exercise solve: (a) the maximization problem graphically as in Section 5.3, (b) the minimization problem graphically, and (c) both dual problems by the simplex algorithm.

3. Exercise 1.

4. Exercise 2.

5. Use the simplex algorithm to solve both dual problems for the tableau (16).

Consider the simplex tableau

	C_1	C_2	C_3	E_1	E_2	E_3	
E_1	1	0	1	1	0	0	5
E_2	0	1	2	0	1	0	9
E_3	1	2	1	0	0	1	8
	-5	-9	-8	0	0	0	0

6. State the maximization problem in terms of x, y, and z.
7. State the minimization problem in terms of u, v, and w.
8. Use the simplex algorithm to solve both dual problems.

Consider the simplex tableau

	C_1	C_2	C_3	E_1	E_2	E_3	
E_1	2	2	3	1	0	0	3
E_2	3	-1	2	0	1	0	1
E_3	0	1	5	0	0	1	1
	-3	-2	-6	0	0	0	0

9. State the maximization problem in terms of x, y, and z.
10. State the minimization problem in terms of u, v, and w.
11. Use the simplex algorithm to solve both dual problems.
12. A frozen foods company has 500 pounds of carrots and 800 pounds of peas ready for packaging. Suppose that one pound of frozen carrots can be sold at a profit of 10 cents, one pound of mixed vegetables (one-third carrots and two-thirds peas by weight) can be sold at a profit of 8 cents, and one pound of frozen peas can be sold at a profit of 6 cents.

    a) Let x be the number of pounds of frozen carrots sold,

    y be the number of pounds of mixed vegetables sold, and
    z be the number of pounds of peas sold.

    State the constraints.

    b) For maximum profit state the objective function in cents.

    c) How should the carrots and peas be packaged for a maximum profit?

    d) The variables u (per pound of carrots) and v (per pound of peas) of the dual problem are sometimes called *implicit prices* or *opportunity costs*. State the objective function, the constraints, and the solution for the dual problem.

REVIEW EXERCISES FOR CHAPTER 5

1. Graph $1 + x \geq 0$ on a number line.
2. For the function p: $10 - 2x$ subject to the constraints
$$\begin{cases} 0 \leq x, \\ 3x - 6 \leq 0 \end{cases}$$

a) graph the system of constraints on a number line,
b) find the maximum value of the function p subject to the given constraints and the value of x for this maximum.

3. Graph on a coordinate plane
$$\begin{cases} 0 \leq x, \\ 0 \leq y, \\ x + y \leq 5, \\ y \leq 3. \end{cases}$$

4. Find (a) the maximum and (b) the minimum value of $2x + 3y$ subject to the system of statements in Exercise 3 as constraints.

5. Write in the form $a \leq b$:

a) $2x \geq -3$;   b) $-x \geq 4$;   c) $x \geq 5$.

6. Write in the form $a \geq b$:

a) $3x + 1 \leq 7$;   b) $5 - x \leq 8$;   c) $2x - 5 \leq 7$.

7. Write the statement
$$x_1 + 2x_2 \leq 5$$
as a system consisting of an equation and an inequality of the form $x_j \geq 0$, where x_j is a slack variable.

For the system of constraints
$$\begin{cases} x - 2y + z = 6, \\ x - y = 4, \\ x + 2z = 5. \end{cases}$$

use a tableau to find the value of:

8. $3x - 2y$.
9. $7x + 5y - 2z$.

For the constraints
$$\begin{cases} 0 \leq x, \quad 0 \leq y, \\ x + 2y \leq 6, \\ y \leq 2 \end{cases}$$

and the objective function $4x - y$ to be maximized:

10. State the simplex tableau.

11. Solve using the simplex tableau.

12. Graph the constraints and solve graphically.

13. State the dual of the problem solved in Exercise 11.

14. Solve the dual problem graphically.

For the system of constraints used for Exercises 8 and 9 and the maximization of $5x - y + 3z$:

15. State the simplex tableau.

16. Solve this maximization problem using the simplex tableau.

17. State the dual minimization problem in terms of u, v, and w.

18. Solve the minimization problem.

A farmer picked 100 bushels of Macintosh apples and 80 bushels of Cortland apples. He has storage facilities for 75 bushels of apples. If he sells the apples immediately his profits are 20 cents a bushel on the Macintosh apples and 25 cents a bushel on the Cortland apples. If he stores the apples for future sales, his expected profits are 24 cents a bushel on the Macintosh apples and 22 cents a bushel on the Cortland apples.

Let w be the number of bushels of Macintosh apples sold immediately, x the number of bushels of Macintosh apples stored, y the number of bushels of Cortland apples sold immediately, and z the number of bushels of Cortland apples stored.

19. State the constraints and the objective function for maximum profit.

20. Find the maximum profit and the manner in which the apples should be sold to realize this profit.

game theory   6

Finite sets, sample spaces, probabilities, matrices, and linear programming are all used in the study of the behavior of two or more people, teams, or even nations engaged in competition or conflict. The systematic study of games has been developed during the last fifty years. Specific applications range from parlor games to economic theories to nuclear warfare.

We conclude our introduction to finite mathematics with a brief introduction to the theory of games. Basic techniques and simplified examples are considered.

6.1 GAMES

Any competition or conflict may be treated as a **game**. In this introduction to the theory of games we shall consider only games between two contestants. The contestants may be individuals, teams, nations, or other groups of people. We refer to each contestant as a **player** and discuss the game as if the player was an individual. In this sense we consider only **two-person games**.

The actions of the players in a game are called **moves**. We consider games in which each player has a finite number of moves, that is,

finite games. The moves of the game may be based upon *personal decisions* or made at *random*. For example, a move based upon a flip of a coin or a toss of two dice is a random move. As in these two examples the probabilities of random moves are assumed to be known. This assumption is illustrated by the common consideration of the use of biased coins or loaded dice as "cheating."

Some games consist of a single move such as matching coins just once to decide who buys coffee. Other games involve a sequence of moves as in chess or matching coins for coffee each work day. When a game involves a sequence of moves, a player may have access to complete information about previous moves, as in chess, or may have very little information, as in some card games.

The reward, or **payoff**, for winning a game may be personal satisfaction, money, fame, or even survival. In the study of games numerical values are usually assigned to each reward. The particular reward that one player receives as a consequence of a particular move usually depends upon the move made by the other player. These rewards may be tabulated as entries in a matrix called the **game matrix**, or the **payoff matrix**.

A two-person game in which each player loses exactly what the other player wins is called a **zero-sum game**. In our brief introduction we shall consider only zero-sum games. For any zero-sum game it is sufficient to consider the payoffs to only one of the players. Then a win of x by this player is entered in the payoff matrix as x; a win of x by the other player is entered in the matrix as a payoff of $-x$ to the player whose payoffs are being recorded.

Each move of one of the players, for convenience called the **row player**, is associated with a row of the payoff matrix. Each move of the other player, the **column player**, is associated with a column of the matrix. The entries in the payoff matrix are the payoffs to the row player. In other words, a payoff to the row player is entered as a positive number, and a payoff to the column player is entered as a negative number.

6.2 PAYOFF MATRICES

Suppose that Ron and Carl are playing the game of **matching pennies**. Each person places a penny heads up or tails up so that the other person cannot see it. They have decided that if the pennies match (both heads or both tails), then Ron gets both pennies—a win of one penny for Ron; if the pennies don't match, then Carl gets both pennies—a loss of one penny for Ron. Note that this is a zero-sum game.

A payoff matrix may be set up with Ron as the row player and Carl as the column player. Then Ron's two moves are each associated with a row of the payoff matrix; Carl's moves are each associated with a column of the matrix. Headings may be used for these rows and columns whenever desired. For example, the columns and rows of the matrix could be annotated as follows:

$$\begin{array}{cc} & \text{Carl} \\ & \text{heads} \quad \text{tails} \end{array}$$

$$\text{Ron} \quad \begin{array}{c} \text{heads} \\ \text{tails} \end{array} \begin{pmatrix} 1 & -1 \\ -1 & 1 \end{pmatrix}.$$

The construction and use of payoff matrices are considered in the exercises. Whenever Ron and Carl are the players it is assumed that Ron is the row player and Carl the column player.

. . . .

Exercises

State the payoff matrix for each game:

1. Ron flips a coin. Carl calls "heads" or "tails." If Carl calls the coin correctly, Ron pays him one penny. If Carl does not call the coin correctly, he pays Ron one penny.

2. Ron and Carl simultaneously each show one or two fingers. If they show the same number of fingers, Ron pays Carl one penny. If they show different numbers of fingers, Carl pays Ron one penny.

3. Ron and Carl simultaneously each show one or two fingers. If the total numbers of fingers shown is even, Ron pays Carl that number of pennies. If the total number of fingers shown is odd, Carl pays Ron that number of pennies.

4. The game of Paper-Scissors-Stone is played with values of $+1$ for winning, -1 for losing, and 0 when there is no winner. The winners are determined by the rules: paper covers stone, stone breaks scissors, scissors cut paper.

5. Ron and Carl simultaneously and independently each write down one of the numbers 1, 2, or 3. If the sum of the numbers is even, Ron pays Carl that number of dollars. If the sum of the numbers is odd, Carl pays Ron that number of dollars.

Consider these payoff matrices:

a) $\begin{pmatrix} 1 & 2 \\ -1 & 1 \end{pmatrix}$;

b) $\begin{pmatrix} 1 & -1 & 1 \\ 2 & -2 & -1 \\ 1 & 3 & -2 \end{pmatrix}$;

c) $\begin{pmatrix} 1 & -1 \\ -1 & 1 \end{pmatrix};$ d) $\begin{pmatrix} 1 & 2 & 4 \\ 2 & 3 & 4 \\ 2 & 1 & 1 \end{pmatrix}.$

6. Suppose that you are the row player. Is there a row with payoffs that are always at least as favorable to you as those on some other row and in at least one instance better than that other row? If so, state which row is better than (dominates) which row(s).

7. Columns are considered relative to the point of view of the column player. He wants to pay as little as possible. Therefore, a column with smaller elements dominates a column with large elements. Suppose that you are the column player. Is there a column with payoffs that are always at least as favorable to you as those on some other column and in at least one instance better than that other column? If so, state which column dominates which column(s).

8. Relative to the row player find the worst (minimum) payoff for each row and name the row for which this minimum is as large as possible. In other words, name the row for which the least amount received is as large as possible.

9. Relative to the column player find the worst (maximum) payoff for each column and name the column for which this maximum is as small as possible. In other words, name the column for which the largest amount paid out is as small as possible.

Ron rolls a die. Carl flips a coin. If the number on the die is odd and the coin is heads, then Carl pays Ron that number of dollars. If the number is even and the coin is tails, then Carl pays Ron that number of dollars. Otherwise Ron pays Carl the number of dollars shown on the die.

10. State the payoff matrix.

11. a) Is this a zero-sum game?

 b) List Ron's moves and the probability of each one for an unbiased die.

 c) List Carl's moves and the probability of each one for an unbiased coin.

12. a) Which move of Ron's maximizes his minimal gain?

 b) Which move of Carl's minimizes his maximal loss?

. . . .

6.3 PURE STRATEGIES

A decision to select exactly one of the available moves is called a **pure strategy**. The use of a pure strategy, if feasible, depends upon the conditions considered in Exercises 6 through 9 of Section 6.2.

Consider the payoff matrix:

$$\begin{pmatrix} 6 & 3 & 2 \\ 4 & 1 & 1 \\ 3 & 2 & 1 \end{pmatrix}. \tag{1}$$

First, assume that you are the row player. If the column player selects the first column, you would win the most if you had selected the first row. If the column player selects the second column, you would win the most if you had selected the first row. If the column player selects the third column, you would win the most if you had selected the first row.

The first row of (1) is always at least as favorable to the row player as the second row and is better than the second row in at least one instance; that is, the first row *dominates* the second row. Similarly, the first row dominates the third row. Thus, the first row is the **dominant row**. Under all circumstances the best strategy for the row player is to select the first row.

Next, assume that you are the column player for the same payoff matrix (1). As column player you want to lose (pay) as little as possible. If the row player selects the first row, you would lose the least if you had selected the third column. If the row player selects the second row, you would lose the least if you had selected the third column. If the row player selects the third row, you would lose the least if you had selected the third column. The third column dominates the first column, dominates the second column, and is the **dominant column**.

The matrix (1) has a dominant row and a dominant column. Whenever such is the case the game can be easily solved. In general, the **solution of a game** consists of the identification of the best strategy, usually called the **optimum strategy**, for each player. For the game with payoff matrix (1) the first row is the optimum strategy for the row player, and the third column is the optimum strategy for the column player. The element 2 on the first row and third column is the **value of the game**. The game favors the row player since the value of the game is positive. If the column player plays well, the row player will not win any more than the value of the game. If the row player plays well, he will not win any less than the value of the game.

Many payoff matrices do not have a dominant row and a dominant column. Consider the matrix:

$$\begin{pmatrix} 2 & 0 & 0 \\ 3 & 1 & 1 \\ 1 & 2 & 0 \end{pmatrix}. \tag{2}$$

The matrix (2) does not have a dominant row. Accordingly, we look for the minimum gain on each row; namely, 0 on the first row, 1 on the second row, and 0 on the third row. These minimum payoffs are the worst that could happen. Frequently they are listed at the ends of the rows:

$$
\begin{pmatrix} 2 & 0 & 0 \\ 3 & 1 & 1 \\ 1 & 2 & 0 \end{pmatrix}
\quad
\begin{array}{c} \text{row} \\ \text{minimums} \\ 0 \\ 1 \quad \text{maximin 1} \\ 0 \end{array}
$$

The maximum of the row minimums is 1 on the second row. Accordingly, the **maximin strategy** of the row player is the second row.

The column player for the matrix (2) considers the maximum that he might have to pay on each column:

$$
\begin{pmatrix} 2 & 0 & 0 \\ 3 & 1 & 1 \\ 1 & 2 & 0 \end{pmatrix}
$$

column
maximums   3   2   1

minimax 1

The minimum of the column maximums is 1 in the third column. Accordingly, the **minimax strategy** for the column player is the third column.

Note that the element 1 on the second row and the third column of (2) serves as both the maximin for the rows and the minimax for the columns. This element 1 is the minimum of the elements in its row and the maximum of the elements in its column. Any such element is called a **saddle point** of the matrix. Neither player can improve his expected payoff by changing from the row or column of a saddle point. Accordingly, the associated strategies are *optimum strategies* for the players.

The name *saddle point* comes from the property of the point as the minimum on its row (left to right) and the maximum on its column (front to back) as visualized for the point X in Fig. 6.1.

The solution of the game with payoff matrix (2) is the second row as the row player's pure strategy and the third column as the column player's pure strategy. The value of the game is 1.

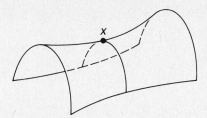

Fig. 6.1

The search for a saddle point for a matrix game can be systematically performed as follows:

1. Copy the minimum element of each row at the end of that row. Identify the maximum of these minimum elements as the maximin. The rows with the maximin as minimum are **maximin rows**.

2. Copy the maximum element of each column below that column. Identify the minimum of these maximum elements as the minimax. The columns with the minimax as maximum are **minimax columns**.

3. The game has a saddle point if and only if the maximin and the minimax are the same number and that number occurs at the intersection of a maximin row and a minimax column. As in Exercises 12 and 16 a matrix (game) may have more than one saddle point.

If there is a saddle point, the value at this saddle point is the value of the game as well as the common value of the minimax and the maximin. The row of a saddle point and the column of that point constitute the solution, or one of two or more equivalent solutions, of the game. For the matrix game (2) the procedure above may be performed and reported as follows:

$$
\begin{array}{ccc}
 & \text{minimums} & \\
\begin{pmatrix} 2 & 0 & 0 \\ 3 & 1 & 1 \\ 1 & 2 & 0 \end{pmatrix} & \begin{matrix} 0 \\ 1 \\ 0 \end{matrix} & \text{maximin 1}
\end{array}
$$

maximums   3   2   1

minimax 1

Solution: second row, third column
Value of game: 1

If a payoff matrix has a dominant row and a dominant column, there exists a pure optimum strategy of that row and that column. Actually, the element at the intersection of the dominant row and the dominant column is also a saddle point (Supplementary Exercise 9). Thus, the use of dominant rows and dominant columns may be viewed as another procedure for finding saddle points. If a payoff matrix has a saddle point, there exists a pure optimum strategy of the row and column of that saddle point. In all other cases a mixed strategy (Section 6.4) is needed.

Any game that has a saddle point is called a **strictly determined game**. Any game that has value 0 is a **fair game**. If a game has a positive value, the game favors the row player. If a game has a negative value, the game favors the column player. Remember that a zero-sum game is a game in which each player loses exactly what the other player wins (Section 6.1) and thus may have values different from zero.

. . . .

Exercises

Find the dominant row, if any, for each matrix:

1. $\begin{pmatrix} 1 & 2 \\ 2 & 3 \end{pmatrix}$.

2. $\begin{pmatrix} 1 & 0 & -1 \\ 3 & 1 & 2 \end{pmatrix}$.

3. $\begin{pmatrix} 2 & 1 & -3 \\ 1 & 0 & -1 \\ -2 & 1 & -2 \end{pmatrix}$.

4. $\begin{pmatrix} 2 & 1 & 1 \\ 1 & -3 & 2 \\ 2 & 1 & 2 \end{pmatrix}$.

5 through 8. Find the dominant column, if any, for each matrix in Exercises 1 through 4.

9 through 12. Use the minimax-maximin procedure to find the saddle point(s), if any, for each matrix in Exercises 1 through 4. If there is a dominant row and a dominant column, check that their intersection is a saddle point.

Determine whether or not the game with each payoff matrix is (a) strictly determined, (b) fair:

13. $\begin{pmatrix} 0 & 2 \\ -2 & 5 \end{pmatrix}$.

14. $\begin{pmatrix} 4 & 1 \\ -4 & -2 \end{pmatrix}$.

15. $\begin{pmatrix} 1 & 0 \\ -1 & 1 \end{pmatrix}$.

In Exercises 16 and 17 solve and find the value of the game with payoff matrix:

16. $\begin{pmatrix} 2 & -1 & -5 & -4 \\ 1 & 2 & 0 & 1 \\ -5 & 1 & -2 & 2 \end{pmatrix}$.

17. $\begin{pmatrix} 10 & 0 & 23 & -12 \\ 14 & 1 & 2 & 8 \\ -4 & -3 & 14 & -2 \\ 12 & -6 & 6 & 4 \end{pmatrix}$.

18. Ron and Carl match pennies with payoffs of 1 penny to Ron if the coins are both heads, 1 penny to Carl if the coins are both tails, and no payments if the coins do not match.

   a) Let Ron be the row player and Carl the column player. Find the payoff matrix.

   b) Is the game strictly determined?

   c) Is the game fair?

19. Ron and Carl simultaneously each show one or two fingers. The payoff is $2 to Carl if they both show one finger, $4 to Ron if they both show two fingers, and no payoff if they do not show the same number of fingers.

   a) What is Ron's row maximin strategy?

   b) What is Carl's minimax strategy?

   c) Is the game strictly determined?

   d) Is the game fair?

20. Ron and Carl simultaneously show one, two, or three fingers. The payoffs are indicated in the following matrix:

		Carl		
		one finger	two fingers	three fingers
	one finger	1	2	0
Ron	two fingers	0	1	-1
	three fingers	1	0	0

   a) Does Ron have a dominant row strategy?

   b) Does Carl have a dominant column strategy?

   c) Is the game strictly determined?

   d) Is the game fair?

Supplementary Exercises

These exercises are designed to explore the conditions under which a 2×2 payoff matrix is not strictly determined, that is, does not have a saddle point.

1. Is the game with payoff matrix

$$\begin{pmatrix} 3 & 2 \\ b & 0 \end{pmatrix}$$

   strictly determined for
   a) $b = 1$?   b) $b > 0$?   c) $b < 0$?

2. Consider a strictly determined game with a 2×2 payoff matrix and a saddle point v. Suppose that x is the element of the matrix that is not on a row or a column with v. Explain whether or not a change in the value of x can make the game strictly determined?

3. Is the game with payoff matrix

$$\begin{pmatrix} 1 & c \\ c & 10 \end{pmatrix}$$

   strictly determined for
   a) $c < 1$?   b) $c = 1$?   c) $1 < c < 10$?
   d) $c = 10$?   e) $c > 10$?

4. In order for a game to be strictly determined, an element (saddle point) is needed that is both a minimum of its row and a maximum of its column. For a 2×2 matrix

$$\begin{pmatrix} a & b \\ c & d \end{pmatrix}$$

   each element is on the *principal diagonal* (the elements a and d) or on the *minor diagonal* (the elements b and c).
   a) List the inequalities needed for b to be a saddle point.
   b) List the inequalities needed for c to be a saddle point.

For the matrix considered in Exercise 4 think of A, B, C, and D as the points on a number line with the coordinates a, b, c, and d, respectively.

5. Relative to the line segment $\overline{AD}$ describe the position of the point:
   a) B if b is to be a saddle point;
   b) C if c is to be a saddle point;
   c) B if b is not to be a saddle point;
   d) C if c is not to be a saddle point.

6. Determine whether or not the game is strictly determined if:
   a) $B \in \overline{AD}$ or $C \in \overline{AD}$;
   b) $A \in \overline{BC}$ or $D \in \overline{BC}$;
   c) $A \notin \overline{BC}$ and $\overline{AD} \cap \overline{BC} = \emptyset$.

7. In Exercise 6 are there any other possible cases; that is, do the three cases considered fail to provide a partition (mutually exclusive and exhaustive) of the possibilities?
8. Restate the implication of Exercise 6(c) and Exercise 7 in terms of the values of the elements on one diagonal compared with the values of the elements on the other diagonal.

. . . .

6.4 MIXED STRATEGIES AND SUBGAMES

The modified game of matching pennies considered in Section 6.3 Exercise 18 has payoff matrix

$$\begin{pmatrix} 1 & 0 \\ 0 & -1 \end{pmatrix}.$$

This game is strictly determined with the first row as the maximin row strategy and the second column as the minimax column strategy. The row strategy may be represented by the **row strategy matrix** (vector) (1, 0). The product of this row strategy matrix and the payoff matrix is a matrix of the possible payoffs when this row strategy is used:

$$(1 \quad 0) \begin{pmatrix} 1 & 0 \\ 0 & -1 \end{pmatrix} = (1 \quad 0).$$

The column strategy may be similarly represented by a column strategy matrix $(0, 1)^t$. The product of the payoff matrix and this column strategy matrix is a matrix of the possible payoffs when this column strategy is used;

$$\begin{pmatrix} 1 & 0 \\ 0 & -1 \end{pmatrix} \begin{pmatrix} 0 \\ 1 \end{pmatrix} = \begin{pmatrix} 0 \\ -1 \end{pmatrix}.$$

The product of the three matrices—the row strategy matrix, the payoff matrix, and the column strategy matrix—is a matrix with the value of the game as its only element;

$$(1 \quad 0) \begin{pmatrix} 1 & 0 \\ 0 & -1 \end{pmatrix} \begin{pmatrix} 0 \\ 1 \end{pmatrix} = (1 \quad 0) \begin{pmatrix} 0 \\ 1 \end{pmatrix} = (0).$$

The use of row strategy matrices and column strategy matrices is particularly helpful when the game is not strictly determined and a mixed strategy is needed. The elements of the strategy matrices then become the probabilities with which the rows (or columns) are randomly selected.

Consider again the usual game of matching pennies with payoff matrix

$$\begin{pmatrix} 1 & -1 \\ -1 & 1 \end{pmatrix}.$$

This game is not strictly determined. If the row player adopts a pure strategy of a particular row, say heads, then the column player will soon "catch on" and play tails consistently for repeated wins. Thus, the row player must show heads part of the time and tails part of the time. If he has a fixed pattern for doing this, the column player is apt to discover that pattern and take advantage of it. Thus, a random selection is desirable. Indeed, to make certain that the opponent does not discover a pattern, it is best not to have a pattern at all. Instead, a random procedure such as flipping a coin should be used to decide whether to show heads or tails. The resulting strategy in which pure strategies, heads or tails, are mixed at random but according to some definite proportion is a **mixed strategy**.

Let the payoff matrix of a general 2×2 game be

$$\begin{pmatrix} a & b \\ c & d \end{pmatrix}.$$

Let the row strategy matrix be $(p, 1 - p)$. Then

$$(p, \ 1 - p) \begin{pmatrix} a & b \\ c & d \end{pmatrix} = (ap + c(1 - p), \ bp + d(1 - p)).$$

The row player's expected payoff is $ap + c(1 - p)$ if the column player selects the first column. The row player's expected payoff is $bp + d(1 - p)$ if the column player selects the second column. The optimum strategy for the row player is obtained by equating these two expected payoffs. Then

$$ap + c(1 - p) = bp + d(1 - p),$$

$$p(a - b - c + d) = d - c,$$

$$p = \frac{d - c}{a - b - c + d},$$

$$1 - p = \frac{a - b}{a - b - c + d},$$

and for the row strategy matrix

$$(p, 1 - p) = \left(-\frac{d - c}{a - b - c + d}, \frac{a - b}{a - b - c + d}\right). \tag{3}$$

Similarly, if the column strategy matrix is $(q, 1 - q)^t$, then

$$\begin{pmatrix} a & b \\ c & d \end{pmatrix} \begin{pmatrix} q \\ 1 - q \end{pmatrix} = \begin{pmatrix} aq + b(1 - q) \\ cq + d(1 - q) \end{pmatrix},$$

$$aq + b(1 - q) = cq + d(1 - q),$$

$$q(a - b - c + d) = d - b,$$

$$q = \frac{d - b}{a - b - c + d},$$

$$(q, 1 - q)^t = \left(\frac{d - b}{a - b - c + d}, \frac{a - c}{a - b - c + d}\right). \tag{4}$$

The value of the game (to the row player) is v, where

$$v = ap + c(1 - p),$$

$$v = \frac{ad - ac + ac - bc}{a - b - c + d},$$

$$v = \frac{ad - bc}{a - b - c + d}. \tag{5}$$

For the column player the value of the game is also v, payable to the row player. Thus, v is the *value of the game*. As in the case of pure strategies the value of the game may be considered as the value for a good player against a good player. A good player, in general, cannot win more unless his opponent plays badly and cannot win less unless he plays badly. In other words, the above strategies (3) and (4) are the optimum mixed strategies.

Example Find the optimum strategies and the value of the game for the usual game of matching pennies.

Solution. The payoff matrix is

$$\begin{pmatrix} 1 & -1 \\ -1 & 1 \end{pmatrix}.$$

For $a = d = 1$ and $b = c = -1$, we use the strategies (3) and (4) to obtain $(p, 1 - p) = (\frac{1}{2}, \frac{1}{2})$ and $(q, 1 - q)^t = (\frac{1}{2}, \frac{1}{2})^t$. The value of the game may be found either from (5) or from the product of matrices

$$(\tfrac{1}{2} \ \ \tfrac{1}{2}) \begin{pmatrix} 1 & -1 \\ -1 & 1 \end{pmatrix} \begin{pmatrix} \frac{1}{2} \\ \frac{1}{2} \end{pmatrix} = (0 \ \ 0) \begin{pmatrix} \frac{1}{2} \\ \frac{1}{2} \end{pmatrix} = (0).$$

The value of the game is 0; the game is a fair game.

The mixed strategies (3) and (4) are used only for games that cannot be solved by pure strategies (Section 6.3). Similar strategies may be developed for matrices with more rows and/or columns. Except for the use of techniques of linear programming (Section 6.5) and the reduction of matrices by the elimination of dominated rows and/or columns, such details are beyond the scope of this book.

Consider the payoff matrix

$$\begin{pmatrix} 1 & 3 & 2 & 4 & 3 \\ 4 & 2 & 5 & 3 & 3 \end{pmatrix}. \tag{6}$$

The matrix (6) does not have a saddle point. Neither row is dominant. However, the first column dominates (is preferable to the column player under all circumstances) the third column; the second column dominates the fourth column and the fifth column. Accordingly, the third, fourth, and fifth columns do not need to be considered further. The game (6) may be solved by solving the **subgame** with matrix

$$\begin{pmatrix} 1 & 3 \\ 4 & 2 \end{pmatrix}. \tag{7}$$

Since the subgame is not strictly determined, the mixed strategies (3) and (4) are used (Exercise 3). For the subgame

$$(p, 1 - p) = (\tfrac{1}{2}, \tfrac{1}{2}),$$
$$(q, 1 - q)^t = (\tfrac{1}{4}, \tfrac{3}{4})^t.$$

The row strategy matrix for the game (6) is the same as for the game (7). The column strategy matrix for (6) is obtained from the column strategy matrix for (7) by inserting zeros for the dominated columns of (6). Thus, we have

$$(\tfrac{1}{4}, \tfrac{3}{4}, 0, 0, 0)^t.$$

The values of the games (6) and (7) are each $\frac{5}{2}$.

The elimination of dominated rows and/or columns can be very useful and can be done for the payoff matrices of subgames as well as for the original matrices.

. . . .

Exercises

Find the optimum strategies and the value of the game for the game with payoff matrix:

1. $\begin{pmatrix} 1 & 0 \\ 0 & 2 \end{pmatrix}$.

2. $\begin{pmatrix} 1 & 2 \\ 5 & -8 \end{pmatrix}$.

3. $\begin{pmatrix} 1 & 3 \\ 4 & 2 \end{pmatrix}$.

4. $\begin{pmatrix} 2 & -1 \\ -2 & 1 \end{pmatrix}$.

Obtain (a) the payoff matrix for a subgame by eliminating the dominated rows and columns from each payoff matrix; (b) the optimum strategies and the value of the subgame; (c) the optimum strategies and the value of the original game.

5. $\begin{pmatrix} 1 & 2 & -1 \\ 3 & 2 & 0 \\ -1 & 1 & 0 \end{pmatrix}$.

6. $\begin{pmatrix} 2 & 1 & 3 \\ 4 & -10 & 5 \\ 1 & -20 & 2 \end{pmatrix}$.

7. $\begin{pmatrix} 2 & 1 & -3 & -4 & 5 \\ 1 & 0 & -4 & -4 & 3 \\ 0 & -2 & 1 & 0 & 4 \end{pmatrix}$.

8. $\begin{pmatrix} 2 & 0 & -2 & 1 & -1 & 5 \\ 1 & 0 & -3 & 4 & 2 & 4 \\ 3 & 4 & 4 & 1 & 0 & 5 \end{pmatrix}$.

Find the optimum strategies and the value of the game for the game described in Section 6.2:

9. Exercise 1.   10. Exercise 3.

Show that the mixed strategies (3) and (4) are not affected by:

11. Multiplying each element of a payoff matrix by a constant k different from zero.

12. Adding the same number t to each element of a payoff matrix.

Show that:

13. If each element of a payoff matrix is multiplied by a constant k, then the value of the game is multiplied by k.

14. If the same number t is added to each element of a payoff matrix, then the value of the game is increased by that number.

. . . .

6.5 GAME THEORY AND LINEAR PROGRAMMING

The simplex algorithm for linear programming problems enables us to consider many games with payoff matrices that are larger than 2×2 matrices. However, we first develop the theory for a general 2×2 payoff matrix

$$\begin{pmatrix} a_{11} & a_{12} \\ a_{21} & a_{22} \end{pmatrix} \tag{8}$$

for a game that is *not* strictly determined. Let the row strategy matrix be (p_1, p_2), where $p_1 + p_2 = 1$. Let the column strategy matrix be $(q_1, q_2)^t$, where $q_1 + q_2 = 1$.

The value v of the game is the same as the minimum of the expected payoffs to the row player. Since

$$(p_1 \quad p_2) \begin{pmatrix} a_{11} & a_{12} \\ a_{21} & a_{22} \end{pmatrix} = (a_{11}p_1 + a_{21}p_2, \ a_{12}p_1 + a_{22}p_2),$$

we have

$$\begin{cases} a_{11}p_1 + a_{21}p_2 \geq v, \\ a_{12}p_1 + a_{22}p_2 \geq v. \end{cases} \tag{9}$$

Also, we have

$$\begin{cases} 0 \leq p_1, \\ 0 \leq p_2, \\ p_1 + p_2 = 1. \end{cases}$$

To obtain a standard linear programming form for this problem, we need to introduce new variables p_1/v and p_2/v. This requires the division of both sides of an inequality by v and thus raises a question as to whether $0 < v, 0 = v$, or $0 > v$. Fortunately, the strategies for any game (8) are the same as the strategies for any game obtained from (8) by adding the same number to each element of (8) (Section 6.4 Exercise 12). Thus, if we increase each element of (8) by $1 + |v|$, then the new matrix will have the same associated strategies as (8) and, as in Section 6.4 Exercise 14, the value of the new game will be a positive number $v + 1 + |v|$. In other words, any game with matrix (8) can be replaced by an equivalent game with a positive value. Accordingly, we may assume that we are concerned with a game with a positive value and make the change of variables just described.

The system (9) and related statements for the new variables become

$$\begin{cases} a_{11}(p_1/v) + a_{12}(p_2/v) \geq 1, \\ a_{12}(p_1/v) + a_{22}(p_2/v) \geq 1, \\ 0 \leq p_1/v, \\ 0 \leq p_2/v, \\ (p_1/v) + (p_2/v) = 1/v. \end{cases}$$

Each player wishes to maximize the payoff of the game to him. For example, the row player tries to maximize v, the minimum payoff to him. The maximization of v is equivalent to the minimization of $1/v$. In the notation of the simplex algorithm for minimization, we let $(p_1/v) = u$, $(p_2/v) = w$, recognize that then $u + w = 1/v$, and minimize $u + w$ subject to the set of constraints

$$\begin{cases} u \geq 0, w \geq 0, \\ a_{11}u + a_{21}w \geq 1, \\ a_{12}u + a_{22}w \geq 1. \end{cases}$$

This problem is in the usual form for a linear programming problem and has simplex tableau

	C_1	C_2	E_1	E_2	
E_1	a_{11}	a_{12}	1	0	1
E_2	a_{21}	a_{22}	0	1	1
	-1	-1	0	0	0

$$(10)$$

The dual problem is the maximization of $x + y$ subject to the constraints

$$\begin{cases} 0 \leq x, 0 \leq y, \\ a_{11}x + a_{12}y \leq 1, \\ a_{21}x + a_{22}y \leq 1. \end{cases}$$

For $x = q_1/v$ and $y = q_2/v$, we have the conditions

$$\begin{cases} a_{11}q_1 + a_{12}q_2 \leq v, \\ a_{21}q_1 + a_{22}q_2 \leq v, \\ 0 \leq q_1, 0 \leq q_2, \\ q_1 + q_2 = 1. \end{cases}$$

$$(11)$$

In other words, the dual linear programming problem is precisely the problem of solving the game from the point of view of the column player. The common value of the objective function for the minimization problem and the objective function for the maximization problem is the value of the game when the problems are stated as in (9) and (11). This common value is modified according to an established plan to find the value of the game when the problems are stated in the usual form for linear programming problems.

Example 1 Use the simplex algorithm to solve and find the value of the usual game of matching pennies.

Solution. The payoff matrix is

$$\begin{pmatrix} 1 & -1 \\ -1 & 1 \end{pmatrix}.$$

For this particular game we know from the Example of Section 6.4 that the value of the game is 0. Thus, we could add 1 to each element of the matrix to obtain a game with the same strategies and a positive value. If we did not know the value of the game, we could add 2 to each element of the matrix to obtain a matrix that has only positive elements and therefore must have a positive value.

We add 2 to illustrate this general procedure and obtain the payoff matrix

$$\begin{pmatrix} 3 & 1 \\ 1 & 3 \end{pmatrix}.$$

The game with this payoff matrix is not strictly determined. The simplex tableau (10) for this payoff matrix is

	C_1	C_2	E_1	E_2	
E_1	3	1	1	0	1
E_2	1	3	0	1	1
	-1	-1	0	0	0

We solve the linear programming problem as in Chapter 5:

	C_1	C_2	E_1	E_2	
C_1	1	$\frac{1}{3}$	$\frac{1}{3}$	0	$\frac{1}{3}$
E_2	0	$\frac{8}{3}$	$-\frac{1}{3}$	1	$\frac{2}{3}$
	0	$-\frac{2}{3}$	$\frac{1}{3}$	0	$\frac{1}{3}$

	C_1	C_2	E_1	E_2	
C_1	1	0	$\frac{3}{8}$	$-\frac{1}{8}$	$\frac{1}{4}$
C_2	0	1	$-\frac{1}{8}$	$\frac{3}{8}$	$\frac{1}{4}$
	0	0	$\frac{1}{4}$	$\frac{1}{4}$	$\frac{1}{2}$

The new game has

$$(p_1, p_2) = \tfrac{2}{1}(\tfrac{1}{4}, \tfrac{1}{4}) = (\tfrac{1}{2}, \tfrac{1}{2}),$$

$$(q_1, q_2) = \tfrac{2}{1}(\tfrac{1}{4}, \tfrac{1}{4}) = (\tfrac{1}{2}, \tfrac{1}{2}),$$

and $v = 2$. The original game has these same strategies but has value $2 - 2$, that is, 0.

Consider any two-person game. The following steps for solving the game are now available to us:

1. If the payoff matrix has a saddle point, then the game is strictly determined and the pure strategies may be found as in Section 6.3.

2. If the payoff matrix does not have a saddle point, then the dominated rows and columns, if any, may be eliminated to obtain an equivalent subgame. If the payoff matrix of this subgame has a saddle point, then pure strategies may be found as in Section 6.4.

3. If neither the payoff matrix of the original game nor the payoff matrix of a subgame found by eliminating dominated rows and columns has a saddle point, then mixed strategies are needed. These strategies may be obtained for the subgame.

In order to be sure that the value of the game is positive, an appropriate positive number k is added to each element of the payoff matrix to obtain a payoff matrix with only positive elements:

$$\begin{pmatrix} a_{11} & a_{12} & \cdots & a_{1m} \\ a_{21} & a_{22} & \cdots & a_{2m} \\ \cdots & \cdots & \cdots & \cdots \\ a_{n1} & a_{n2} & \cdots & a_{nm} \end{pmatrix}.$$

The row strategy matrix is then

$$(p_1, p_2, \ldots, p_n);$$

the column strategy matrix is

$$(q_1, q_2, \ldots, q_m)^t.$$

Subject to the usual restrictions on the use of the simplex algorithm, the game may be solved using a simplex tableau of the form

	C_1	C_2	$\cdots$	C_m	E_1	E_2	$\cdots$	E_m	
E_1	a_{11}	a_{12}	$\cdots$	a_{1m}	1	0	$\cdots$	0	1
E_2	a_{21}	a_{22}	$\cdots$	a_{2m}	0	1	$\cdots$	0	1
$\cdots$	$\cdots$	$\cdots$	$\cdots$	$\cdots$	$\cdots$	$\cdots$	$\cdots$	$\cdots$	$\cdots$
E_n	a_{n1}	a_{n2}	$\cdots$	a_{nm}	0	0	$\cdots$	1	1
	-1	-1	$\cdots$	-1	0	0	$\cdots$	0	0

The common value of the objective functions for the minimization and maximization problems is $1/(v + k)$, where k is the number that was added to each element of the original payoff matrix and v is the value of the game. The row strategy matrix may be obtained as $1/(v + k)$ times the solution of the minimization problem; the column strategy matrix may be similarly obtained from the solution of the maximization problem. If a subgame has been solved, then zeros must be added in the strategy matrices for the dominated rows and columns that were eliminated.

Example 2   Solve the game with payoff matrix

$$\begin{pmatrix} -1 & 2 & 0 \\ 3 & 0 & 1 \\ 0 & 1 & 2 \end{pmatrix}.$$

Solution. We first check for a saddle point as in Section 6.3.

minimums

$$\begin{pmatrix} -1 & 2 & 0 \\ 3 & 0 & 1 \\ 0 & 1 & 2 \end{pmatrix} \quad \begin{matrix} -1 \\ 0 \\ 0 \end{matrix} \quad \text{maximin } 0$$

maximums   3   2   2

minimax 2

Since the maximin and the minimax are different, the matrix does not have a saddle point.

We next look for dominated rows and columns. There are none.

We add 2 to each element of the matrix to obtain a new matrix with only positive terms:

$$\begin{pmatrix} 1 & 4 & 2 \\ 5 & 2 & 3 \\ 2 & 3 & 4 \end{pmatrix}.$$

The simplex tableau is

	C_1	C_2	C_3	E_1	E_2	E_3	
E_1	1	4	2	1	0	0	1
E_2	5	2	3	0	1	0	1
E_3	2	3	4	0	0	1	1
	-1	-1	-1	0	0	0	0

We proceed as in Chapter 5. Note that the smallest quotient of the last element of a row divided by an element a_{ij} is obtained using the element 5 in the second row and first column.

	C_1	C_2	C_3	E_1	E_2	E_3	
E_1	0	$\frac{18}{5}$	$\frac{7}{5}$	1	$-\frac{1}{5}$	0	$\frac{4}{5}$
C_1	1	$\frac{2}{5}$	$\frac{3}{5}$	0	$\frac{1}{5}$	0	$\frac{1}{5}$
E_3	0	$\frac{11}{5}$	$\frac{14}{5}$	0	$-\frac{2}{5}$	1	$\frac{3}{5}$
	0	$-\frac{3}{5}$	$-\frac{2}{5}$	0	$\frac{1}{5}$	0	$\frac{1}{5}$

	C_1	C_2	C_3	E_1	E_2	E_3	
C_2	0	1	$\frac{7}{18}$	$\frac{5}{18}$	$-\frac{1}{18}$	0	$\frac{2}{9}$
C_1	1	0	$\frac{4}{9}$	$-\frac{1}{9}$	$\frac{2}{9}$	0	$\frac{1}{9}$
E_3	0	0	$\frac{35}{18}$	$-\frac{11}{18}$	$-\frac{5}{18}$	1	$\frac{1}{9}$
	0	0	$-\frac{1}{6}$	$\frac{1}{6}$	$\frac{1}{6}$	0	$\frac{1}{3}$

	C_1	C_2	C_3	E_1	E_2	E_3	
C_2	0	1	0	$\frac{2}{5}$	0	$-\frac{1}{5}$	$\frac{1}{5}$
C_1	1	0	0	$\frac{1}{35}$	$\frac{2}{7}$	$-\frac{8}{35}$	$\frac{3}{35}$
C_3	0	0	1	$-\frac{11}{35}$	$-\frac{1}{7}$	$\frac{18}{35}$	$\frac{2}{35}$
	0	0	0	$\frac{4}{35}$	$\frac{1}{7}$	$\frac{3}{35}$	$\frac{12}{35}$

Then $1/(v + k) = \frac{12}{35}$, $v + k = \frac{35}{12}$,

$$(p_1, p_2, p_3) = (\tfrac{35}{12})(\tfrac{4}{35}, \tfrac{1}{7}, \tfrac{3}{35}) = (\tfrac{1}{3}, \tfrac{5}{12}, \tfrac{1}{4});$$

$$(q_1, q_2, q_3)^t = (\tfrac{35}{12})(\tfrac{3}{35}, \tfrac{1}{5}, \tfrac{2}{35})^t = (\tfrac{1}{4}, \tfrac{7}{12}, \tfrac{1}{6})^t.$$

Since $k = 2$, $v = \frac{35}{12} - 2 = \frac{11}{12}$.

The optimum row strategy is $(\tfrac{1}{3}, \tfrac{5}{12}, \tfrac{1}{4})$, the optimum column strategy is $(\tfrac{1}{4}, \tfrac{7}{12}, \tfrac{1}{6})^t$, and the value of the game is $\frac{11}{12}$, that is, the game favors the row player by $\frac{11}{12}$.

. . . .

Exercises

For an equivalent game with a positive value, find a payoff matrix with least element $+1$.

1. $\begin{pmatrix} 3 & 0 & -3 \\ -6 & -1 & 2 \end{pmatrix}.$

2. $\begin{pmatrix} 3 & 0 & -1 \\ 0 & 3 & 2 \\ -1 & 2 & 1 \end{pmatrix}.$

In Exercises 3, 4, and 5 find the optimum row strategy, the optimum column strategy, and the value of the game with the given payoff matrix.

3. $\begin{pmatrix} 6 & 3 & 0 \\ -3 & 2 & 5 \end{pmatrix}.$

4. $\begin{pmatrix} 7 & 6 & 8 & 2 \\ 3 & 5 & 4 & 6 \end{pmatrix}.$

5. $\begin{pmatrix} 5 & 2 & 1 \\ 2 & 5 & 4 \\ 1 & 4 & 3 \end{pmatrix}.$

6. For the usual game Paper-Scissors-Stone (Section 6.2, Exercise 4) find the optimum row strategy, the optimum column strategy, and the value of the game.

7. Consider the game of rolling a die and flipping a coin (Section 6.2, Exercises 10 through 12).

   a) What is the row strategy for rolling an unbiased die?

   b) What is the column strategy for flipping an unbiased coin?

   c) What is the value of the game when played with an unbiased die and an unbiased coin?

   d) Is this game a fair game?

8. For the game in Exercise 7 suppose that the die may be biased and the coin may be biased. What is the value of the game if the coin has two heads and:

   a) the die always shows 6?

   b) the die always shows 5?

   c) the die shows 6 and 5 with equal probabilities?

   d) the die shows 6 with probability $\frac{5}{11}$ and 5 with probability $\frac{6}{11}$?

   e) the die shows 2 with probability $\frac{3}{5}$ and 3 with probability $\frac{2}{5}$?

9. Suppose that the game of rolling a die and flipping a coin (Exercise 7) is modified to give each player complete control of his moves. For example, suppose that each player independently and without any knowledge of the other player's move writes down his move.

   a) Use $k = 7$ and write down the simplex tableau for this game.

   b) Select the element on the sixth row and second column of the tableau (a) as the pivotal element and write the tableau for the next step in the simplex solution of the problem.

   c) Note in the tableau (b) that a negative indicator is obtained in the E_6 column if the next pivotal element is selected on the second or fourth rows.

   d) Select the next pivotal element on the fifth row of the tableau (b) and find the simplex solution.

   e) Select the next pivotal element on the first row of the tableau (b) and find the simplex solution.

10. Modify the game in Exercise 9 so that the row player flips the coin and the column player rolls the die. Use a simplex tableau to solve this game.

. . . .

REVIEW EXERCISES FOR CHAPTER 6

State the payoff matrix for each game:

1. Ron holds a dime in one hand and a penny in the other. If Carl guesses the coin in Ron's right hand correctly, Ron gives the coin to Carl. If Carl does not guess the coin correctly, Carl gives Ron a nickel.

2. Ron and Carl each roll an unbiased die. If the numbers on the dice match, Carl pays Ron the sum of the two numbers in cents; if the numbers do not match, Ron pays Carl one cent.

Does the game described in (a) Exercise 1, (b) Exercise 2, have:

3. A saddle point?

4. A dominated row?

5. A dominated column?

6. A pure strategy?

Find the optimal row strategy, the optimal column strategy, and the value of the game with the given payoff matrix:

7. $\begin{pmatrix} 0 & 3 \\ 1 & 2 \end{pmatrix}$.

8. $\begin{pmatrix} 5 & 4 \\ 6 & 3 \end{pmatrix}$.

9. $\begin{pmatrix} 0 & 0 & -1 & 1 \\ 0 & 0 & -1 & 0 \\ 0 & -2 & 0 & -1 \\ 2 & 1 & 0 & 1 \end{pmatrix}$.

10. $\begin{pmatrix} 7 & 6 & 2 \\ 3 & 5 & 4 \end{pmatrix}$.

11. $\begin{pmatrix} 3 & 0 \\ 2 & 4 \end{pmatrix}$.

12. $\begin{pmatrix} 4 & 1 \\ 3 & 5 \end{pmatrix}$.

For the game described in Exercise 1:

13. Let the row strategy matrix be $(p, 1 - p)$ and find the row player's expected payoffs.

14. Equate the expected payoffs obtained in Exercise 13 to find the optimum row strategy matrix and the value of the game.

15. Use a simplex tableau to solve this game.

answers to odd-numbered exercises

CHAPTER 1

1.1 Sets

1. No.
   1) Read the letters h, e, l, p in order.
   2) Think of the first letter h. Is the first letter a? No.
   3) Think of the next letter e. Is this letter a? No.
   4) Think of the next letter l. Is this letter a? No.
   5) Think of the next letter p. Is this letter a? No.
   6) There are no more letters; $a \notin B$.
3. a) False;   b) true;   c) true;
   d) true;   e) false;   f) true;
   g) false;   h) true;   i) false.
5. t, a, r; since $\{t, a, r, t\} = \{t, a, r\}$ the steps are the same as in Exercise 4.
7. b) 1) Read the answers a, l, t and a, b, e, l, t for Exercise 6(a). Let $P = \{a, l, t\}$ and $Q = \{a, b, e, l, t\}$.
   2) Each element that is a member of both sets must be a member of P. We select the elements of P that are also elements of Q.

3) The first element of P is a. Is $a \in Q$? Yes, a is a member of both sets.

4) The next element of P is l. Is $l \in Q$? Yes, l is a member of both sets.

5) The next element of P is t. Is $t \in Q$? Yes, t is a member of both sets.

6) There are no more members of P. Thus, there are no more members of both sets. The set of members of both sets is $\{a, l, t\}$.

c) 1) As in part (b) let $P = \{a, l, t\}$ and $Q = \{a, b, e, l, t\}$. Let S be the set of letters that are members of at least one of the sets P and Q. Then, in particular, each element of P is a member of S; $a \in S$, $l \in S$, and $t \in S$.

2) We next consider the members of Q. Is a already included as an element of S? Yes.

3) Is b already included as an element of S? No; we need $b \in S$.

4) Is e already included as an element of S? No; we need $e \in S$.

5) Is l already included as an element of S? Yes.

6) Is t already included as an element of S? Yes.

7) There are no more elements in Q; $S = \{a, l, t, b, e\}$.

d) 1) $\{a, l, t\} \neq \{a, b, e, l, t\}$ because b, also e, is an element of the second set but not an element of the first set.

9. a) d, e, n, s, t, u; d, e, n, s, t.
   b) $\{d, e, n, s, t\}$.   c) $\{d, e, n, s, t, u\}$.
   d) No.

11. a) 101, 103, 105, 107, 109.
    b) 102, 104, 106, 108, 110.
    c) 102, 105, 108, 111, 114.
    d) 105, 112, 119, 126, 133.

1.2 Statements

1. a) $\{1, 5\}$;   b) $\{0, 1, 2, 3, 5, 6, 7, 9\}$.
3. a) $\{\ \}$;   b) $\{0, 1, 2, 3, 4, 5, \ldots\}$.
5. a) $\{12, 24, 36, 48, \ldots\}$;
   b) $\{3, 4, 6, 8, 9, 12, 15, 16, 18, 20, 21, \ldots\}$.
7. b, c, d, e, f.
9. a) p: I would like to buy that red car.
      q: I can't afford to buy that red car.

         $p \wedge q$

b) p: I'll give you the book in class.
   q: I'll bring the book to your room.

   $p \lor q$

c) p: Bill is smart.
   q: Bill is lazy.

   $p \land q$

d) p: Don will take Judy to the dance.
   q: Don will take Ruth to the dance.

   $p \lor q$

11.

p	q	p	$\land$	$\sim q$
T	T	T	F	F
T	F	T	T	T
F	T	F	F	F
F	F	F	F	T

              (a)   (c)   (b)

13.

p	q	$(\sim p)$	$\land$	$\sim q$
T	T	F	F	F
T	F	F	F	T
F	T	T	F	F
F	F	T	T	T

              (a)   (c)   (b)

1.3 Implications

1. p: You don't like the heat.
   q: You get out of the kitchen.

3. p: You graduate from college.
   q: You survive college.

5.

p	q	p	$\rightarrow$	$\sim q$
T	T	T	F	F
T	F	T	T	T
F	T	F	T	F
F	F	F	T	T

       (a)   (c)   (b)

7.

p	q	$[(p \rightarrow q)$	$\wedge$	$(q \rightarrow p)]$	$\leftrightarrow$	$p \leftrightarrow q$
T	T	T	T T T T	T		T
T	F	F	F F T T	T		F
F	T	T	F T F F	T		F
F	F	T	T F T F	T		T

     (a)   (e) (b) (d) (c) (g)   (f)

9. If John does not live in Illinois, then John does not live in Chicago.

11. If $x \neq 3$, then $x + 2 \neq 5$.

13. If a triangle is not isosceles, then it is not equilateral.

15. a) If John does not live in Chicago, then John does not live in Illinois. Not necessarily true.

    b) If Ruth is not a mathematics major, then she cannot do algebra problems. Not necessarily true.

1.3 Supplementary Exercises

1.

p	q	$(p \rightarrow q)$	$\leftrightarrow$	$(q \rightarrow p)$
T	T	T	T	T
T	F	F	F	T
F	T	T	F	F
F	F	T	T	T

       (a)   (c)   (b)

The statements $p \rightarrow q$ and $q \rightarrow p$ are equivalent only when $p \leftrightarrow q$.

3.

p	q	$[\sim(p \wedge q)]$	$\leftrightarrow$	$[(\sim p)$	$\vee$	$\sim q]$
T	T	F	T	T	F	F	F
T	F	T	F	T	F	T	T
F	T	T	F	T	T	T	F
F	F	T	F	T	T	T	T

(b)   (a)   (f)   (c)   (e)   (d)

5. Bill can swim and dive.

7. Jane will not go to the dance and will not study.

1.4 Quantifiers

1. $\exists x: x > 100$, where x is a whole number.

3. $\forall x: x > -1$, where x is a whole number.

5. There exists a whole number x such that $x^2 = 1$.

7. For all numbers x, where x is a whole number, $x^2 \geq 0$.

9. a) $\exists x: 7 - x = 25$, where x is a whole number.

  b) $\exists x: x$ is too long, where x is a mathematics assignment.

11. a) There exists no one who is home tonight.

  b) There exist courses that are worth taking.

  c) For all tires on this car, the tires are flat.

  d) There exists someone in this class who did not pass in a paper.

1.5 Finite sets

1. $\{t, \quad a, \quad n\}$
   $\updownarrow \quad \updownarrow \quad \updownarrow$
   $\{s, \quad u, \quad n\}$

3. $\{3, 6, 9, 12, 15, 18, 21\}$
   $\updownarrow \updownarrow \updownarrow \quad \updownarrow \quad \updownarrow \quad \updownarrow \quad \updownarrow$
   $\{1, 2, 3, \quad 4, \quad 5, \quad 6, \quad 7\}$

5. $\{5, 10, 15, \ldots, 5n, \ldots\}$
   $\updownarrow \quad \updownarrow \quad \updownarrow \qquad \updownarrow$
   $\{1, \quad 2, \quad 3, \ldots, \quad n, \ldots\}$

7. Finite, $n(B) = 50$.

9. Infinite.

11. Finite, $n(F) = 101$ since 0 is a whole number.

13. a) $\subseteq$;   b) $\subseteq$;   c) $\subseteq$;   d) $\subset$.

15. a) $=$;   b) $=$;   c) $=$;   d) $=$;   e) $\neq$.

17. $\{\ \}$, $\{a\}$, $\{b\}$, $\{c\}$, $\{a, b\}$, $\{a, c\}$, $\{b, c\}$, $\{a, b, c\}$.

1.6 Flowcharts

1.

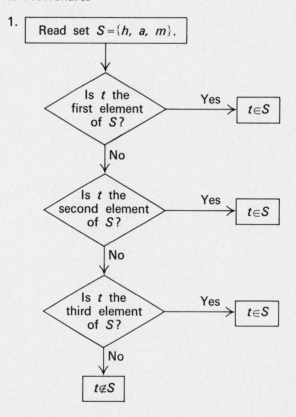

3. For the chart given as the answer for Exercise 1:

   1) Read set $S = \{h, a, m\}$.

   2) Is t the first element h of S? No, go to the second diamond.

   3) Is t the second element a of S? No, go to the third diamond.

   4) Is t the third element m of S? No, go to the last box.

   5) $t \notin S$.

5.

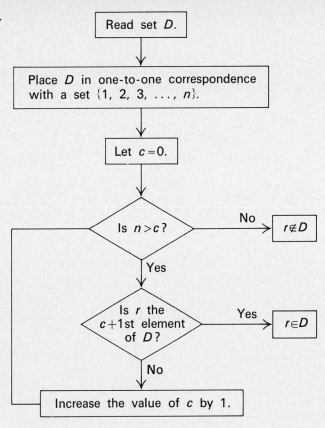

Read set *D*.

Place *D* in one-to-one correspondence with a set $\{1, 2, 3, \ldots, n\}$.

Let $c = 0$.

Is $n > c$?

No → $r \notin D$

Yes

Is *r* the $c+1$st element of *D*?

Yes → $r \in D$

No

Increase the value of *c* by 1.

7.

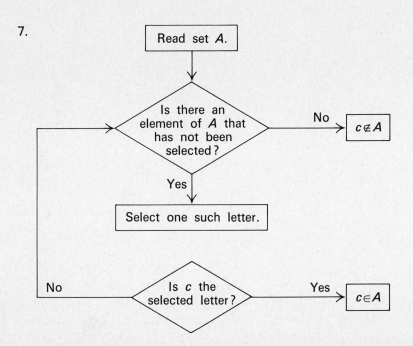

Read set *A*.

Is there an element of *A* that has not been selected?

No → $c \notin A$

Yes

Select one such letter.

Is *c* the selected letter?

No

Yes → $c \in A$

9.

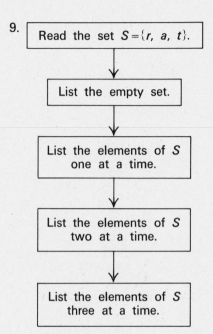

Read the set $S = \{r, a, t\}$.

List the empty set.

List the elements of S one at a time.

List the elements of S two at a time.

List the elements of S three at a time.

1.7 Uses of numbers

1. a) Cardinal;   b) cardinal;   c) ordinal;
   d) identification;   e) identification;   f) ordinal;
   g) cardinal.

3. Among the many possible answers are the following:
   a) Inch, foot, mile, centimeter, meter,
   b) square inch, square foot, square mile, square centimeter, acre,
   c) cubic inch, cubic foot, cubic centimeter, cubic meter, cubic yard,
   d) degree, right angle, straight angle, revolution, radian.

5. a) 4.5 yards;   b) 5372 yards;
   c) 7 hours 35 minutes.

7. a) 3-digit accuracy and precision 0.01;
   b) 5-digit accuracy and precision 0.001;
   c) 2-digit accuracy and precision 0.001;
   d) 3-digit accuracy and precision 0.0001.

1.8 Approximations

1. a) 26;   b) 78.
3. a) 4.41;   b) 90,000.
5. a) 0.008;   b) 0.5.
7. a) 20;   b) 0.2.
9. a) 20;   b) 4.

11. a) ≈ 224.7;   b) ≈ 2.526.

13. a) 10;   b) 1.

15. a) 2.0×10^1;   b) 3.3×10^2.

Review Exercises for Chapter 1

1. 1001, 1008, 1015, 1022, 1029.

3.

p	q	p	$\rightarrow$	$[q$	$\vee$	$(p$	$\wedge$	$\sim q)]$
T	T	T	T	T	T	T	F	F
T	F	T	T	F	T	T	T	T
F	T	F	T	T	T	F	F	F
F	F	F	T	F	F	F	F	T
		(a)	(g)	(b)	(f)	(c)	(e)	(d)

5. Every textbook is easy reading.

7. a) If $x = -1$, then $x^2 = 1$.

   b) If $x + 1 = 5$, then $x = 4$.

9. $\{t, \quad a, \quad p, \quad e\}$ 11. Finite, $n(A) = 8$.
     $\updownarrow \quad \updownarrow \quad \updownarrow \quad \updownarrow$
     $\{t, \quad r, \quad a, \quad p\}$

13.

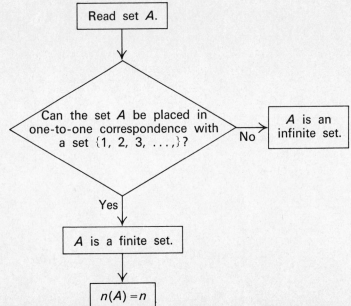

15. 27 inches.

17. 24.01.

19. 782.0.

CHAPTER 2

2.1 Sample Spaces

1. {red, black}.

3. {ace, 2, 3, 4, 5, 6, 7, 8, 9, 10, jack, queen, king}.

5. $\frac{1}{2}$.

7. a) 1 to 51;   b) 4 to 48.

9. a) $\frac{1}{52}$;   b) $\frac{4}{52}$, that is, $\frac{1}{13}$.

11. a) $\{H_p, T_p\}$;   b) $\{H_pH_d, T_pH_d\}$;   c) $\{H_pT_d, T_pH_d\}$.

13. a) 2;   b) 2;   c) 4.

15. a) {1, 2, 3, 4, 5, 6};
    b) {1H, 2H, 3H, 4H, 5H, 6H};
    c) {1T, 2T, 3T, 4T, 5T, 6T}.

17. {H1, H2, H3, H4, H5, H6, T1, T2, T3, T4, T5, T6}.

19. $\{R_1G_1,\ R_1G_2,\ R_1G_3,\ R_1G_4,\ R_1G_5,\ R_1G_6,$
    $R_2G_1,\ R_2G_2,\ R_2G_3,\ R_2G_4,\ R_2G_5,\ R_2G_6,$
    $R_3G_1,\ R_3G_2,\ R_3G_3,\ R_3G_4,\ R_3G_5,\ R_3G_6,$
    $R_4G_1,\ R_4G_2,\ R_4G_3,\ R_4G_4,\ R_4G_5,\ R_4G_6,$
    $R_5G_1,\ R_5G_2,\ R_5G_3,\ R_5G_4,\ R_5G_5,\ R_5G_6,$
    $R_6G_1,\ R_6G_2,\ R_6G_3,\ R_6G_4,\ R_6G_5,\ R_6G_6\}.$

21. a) 36;   b) 216;   c) 8;   d) 16;   e) 2^n.

2.2 Tree diagrams

1.

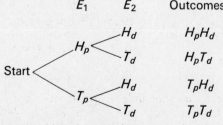

$\{H_pH_d,\ H_pT_d,\ T_pH_d,\ T_pT_d\}$

3.

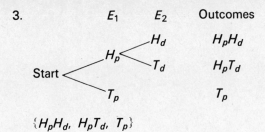

$\{H_pH_d,\ H_pT_d,\ T_p\}$

5.

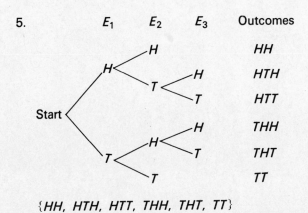

$\{HH,\ HTH,\ HTT,\ THH,\ THT,\ TT\}$

7.

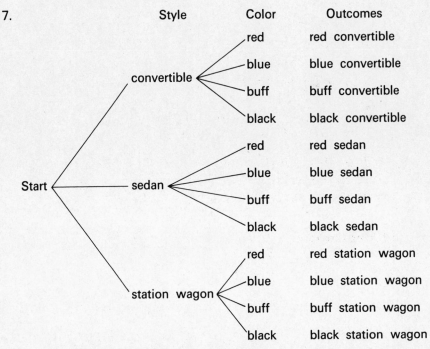

{red convertible, blue convertible, buff convertible, black convertible, red sedan, blue sedan, buff sedan, black sedan, red station wagon, blue station wagon, buff station wagon, black station wagon}

9. a) 12;   b) 8;
   c) 12;   d) 16;
   e) 24.

11.

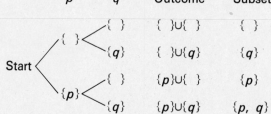

	p	q	Outcome	Subset
Start	{ }	{ }	{ }∪{ }	{ }
		{q}	{ }∪{q}	{q}
	{p}	{ }	{p}∪{ }	{p}
		{q}	{p}∪{q}	{p, q}

13.

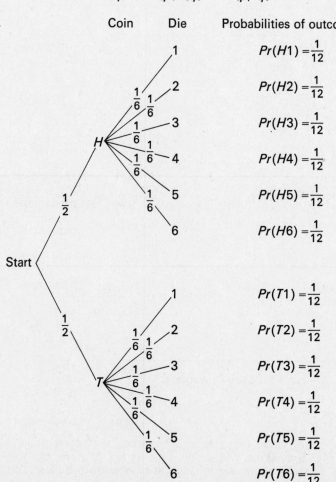

	Coin	Die	Probabilities of outcomes
		1	$Pr(H1) = \frac{1}{12}$
		2	$Pr(H2) = \frac{1}{12}$
	H	3	$Pr(H3) = \frac{1}{12}$
		4	$Pr(H4) = \frac{1}{12}$
		5	$Pr(H5) = \frac{1}{12}$
		6	$Pr(H6) = \frac{1}{12}$
Start		1	$Pr(T1) = \frac{1}{12}$
		2	$Pr(T2) = \frac{1}{12}$
	T	3	$Pr(T3) = \frac{1}{12}$
		4	$Pr(T4) = \frac{1}{12}$
		5	$Pr(T5) = \frac{1}{12}$
		6	$Pr(T6) = \frac{1}{12}$

15.

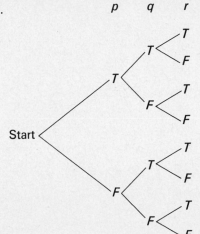

p	q	r
T	T	T
T	T	F
T	F	T
T	F	F
F	T	T
F	T	F
F	F	T
F	F	F

2.3 Venn diagrams

1.

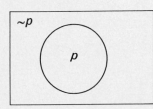

3.

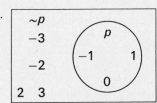

5. a)

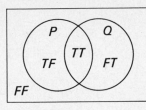

b)

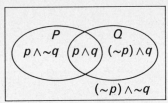

7. a)

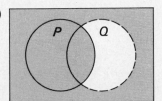

b)

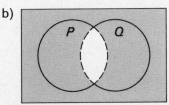

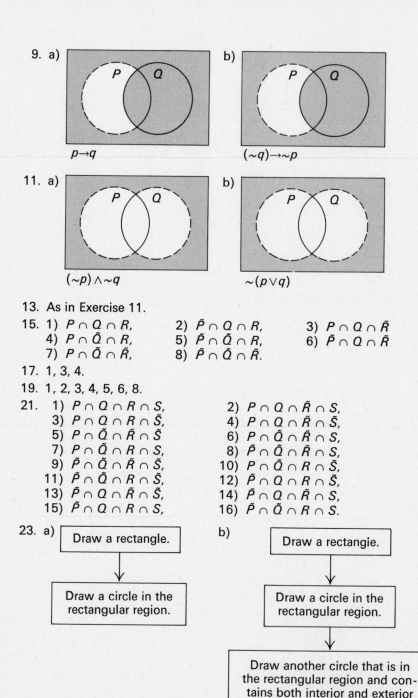

9. a) $p \rightarrow q$
   b) $(\sim q) \rightarrow \sim p$

11. a) $(\sim p) \wedge \sim q$
    b) $\sim(p \vee q)$

13. As in Exercise 11.

15. 1) $P \cap Q \cap R$,   2) $\breve{P} \cap Q \cap R$,   3) $P \cap Q \cap \breve{R}$
    4) $P \cap \breve{Q} \cap R$,   5) $\breve{P} \cap \breve{Q} \cap R$,   6) $\breve{P} \cap Q \cap \breve{R}$
    7) $P \cap \breve{Q} \cap \breve{R}$,   8) $\breve{P} \cap \breve{Q} \cap \breve{R}$.

17. 1, 3, 4.

19. 1, 2, 3, 4, 5, 6, 8.

21. 1) $P \cap Q \cap R \cap S$,   2) $P \cap Q \cap \breve{R} \cap S$,
     3) $P \cap Q \cap R \cap \breve{S}$,   4) $P \cap Q \cap \breve{R} \cap \breve{S}$,
     5) $P \cap \breve{Q} \cap \breve{R} \cap \breve{S}$ 6) $P \cap \breve{Q} \cap \breve{R} \cap S$,
     7) $P \cap \breve{Q} \cap R \cap S$,   8) $\breve{P} \cap \breve{Q} \cap \breve{R} \cap S$,
     9) $\breve{P} \cap \breve{Q} \cap \breve{R} \cap \breve{S}$,   10) $P \cap \breve{Q} \cap R \cap \breve{S}$,
    11) $\breve{P} \cap \breve{Q} \cap R \cap \breve{S}$,   12) $\breve{P} \cap Q \cap R \cap \breve{S}$,
    13) $\breve{P} \cap Q \cap \breve{R} \cap \breve{S}$,   14) $\breve{P} \cap Q \cap \breve{R} \cap S$,
    15) $\breve{P} \cap Q \cap R \cap S$,   16) $\breve{P} \cap \breve{Q} \cap R \cap S$.

23. a)
```
Draw a rectangle.
```
↓
```
Draw a circle in the
rectangular region.
```

   b)
```
Draw a rectangie.
```
↓
```
Draw a circle in the
rectangular region.
```
↓
```
Draw another circle that is in
the rectangular region and con-
tains both interior and exterior
points of the first circle.
```

c)

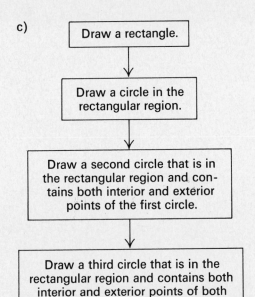

2.4 Partitions

1. a) Yes;   b) matching coins.

3. a) $\{P \cap Q, \tilde{P} \cap Q, P \cap \tilde{Q}, \tilde{P} \cap \tilde{Q}\}$;

   b) $\{P \cap Q \cap R, P \cap \tilde{Q} \cap R, \tilde{P} \cap Q \cap R, \tilde{P} \cap \tilde{Q} \cap R,$
   $P \cap Q \cap \tilde{R}, P \cap \tilde{Q} \cap \tilde{R}, \tilde{P} \cap Q \cap \tilde{R}, \tilde{P} \cap \tilde{Q} \cap \tilde{R}\}$.

5. a) 0;   b) 11;   c) 7;   d) 18;
   e) 13;   f) 24;   g) yes;   h) yes.

7. 120.

9. 10.

11. a)   b) 33.

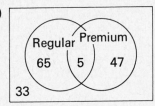

13. a) 175;   b) 83;   c) 40;
    d) 218;   e) 233;   f) 80.

15. a) b) 445.

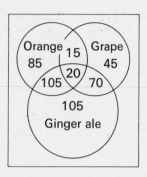

17. Yes.

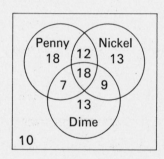

2.5 Permutations of distinct elements

1.

First element	Permutations one at a time
a	a
b	b
c	c
d	d

Start

3.

First element	Second element	Third element	Permutations three at a time

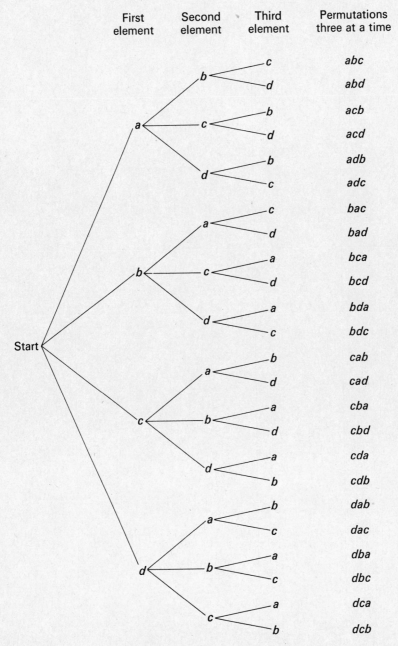

5. a) 6;   b) 24.

7. a) $\dfrac{6 \times 5 \times 4 \times 3 \times 2 \times 1}{4 \times 3 \times 2 \times 1} = 30$;

   b) $\dfrac{10 \times 9 \times 8 \times 7 \times 6 \times 5 \times 4 \times 3 \times 2 \times 1}{9 \times 8 \times 7 \times 6 \times 5 \times 4 \times 3 \times 2 \times 1} = 10.$

9. a) 25;   b) 26×51, that is, 1326.

11. a) $\dfrac{6!}{4!}$;   b) $\dfrac{10!}{7!}$.

13. 6.

15. a) 5!, that is, 120;   b) 5!, that is, 120.

17. a) 5!, that is, 120;   b) 60.

19. a) $12 \times 11 \times 10$, that is, 1320;

    b) $12 \times 11 \times 10 \times 9 \times 8 \times 7 \times 6$, that is, 3,991,680.

21. 720.

23. $200 \times 199 \times 198 \times 197 \times 196 \times 195 \times 194 \times 193 \times$
    $192 \times 191.$

2.6 Counting

1. a) 26×26, that is, 676;

   b) $26 \times 26 \times 26$, that is, 17,576.

3. a) 120;   b) 5^5, that is, 3125.

5. a) 4;   b) 4.

7. $_7C_2\,_9C_2$, that is, 756.

9. a) $\dfrac{6 \times 5}{2 \times 1} \times \dfrac{4 \times 3}{2 \times 1} \times \dfrac{2 \times 1}{2 \times 1}$, that is, 90;

   b) $90 - 3 \times \dfrac{4 \times 3}{2 \times 1} \times \dfrac{2 \times 1}{2 \times 1}$, that is, 72.

11. a) $26 \times 26 \times 10 \times 10 \times 10 \times 10 \times 10$, that is, 67,600,000;

    b) $26 \times 26 \times 26 \times 10 \times 10 \times 10 \times 10$, that is, 175,760,000;

    c) 10,000.

13. $4 \times 3 \times 3 \times 2 \times 2 \times 1 \times 1$, that is, 144.

2.6 Supplementary Exercises

1. a) $_5C_0$ b) $_7C_6$;   c) $_9C_5.$

3. a) 2;   b) 4;   c) 8.

5. a) $9 \times 10 \times 10 \times 10$, that is, 9000;

   b) $9 \times 10 \times 10 \times 2$, that is, 1800;

   c) $9 \times 10 \times 10 \times 5$, that is, 4500.

7. $$_{n+1}C_r = \frac{(n+1)!}{r!\,(n+1-r)!}$$

   $$_nC_r + {}_nC_{r-1} = \frac{n!}{r!(n-r)!} + \frac{n!}{(r-1)!(n-r+1)!}$$

   $$= \frac{n!(n-r+1)}{r!(n-r+1)!} + \frac{n! \times r}{r!(n-r+1)!}$$

   $$= \frac{n!(n+1)}{r!(n-r+1)!} = {}_{n+1}C_r$$

2.7 The binomial theorem

1. $x^{10} + 10x^9y + 45x^8y + 120x^7y^3$.

3. $a^6 - 6a^5b + 15a^4b^2 - 20a^3b^3$.

5. $a^7 + 14a^6b + 84a^5b^2 + 280a^4b^3$.

7. $a^{11} - 22a^{10}b + 220a^9b^2 - 1320a^8b^3$.

9.
```
                        1   1
                     1    2    1
                  1    3    3    1
               1    4    6    4    1
            1    5   10   10    5    1
         1    6   15   20   15    6    1
      1    7   21   35   35   21    7    1
   1    8   28   56   70   56   28    8    1
 1   9   36   84  126  126   84   36    9    1
1  10   45  120  210  252  210  120   45   10   1
 1  11   55  165  330  462  462  330  165   55   11   1
1  12   66  220  495  792  924  792  495  220   66   12   1
```

11. $220a^3(2b)^9$, that is, $112{,}640a^3b^9$.

13. $-330(2x)^4y^7$, that is, $-5280x^4y^7$.

15. $1 + 5(0.02) + 10(0.02)^2 + 10(0.02)^3 + \cdots$
    $= 1 + 0.1 + 0.004 + 0.00008 + \cdots \approx 1.10408 \approx 1.1041$.

17. $64[1 + 6(0.01) + 15(0.0001) + 20(0.000001) + 15(0.00000001) + \cdots] \approx 64(1.06152015) \approx 67.9373$.

2.8 The multinomial theorem—Supplementary Exercises

1. a) $21x^2y^5$;

   b) $\dfrac{7!}{2!\,5!}\,x^2y^5$, that is, $21x^2y^5$.

3. a) $10!$, that is, $3,628,800$;

   b) $\dfrac{10!}{3!\,2!\,1!\,1!\,1!\,1!\,1!}$, that is, $302,400$.

5. a) 1;   b) 2^3, that is, 8;

   c) 3^3, that is, 27.

Review Exercises for Chapter 2

1. a) 1 to 51;   b) 4 to 48;   c) 3 to 49.
3. a) 216;   b) 32.
5. a)   b)   c)

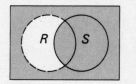 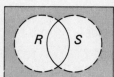 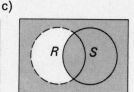

7. a) 14;   b) 16.
9. a) $12 \times 11 \times 10$. that is, 1320;
   b) 220;   c) 220.
11. a) 32;   b) 16.
13. a) 4536;   b) 9000.

15. $\dfrac{12 \times 11 \times 10 \times 9 \times 8 \times 7 \times 6 \times 5 \times 4 \times 3}{2 \times 2 \times 2}$, that is, $29,937,600$

17. $x^5 + 10x^4y + 40x^3y^2 + 80x^2y^3$.
19. $1 + 5(0.03) + 10(0.03)^2 + 10(0.03)^3 + \cdots \approx 1.159$.

CHAPTER 3

3.1 Probability measures

1. a) $\frac{2}{6}$, that is, $\frac{1}{3}$;   b) $\frac{3}{6}$, that is, $\frac{1}{2}$;   c) $\frac{5}{6}$.

3. a)

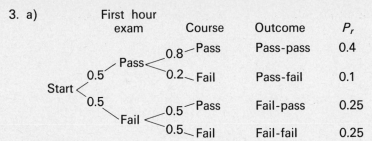

First hour exam · Course · Outcome · P_r

Pass 0.8	Pass	Pass-pass	0.4
0.5 Pass 0.2	Fail	Pass-fail	0.1
Start 0.5 Fail 0.5	Pass	Fail-pass	0.25
0.5	Fail	Fail-fail	0.25

b) 0.65.

5. $\dfrac{13\,C_2}{52\,C_2}$, that is, $\frac{1}{17}$.

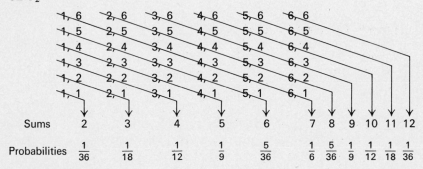

Sums	2	3	4	5	6	7	8	9	10	11	12
Probabilities	$\frac{1}{36}$	$\frac{1}{18}$	$\frac{1}{12}$	$\frac{1}{9}$	$\frac{5}{36}$	$\frac{1}{6}$	$\frac{5}{36}$	$\frac{1}{9}$	$\frac{1}{12}$	$\frac{1}{18}$	$\frac{1}{36}$

9. $2 \times \dfrac{4!}{5!}$, that is, $\frac{2}{5}$.

11. a)

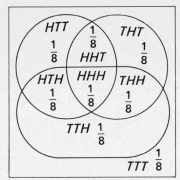

b) $\frac{7}{8}$;   c) $\frac{3}{8}$;

d) $\frac{7}{8}$;   e) $\frac{1}{8}$.

13. True.
15. True.
17. True.
19. a) 0.117;   b) 13 to 100.

21. a) 0.476;   b) 91 to 100.
23. a) 0.569;   b) 132 to 100.
25. a) 0.891;   b) 817 to 100.

3.2 Conditional probability

1. 1.
3. a) $\frac{2}{13}$;   b) $\frac{1}{4}$.
5. a) $\frac{1}{2}$;   b) $\frac{1}{4}$;   c) $\frac{1}{12}$.
7. a) $\frac{2}{3}$;   b) $\frac{1}{3}$.
9. $\frac{4}{10} \times \frac{7}{10} = \frac{28}{100}$, that is, $\frac{7}{25}$.
11. $\frac{3}{10} + \frac{4}{10} - \frac{7}{25}$, that is, $\frac{21}{50}$.
13. $\frac{5}{4}$.
15. By formula (2), $\dfrac{1/3}{1/2}$, that is, $\frac{2}{3}$.

3.3 Bayes' Theorem

1. $\frac{3}{9}$.
3. $\frac{1}{11}$.
5. a) $\frac{1}{8}$;   b) $\frac{27}{64}$;

    c) $\dfrac{\left(\frac{1}{25}\right)\left(\frac{27}{64}\right)}{\left(\frac{1}{25}\right)\left(\frac{27}{64}\right) + \left(\frac{24}{25}\right)\left(\frac{1}{8}\right)}$, that is, $\frac{9}{73}$.

7. a) $\frac{1}{32}$;   b) $\frac{243}{1024}$;

    c) $\dfrac{\left(\frac{1}{25}\right)\left(\frac{243}{1024}\right)}{\left(\frac{1}{25}\right)(243)(1024) + \left(\frac{24}{25}\right)\left(\frac{1}{2}\right)}$, that is, $\frac{81}{337}$.

9. a) $\frac{1}{2}$;   b) $\frac{1}{4}$;

    c) $\dfrac{\left(\frac{1}{25}\right)\left(\frac{1}{4}\right)}{\left(\frac{1}{25}\right)\left(\frac{1}{4}\right) + \left(\frac{24}{25}\right)\left(\frac{1}{2}\right)}$, that is, $\frac{1}{49}$.

11. $\dfrac{0.90}{0.90 + 0.20}$, that is, $\frac{9}{11}$, which is about 81.8%.

13. $\dfrac{0.729}{0.729 + 0.008}$, that is, $\frac{729}{737}$, which is about 98.9%.

15. $\dfrac{(0.9)^5}{(0.9)^5 + (0.2)^5}$, that is, $\dfrac{0.59049}{0.59081}$, which is about 99.94%.

3.3 Supplementary Exercises

1. 20%

3. a) 0.9;   b) 0.92 from the tree diagram

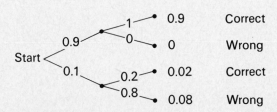

5. $\dfrac{0.92}{0.92 + 0.4}$, that is, $\frac{23}{33}$.

7. $(0.92)^2$, that is, 0.8464, or about 0.85.

9. 0.064.

11. $\dfrac{(0.92)^3}{(0.92)^3 + (0.4)^3}$, that is, about 0.92.

13. a) $\dfrac{0.10}{0.10 + 0.99}$, that is, $\frac{10}{109}$;

    b) 99 to 10.

3.4 Binomial distributions

1. a) $b(2; 4, \frac{1}{2})$, that is, $\frac{3}{8}$;

   b) $b(4; 8, \frac{1}{2})$, that is, $\frac{35}{128}$, or about 0.273;

   c) $b(8; 16, \frac{1}{2})$, that is, $\frac{6,435}{32,768}$, or about 0.196.

3. $b(2; 4, 0.9) + b(3; 4, 0.9) + b(4; 4, 0.9)$,
   that is, $6(0.9)^2(0.1)^2 + 4(0.9)^3(0.1) + 1(0.9)^4$, or 0.9963, which
   is almost 1.

5. a) $b(6; 10, \frac{1}{4})$;

   b) $b(6; 10, \frac{1}{4}) + b(7; 10, \frac{1}{4}) + b(8; 10, \frac{1}{4}) +$
   $b(9; 10, \frac{1}{4}) + b(10; 10, \frac{1}{4})$.

7. $b(3; 5, 0.4) + b(4; 5, 0.4) + b(5; 5, 0.4)$, that is, 0.31744, or
   about 0.32.

9. a) 1;   b) 2.

3.4 Supplementary Exercises

1. $b(0; n, \frac{1}{2}) = {}_nC_0(\frac{1}{2})^n = {}_nC_n(\frac{1}{2})^n = b(n; n, \frac{1}{2})$.
3. $b(2; n, \frac{1}{2}) = {}_nC_2(\frac{1}{2})^n = {}_nC_{n-2}(\frac{1}{2})^n = b(n - 2; n, \frac{1}{2})$.
5. 8.
7. $Pr(x = 2) = b(2; 5, \frac{1}{2}) = \frac{5}{16} = Pr(x = 3)$, $Pr(x = 2 \text{ or } 3) = \frac{5}{8}$.

3.5 Other probability distributions

1. a) $\frac{24}{100}$;　　　　　　　　　　b) $\frac{16}{100}$;
   c) ${}_6C_1(\frac{4}{10})^2(\frac{6}{10})^5$, that is, 0.0746496, or about 0.075.
3. a) $\frac{1}{20}$;
   b) $h(1; 100, 2, 5) = {}_5C_1 \, {}_{95}C_1/{}_{100}C_2$, that is, $\frac{19}{198}$;
   c) $h(1; 100, 5, 5) = {}_5C_1 \, {}_{95}C_4/{}_{100}C_5$, that is,

   $$\frac{5 \times 19 \times 23 \times 31 \times 47}{2^5 \times 3^2 \times 7^2 \times 11 \times 97}, \text{ or about } 0.21.$$

5. a) $\approx b(4; 10, 0.2)$, that is, $2^{13} \times 3 \times 7 \div 5^9$, or about 0.09.
7. $\frac{5}{32}$.
9. $\dfrac{4!}{2! \, 1! \, 1!} \, (\frac{1}{4})^2(\frac{1}{4})(\frac{1}{2})$; that is, $\frac{3}{32}$.

3.6 Expectations

1. a) $\frac{3}{5}$;　　　　　　　　　　b) 500.
3. a) Yes;　　　　　　　　　b) no.
5. a) 3.6 cents;　　　　　　b) $64.
7. 2.
9. $\frac{4}{3}$.　　　　　　　11. $\frac{8}{3}$.　　　　　　13. $1.50.
15. a) $\frac{18}{19}$ dollars, that is, about 94.7 cents;
    b) $1000 - 18,000/19$, that is, about $52.63 loss.

3.7 Markov chains

1.

$$\begin{array}{c}
 \\ N \\ E \\ S \\ W
\end{array}
\begin{array}{cccc}
N & E & S & W \\
\left(\begin{array}{cccc}
1 & 0 & 0 & 0 \\
0 & 1 & 0 & 0 \\
0 & 0 & 1 & 0 \\
0 & 0 & 0 & 1
\end{array}\right).
\end{array}$$

3.
$$
\begin{array}{c}
\\ N \\ E \\ S \\ W
\end{array}
\begin{array}{cccc}
N & E & S & W \\
\end{array}
\left(\begin{array}{cccc}
\frac{1}{2} & \frac{1}{2} & 0 & 0 \\
0 & \frac{1}{2} & \frac{1}{2} & 0 \\
0 & 0 & \frac{1}{2} & \frac{1}{2} \\
\frac{1}{2} & 0 & 0 & \frac{1}{2}
\end{array}\right).
$$

5.

	N	E	S	W
Initial state	1	0	0	0
First step	1	0	0	0
Second step	1	0	0	0
Third step	1	0	0	0
Fourth step	1	0	0	0

7.

	N	E	S	W
Initial state	1	0	0	0
First step	$\frac{1}{2}$	$\frac{1}{2}$	0	0
Second step	$\frac{1}{4}$	$\frac{1}{2}$	$\frac{1}{4}$	0
Third step	$\frac{1}{8}$	$\frac{3}{8}$	$\frac{3}{8}$	$\frac{1}{8}$
Fourth step	$\frac{1}{8}$	$\frac{1}{4}$	$\frac{3}{8}$	$\frac{1}{4}$

9. a) $\frac{3}{8}$;   b) $\frac{7}{32}$.

11. a) $\frac{29}{64}$;   b) $\frac{9}{32}$.

3.7 Supplementary Exercises

1. $0, $100, $200, $300, $400.

3.

	0	100	200	300	400
Initial state	0	0	1	0	0
First step	0	$\frac{1}{2}$	0	$\frac{1}{2}$	0
Second step	$\frac{1}{4}$	0	$\frac{1}{2}$	0	$\frac{1}{4}$
Third step	$\frac{1}{4}$	$\frac{1}{4}$	0	$\frac{1}{4}$	$\frac{1}{4}$
Fourth step	$\frac{3}{8}$	0	$\frac{1}{4}$	0	$\frac{3}{8}$
Fifth step	$\frac{3}{8}$	$\frac{1}{8}$	0	$\frac{1}{8}$	$\frac{3}{8}$
Sixth step	$\frac{7}{16}$	0	$\frac{1}{8}$	0	$\frac{7}{16}$
Seventh step	$\frac{7}{16}$	$\frac{1}{16}$	0	$\frac{1}{16}$	$\frac{7}{16}$
Eighth step	$\frac{15}{32}$	0	$\frac{1}{16}$	0	$\frac{15}{32}$
Ninth step	$\frac{15}{32}$	$\frac{1}{32}$	0	$\frac{1}{32}$	$\frac{15}{32}$

5. a) 0;   b) $\frac{1}{2}$;   c) $\frac{3}{4}$;   d) $\frac{15}{16}$.

7.

	0	100	200	300	400	500	600
0	1	0	0	0	0	0	0
100	$\frac{1}{2}$	0	$\frac{1}{2}$	0	0	0	0
200	0	$\frac{1}{2}$	0	$\frac{1}{2}$	0	0	0
300	0	0	$\frac{1}{2}$	0	$\frac{1}{2}$	0	0
400	0	0	0	$\frac{1}{2}$	0	$\frac{1}{2}$	0
500	0	0	0	0	$\frac{1}{2}$	0	$\frac{1}{2}$
600	0	0	0	0	0	0	1

9. a) 0;   b) $\frac{7}{32}$;   c) $\frac{37}{128}$.

11.

	To John	John holds	To Dave	Dave holds	Answered
To John	0	0.2	0.3	0	0.5
John holds	1	0	0	0	0
To Dave	0.2	0	0	0.1	0.7
Dave holds	0	0	1	0	0
Answered	0	0	0	0	1

13. a) 0.5;   b) 0.71;   c) 0.84.

Review Exercises for Chapter 3

1. {Clubs, diamonds, hearts, spades}.

3. $\frac{1}{16}$.

5. $7!$, that is, 5040.

7. 0.31.

9. $\frac{4}{9}$.

11. $_5C_1(\frac{2}{3})^2(\frac{1}{3})^4$, that is, $\frac{20}{729}$.

13. 120.

15. $\frac{2}{5}$.

17.

$$\begin{array}{c} & 0 & 1 & 2 & 3 & 4 \\ 0 \\ 1 \\ 2 \\ 3 \\ 4 \end{array} \begin{pmatrix} 1 & 0 & 0 & 0 & 0 \\ \frac{2}{3} & 0 & \frac{1}{3} & 0 & 0 \\ 0 & \frac{2}{3} & 0 & \frac{1}{3} & 0 \\ 0 & 0 & \frac{2}{3} & 0 & \frac{1}{3} \\ 0 & 0 & 0 & 0 & 1 \end{pmatrix}.$$

19. $\frac{13}{81}$.

CHAPTER 4

4.1 Vectors

1. a, b.

3. a.

5. a) $(5, -2, 1)$;   b) $(-1, -2, 4)$;   c) $(-4, -4, 9)$.

7. a) $\begin{pmatrix} 8 \\ 1 \\ 4 \\ 7 \end{pmatrix}$;   b) $\begin{pmatrix} -7 \\ 4 \\ 4 \\ -2 \end{pmatrix}$;   c) $\begin{pmatrix} 16 \\ -11 \\ -12 \\ 3 \end{pmatrix}.$

9. $u = 1, v = 4, w = -2.$
11. $a = 1, b = 2, c = -2.$
13. $u_1 = 4, u_2 = 5, u_3 = 6.$
15. $\begin{pmatrix} 3 \\ 7 \\ 11 \\ 8 \end{pmatrix}.$

17. $\begin{pmatrix} 2 \\ 4 \\ 0 \end{pmatrix}.$

4.2 Scalar product of two vectors

1. a) 5;   b) 3.
3. a) -3;   b) 10.
5. a) $4a + 3b + 2c + d$;
   b) $a + b + c + d$;
   c) $x + y + z + w$.
7. a) $(1, 2, -3) \cdot (x, y, 1) = 0$;
   b) $(2, -1, 5) \cdot (x, y, 1) = 0$;
   c) $(1, 0, 3) \cdot (x, y, 1) = 0$.
9. a) 0, on the line;   b) 0, on the line;
   c) 0, on the line.
11. a) $(1, -1, 2, 3) \cdot (x, y, z, 1) = 0$;
    b) $(2, 1, -3, 5) \cdot (x, y, z, 1) = 0.$
13. a) $(1, -2, 0, -5) \cdot (x, y, z, 1) = 0$;
    b) $(0, 3, -5, 0) \cdot (x, y, z, 1) = 0.$
15. a) -2, not on the plane;   b) 0, on the plane;
    c) 8, not on the plane.
17. a) $(1, 4, 6, 4, 0)$;
    b) $(1, 4, 6, 4, 0) \cdot (1, 1, 1, 1, 1)$;
    c) $(1, 4, 6, 4, 0) \cdot (4, 3, 2, 1, 0)$;
    d) $\dfrac{(1, 4, 6, 4, 0) \cdot (4, 3, 2, 1, 0)}{(1, 4, 6, 4, 0) \cdot (1, 1, 1, 1, 1)}.$
19. a) $42(\tfrac{1}{6}, 1, 2)$;
    b) $[42(\tfrac{1}{6}, 1, 2)] \cdot (250, 2, 1) = 1918$, that is, \$19.18.

21. a) $(10, 25, 40, 35, 50, 15) \cdot (1, 1, 1, 1, 1, 1)$,
    $(8, 20, 30, 30, 40, 20) \cdot (1, 1, 1, 1, 1, 1)$,
    $(20, 40, 50, 55, 70, 30) \cdot (1, 1, 1, 1, 1, 1)$,
    $(5, 12, 20, 25, 50, 10) \cdot (1, 1, 1, 1, 1, 1)$;

    b) $(10, 25, 40, 35, 50, 15) \cdot (3, 2, 1, 2, 1, \frac{1}{2})$,
    $(8, 20, 30, 30, 40, 20) \cdot (3, 2, 1, 2, 1, \frac{1}{2})$,
    $(20, 40, 50, 55, 70, 30) \cdot (3, 2, 1, 2, 1, \frac{1}{2})$,
    $(5, 12, 20, 25, 50, 10) \cdot (3, 2, 1, 2, 1, \frac{1}{2})$;

    c) $(10, 25, 40, 35, 50, 15) + (8, 20, 30, 30, 40, 20) +$
    $(20, 40, 50, 55, 70, 30) + (5, 12, 20, 25, 50, 10)$.

4.3 Matrices

1. a) $m = 2, n = 3$;   b) $m = 3, n = 4$;
   c) $m = 4, n = 2$;   d) $m = 1, n = 1$.

3. a) 1;   b) 2;   c) 9;   d) 3.

5. $\begin{pmatrix} 3 & 8 & 0 & 4 & 0 \\ 1 & 4 & 6 & 4 & 0 \\ 4 & 7 & 1 & 4 & 0 \\ 6 & 4 & 3 & 3 & 0 \end{pmatrix}$.

7. $x = 3, y = -5$.

9. $x = 2, y = -4$.

11. $\begin{cases} x_1 = -1, y_1 = 0, z_1 = 1, \\ x_2 = 0, y_2 = 3, z_2 = 2, \\ x_3 = 5, y_3 = -1, z_3 = 3. \end{cases}$

13. $a = 4, b = 2, c = -1,$
    $d = 3, e = -2, f = 7$.

15. $a = \frac{7}{3}, b = \frac{13}{3}, c = \frac{11}{3}, d = -\frac{22}{3}$.

4.3 Supplementary Exercises

1. $ba_{ij} = a_{ij}b$.

3. $(a_{ij} + b_{ij}) + c_{ij} = a_{ij} + (b_{ij} + c_{ij})$.

5. $\begin{pmatrix} 0 & 1 \\ 1 & 0 \end{pmatrix}$.

7. a) $\begin{pmatrix} 0 & 1 & 0 \\ \frac{1}{3} & 0 & \frac{2}{3} \\ \frac{1}{4} & \frac{3}{4} & 0 \end{pmatrix}$;   b) $\begin{pmatrix} 0 & \frac{1}{2} & \frac{1}{2} \\ \frac{1}{4} & 0 & \frac{3}{4} \\ \frac{1}{3} & \frac{2}{3} & 0 \end{pmatrix}$.

9. a) $\begin{pmatrix} 0 & \frac{1}{2} & \frac{1}{2} \\ \frac{1}{2} & 0 & \frac{1}{2} \\ \frac{1}{2} & \frac{1}{2} & 0 \end{pmatrix}$;   b) $\begin{pmatrix} 0 & 1 & 0 \\ \frac{1}{2} & 0 & \frac{1}{2} \\ \frac{3}{4} & \frac{1}{4} & 0 \end{pmatrix}$.

4.4 Matrix multiplication

1. $(a + d + g \quad b + e + h \quad c + f + i)$.

3. $\begin{pmatrix} a + 2e & b + 2f & c + 2g & d + 2h \\ e & f & g & h \\ a & b & c & d \end{pmatrix}$.

5. $\begin{pmatrix} z & y & x \\ w & v & u \\ t & s & r \end{pmatrix}$.

7. $\begin{pmatrix} 2c & 2d \\ 4c & 4d \end{pmatrix}$.

9. $\begin{pmatrix} 0 \\ 0 \end{pmatrix}$.

11. $(0 \quad 0 \quad 0)$.

13. $\begin{cases} 2x + 3y = 7, \\ 4x - y = 7. \end{cases}$

15. $\begin{cases} x \qquad + 2z = 1, \\ 3x - y + z = 1, \\ 2x + 5y + 7z = 12. \end{cases}$

17.
$$AB = \begin{pmatrix} a + g & b + h & c + i \\ d + g & e + h & f + i \\ a + g & b + h & c + i \end{pmatrix} ;$$

$$BA = \begin{pmatrix} a + c & b & a + b + c \\ d + f & e & d + e + f \\ g + i & h & g + h + i \end{pmatrix} \neq AB.$$

19. a) $p_3 = p_2 M$;   b). $p_3 = p_1 M^2$.

4.4 Supplementary Exercises

1. a) $\begin{pmatrix} 1 & 2 \\ 0 & 1 \end{pmatrix}$;   b) $\begin{pmatrix} 1 & 3 \\ 0 & 1 \end{pmatrix}$.

3. a) $\begin{pmatrix} 1 & 0 & 0 \\ 0 & 1 & 0 \\ 0 & 0 & 1 \end{pmatrix}$;   b) $\begin{pmatrix} 0 & 0 & 1 \\ 0 & 1 & 0 \\ 1 & 0 & 0 \end{pmatrix}$.

5. a) $\begin{pmatrix} 1 & 0 & 2 \\ 0 & 1 & -2 \\ 0 & 0 & 1 \end{pmatrix}$;   b) $\begin{pmatrix} 1 & 0 & 3 \\ 0 & 1 & -3 \\ 0 & 0 & 1 \end{pmatrix}$.

11. $Ms^t = \begin{pmatrix} 70 \\ 30 \\ 40 \end{pmatrix}$. The elements of Ms^t are the numbers of hours needed of men, trucks, and tractors.

13. (148, 140, 151, 147, 166, 119). The elements of nM are the total numbers of newspapers sold each day.

15. $\begin{pmatrix} 125 \\ 425 \\ 252 \\ 69 \end{pmatrix}$. The elements of Ms^t are the total numbers of each type of newspaper sold that week.

17. $M^2 = M^3 = M^4 = M^5 = M^n = \begin{pmatrix} 1 & 0 \\ 0 & 1 \end{pmatrix}$.

19. $M^2 = M^3 = M^4 = M^5 = M^n = \begin{pmatrix} \frac{1}{2} & \frac{1}{2} \\ \frac{1}{2} & \frac{1}{2} \end{pmatrix}$.

21. $M^2 = \begin{pmatrix} 1 & 0 \\ \frac{5}{9} & \frac{4}{9} \end{pmatrix}$, $M^3 = \begin{pmatrix} 1 & 0 \\ \frac{19}{27} & \frac{8}{27} \end{pmatrix}$,

$M^4 = \begin{pmatrix} 1 & 0 \\ \frac{65}{81} & \frac{16}{81} \end{pmatrix}$, $M^5 = \begin{pmatrix} 1 & 0 \\ \frac{211}{243} & \frac{32}{243} \end{pmatrix}$,

$M^n = \begin{pmatrix} 1 & 0 \\ 1 - (2^n/3^n) & 2^n/3^n \end{pmatrix}$.

23. $M^2 = M^3 = M^4 = M^5 = M^n = \begin{pmatrix} 1/k & (k-1)/k \\ 1/k & (k-1)/k \end{pmatrix}$.

25. $M^2 = M^5 = M^{3n+2} = \begin{pmatrix} 0 & 0 & 1 \\ 1 & 0 & 0 \\ 0 & 1 & 0 \end{pmatrix}$,

$M^3 = M^6 = M^{3n} = \begin{pmatrix} 1 & 0 & 0 \\ 0 & 1 & 0 \\ 0 & 0 & 1 \end{pmatrix}$,

$M^4 = M^7 = M^{3n+1} = \begin{pmatrix} 0 & 1 & 0 \\ 0 & 0 & 1 \\ 1 & 0 & 0 \end{pmatrix}$.

4.5 Matrices and Markov chains

1. a) Yes;   b) yes;   c) yes;   d) yes.

3. a) Yes;   b) yes;
   c) $p_2 = (\frac{1}{2}, \frac{1}{2})$, $p_3 = (\frac{3}{4}, \frac{1}{4})$, $p_4 = (\frac{7}{8}, \frac{1}{8})$, $p_5 = (\frac{15}{16}, \frac{1}{16})$;
   d) yes.

5. $p_2 = p_1M$, $p_3 = p_1M^2$, $p_4 = p_1M^3$,
   $p_5 = p_1M^4$, $p_{k+1} = p_1M^k$.

7. a)
$$M^2 = \begin{pmatrix} \frac{1}{2} & \frac{1}{4} & \frac{1}{4} \\ 0 & 1 & 0 \\ \frac{1}{4} & \frac{1}{2} & \frac{1}{4} \end{pmatrix},$$

$$M^3 = \begin{pmatrix} \frac{3}{8} & \frac{3}{8} & \frac{1}{4} \\ 0 & 1 & 0 \\ \frac{1}{4} & \frac{5}{8} & \frac{1}{8} \end{pmatrix},$$

$$M^4 = \begin{pmatrix} \frac{5}{16} & \frac{1}{2} & \frac{3}{16} \\ 0 & 1 & 0 \\ \frac{3}{16} & \frac{11}{16} & \frac{1}{8} \end{pmatrix}.$$

b) $p_2 = (\frac{1}{2}, 0, \frac{1}{2})$, $p_3 = (\frac{1}{2}, \frac{1}{4}, \frac{1}{4})$,
   $p_4 = (\frac{3}{8}, \frac{3}{8}, \frac{1}{4})$, $p_5 = (\frac{5}{16}, \frac{1}{2}, \frac{3}{16})$.

9. a) $\begin{pmatrix} 0.46 & 0.54 \\ 0.45 & 0.55 \end{pmatrix}$;   b) 0.46;   c) 0.45.

4.5 Supplementary Exercises

1. a)
$$\begin{array}{cc} & \begin{array}{cc} s_1 & s_2 \end{array} \\ \begin{array}{c} s_1 \\ s_2 \end{array} & \begin{pmatrix} \frac{2}{3} & \frac{1}{3} \\ \frac{2}{3} & \frac{1}{3} \end{pmatrix} \end{array}.$$

b) $p_{12} = (\frac{2}{3}, \frac{1}{3})$, that is, if Bill takes the first shot the probability is $\frac{2}{3}$ that Bill takes the second shot and $\frac{1}{3}$ that Bob takes the second shot.

c) $\begin{pmatrix} \frac{2}{3} & \frac{1}{3} \\ \frac{2}{3} & \frac{1}{3} \end{pmatrix}.$

d) $\frac{2}{3}$ from $p_{13} = (\frac{2}{3}, \frac{1}{3})$.   e) $\frac{2}{3}$ from $p_{23} = (\frac{2}{3}, \frac{1}{3})$.

3. a)
$$\begin{array}{cc} & \begin{array}{cc} s_1 & s_2 \end{array} \\ \begin{array}{c} s_1 \\ s_2 \end{array} & \begin{pmatrix} \frac{1}{10} & \frac{9}{10} \\ \frac{1}{10} & \frac{9}{10} \end{pmatrix} \end{array}.$$

b) $p_{12} = (\frac{1}{10}, \frac{9}{10})$, that is if Bill takes the first shot the probability is $\frac{1}{10}$ that Bill takes the second shot and $\frac{9}{10}$ that Bob takes the second shot.

c) $\begin{pmatrix} \frac{1}{10} & \frac{9}{10} \\ \frac{1}{10} & \frac{9}{10} \end{pmatrix}.$ d) $\frac{1}{10}$.   e) $\frac{1}{10}$.

5. a)
$$\begin{array}{cc} & \begin{array}{cc} s_1 & s_2 \end{array} \\ \begin{array}{c} s_1 \\ s_2 \end{array} & \begin{pmatrix} \frac{6}{10} & \frac{4}{10} \\ \frac{4}{10} & \frac{6}{10} \end{pmatrix} \end{array}.$$

b) $p_{12} = (\frac{6}{10}, \frac{4}{10})$, that is, if Bill takes the first shot the probability is $\frac{6}{10}$ that Bill takes the second shot and $\frac{4}{10}$ that Bob takes the second shot.

c) $\begin{pmatrix} 0.52 & 0.48 \\ 0.48 & 0.52 \end{pmatrix}$.   d) 0.52.   e) 0.48.

7. An absorbing chain.

9. An absorbing chain.

11. Not an absorbing chain.

13. (See figure on facing page.)

4.6 Matrices and systems of linear equations

1. $r_1 - 2r_2$
r_2
$r_3 - 3r_2$

3. a) $r_1 + _3$ b) $r_1/5$
$r_2 + 2r_3$ $r_2 - (\frac{9}{5})r_1$
r_3 $r_3 + 2r_2$
$r_4 + 2r_3$ $r_4 - 2r_1$

5. Among the possible answers is:

$$\rightarrow \begin{pmatrix} 1 & 2 \\ 0 & -11 \end{pmatrix} \begin{matrix} r_1 \\ r_2 - 4r_1 \end{matrix} \rightarrow \begin{pmatrix} 1 & 0 \\ 0 & 1 \end{pmatrix} \begin{matrix} r_1 + 2r_2/11 \\ -r_2/11 \end{matrix}$$

7. Among the possible answers is:

$$\rightarrow \begin{pmatrix} 1 & 5 & -3 \\ 0 & 2 & 7 \\ 0 & -13 & 13 \end{pmatrix} \begin{matrix} r_1 \\ r_2 - 2r_1 \\ r_3 - 3r_1 \end{matrix}$$

$$\rightarrow \begin{pmatrix} 1 & 0 & 2 \\ 0 & 0 & 9 \\ 0 & 1 & -1 \end{pmatrix} \begin{matrix} r_1 + 5r_3/13 \\ r_2 + 2r_3/13 \\ -r_3/13 \end{matrix}$$

$$\rightarrow \begin{pmatrix} 1 & 0 & 0 \\ 0 & 1 & 0 \\ 0 & 0 & 1 \end{pmatrix} \begin{matrix} r_1 - 2r_2/9 \\ r_3 + r_2/9 \\ r_2/9 \end{matrix}$$

9. $\begin{pmatrix} 1 & -1 & 3 \\ 2 & 1 & 0 \end{pmatrix} \rightarrow \begin{pmatrix} 3 & 0 & 3 \\ 0 & 3 & -6 \end{pmatrix} \begin{matrix} r_1 + r_2 \\ r_2 - 2r_1 \end{matrix}$

$$\rightarrow \begin{pmatrix} 1 & 0 & 1 \\ 0 & 1 & -2 \end{pmatrix} \begin{matrix} r_1/3 \\ r_2/3 \end{matrix}$$

$x = 1, y = -2.$

11. $\begin{pmatrix} 1 & 2 & 1 \\ 1 & -1 & 7 \end{pmatrix} \rightarrow \begin{pmatrix} 1 & 2 & 1 \\ 0 & -3 & 6 \end{pmatrix} \rightarrow \begin{pmatrix} 1 & 0 & 5 \\ 0 & 1 & -2 \end{pmatrix};$

$x = 5, y = -2.$

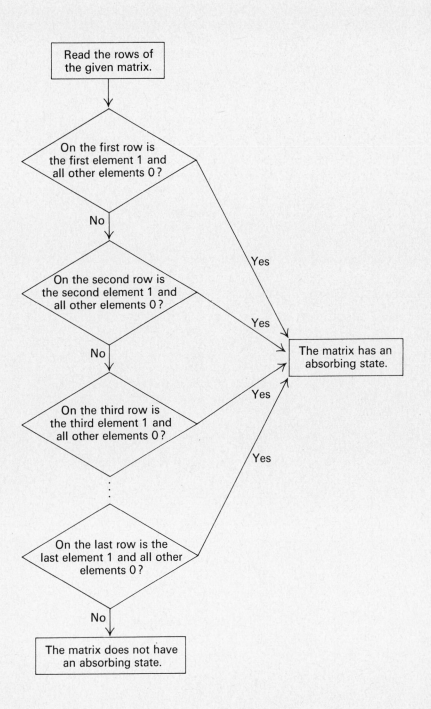

13. $\begin{pmatrix} 1 & -1 & 5 \\ 2 & -2 & 7 \end{pmatrix} \rightarrow \begin{pmatrix} 1 & -1 & 5 \\ 0 & 0 & -3 \end{pmatrix} : \varnothing.$

4.6 Supplementary Exercises

1. $\begin{pmatrix} 1 & -1 & 1 & 4 \\ 2 & 1 & -1 & 2 \\ 0 & 1 & 1 & 4 \end{pmatrix} \rightarrow \begin{pmatrix} 1 & -1 & 1 & 4 \\ 0 & 3 & -3 & -6 \\ 0 & 1 & 1 & 4 \end{pmatrix}$

$\rightarrow \begin{pmatrix} 1 & 0 & 0 & 2 \\ 0 & 1 & -1 & -2 \\ 0 & 0 & 2 & 6 \end{pmatrix} \rightarrow \begin{pmatrix} 1 & 0 & 0 & 2 \\ 0 & 1 & 0 & 1 \\ 0 & 0 & 1 & 3 \end{pmatrix},$

$x = 2, y = 1\ z = 3$

3. $\begin{pmatrix} 1 & -1 & -1 & 3 \\ 4 & 3 & 4 & 4 \\ 0 & 1 & 2 & -2 \end{pmatrix} \rightarrow \begin{pmatrix} 1 & 0 & 1 & 1 \\ 0 & 7 & 8 & -8 \\ 0 & 1 & 2 & -2 \end{pmatrix}$

$\rightarrow \begin{pmatrix} 1 & 0 & 1 & 1 \\ 0 & 1 & -4 & 4 \\ 0 & 0 & 6 & -6 \end{pmatrix} \rightarrow \begin{pmatrix} 1 & 0 & 0 & 2 \\ 0 & 1 & 0 & 0 \\ 0 & 0 & 1 & -1 \end{pmatrix};$

$x = 2, y = 0, z = -1.$

5. $\begin{pmatrix} 1 & -1 & -2 & -3 & -2 \\ 3 & 2 & 0 & 1 & 1 \\ 3 & 0 & -3 & -5 & -3 \\ 2 & 0 & 2 & 7 & 6 \end{pmatrix} \rightarrow \begin{pmatrix} 5 & 0 & -4 & -5 & -3 \\ 4 & 1 & -2 & -2 & -1 \\ 1 & 0 & -5 & -12 & -9 \\ 2 & 0 & 2 & 7 & 6 \end{pmatrix}$

$\rightarrow \begin{pmatrix} 1 & 0 & -8 & -19 & -15 \\ 4 & 1 & -2 & -2 & -1 \\ 0 & 0 & 3 & 7 & 6 \\ 0 & 0 & 12 & 31 & 24 \end{pmatrix} \rightarrow \begin{pmatrix} 1 & 0 & -8 & -19 & -15 \\ 4 & 1 & -2 & -2 & -1 \\ 0 & 0 & 3 & 7 & 6 \\ 0 & 0 & 0 & 3 & 0 \end{pmatrix}$

$\rightarrow \begin{pmatrix} 1 & 0 & 0 & 0 & 1 \\ 0 & 1 & 0 & 0 & -1 \\ 0 & 0 & 1 & 0 & 2 \\ 0 & 0 & 0 & 1 & 0 \end{pmatrix};$

$x = 1, y = -1, z = 2, w = 0.$

7. $\begin{pmatrix} 4 & 8 & 2 \\ 2 & 4 & 1 \end{pmatrix} \rightarrow \begin{pmatrix} 0 & 0 & 0 \\ 2 & 4 & 1 \end{pmatrix} \begin{matrix} r_1 - 2r_2 \\ r_2 \end{matrix}$

Review Exercises for Chapter 4

1. a) Conformable;   b) not conformable;   c) not conformable.

3. a) $(4, 0, 6)$;   b) $(3, 6, -3)$.

5. a) $(7, 6, 3)$;   b) $(2, -4, 8)$.

7. $(1.75, 1, 2.50) \cdot (8, 3, 5)$.

9. a) $\begin{pmatrix} 3 & -1 & 2 \\ 3 & 2 & -1 \end{pmatrix}$; b) $\begin{pmatrix} -1 & -3 & 4 \\ 1 & -2 & 3 \end{pmatrix}$.

11.

$$\begin{array}{c|ccccccc} & 0 & 1 & 2 & 3 & 4 & 5 & 6 \\ \hline 0 & 1 & 0 & 0 & 0 & 0 & 0 & 0 \\ 1 & \frac{1}{2} & 0 & \frac{1}{2} & 0 & 0 & 0 & 0 \\ 2 & 0 & \frac{1}{2} & 0 & \frac{1}{2} & 0 & 0 & 0 \\ 3 & 0 & 0 & \frac{1}{2} & 0 & \frac{1}{2} & 0 & 0 \\ 4 & 0 & 0 & 0 & \frac{1}{2} & 0 & \frac{1}{2} & 0 \\ 5 & 0 & 0 & 0 & 0 & \frac{1}{2} & 0 & \frac{1}{2} \\ 6 & 0 & 0 & 0 & 0 & 0 & 0 & 1 \end{array}.$$

13. $M^2 = \begin{pmatrix} 1 & 0 & -1 \\ 0 & 2 & -1 \\ -1 & -1 & 2 \end{pmatrix}$, $M^3 = \begin{pmatrix} 0 & 2 & -1 \\ 2 & 1 & -3 \\ -1 & -3 & 3 \end{pmatrix}$.

15. a) Yes; b) yes; c) yes;
    d) no; e) yes; f) no.

17. $\rightarrow \begin{pmatrix} 2 & -4 & 2 \\ 0 & 7 & -1 \\ 0 & 2 & -1 \end{pmatrix} \begin{matrix} r_1 - r_2 \\ 2r_2 - r_1 \\ r_3 \end{matrix}$

$\rightarrow \begin{pmatrix} 1 & -2 & 1 \\ 0 & 1 & 2 \\ 0 & 2 & -1 \end{pmatrix} \begin{matrix} r_1/2 \\ r_2 - 3r_3 \\ \end{matrix}$

$\rightarrow \begin{pmatrix} 1 & 0 & 0 \\ 0 & 1 & 0 \\ 0 & 0 & 1 \end{pmatrix} \begin{matrix} r_1 + r_3 \\ r_2 + 2(r_3 - 2r_2)/5 \\ -(r_3 - 2r_2)/5 \end{matrix}$

19. $\begin{pmatrix} 4 & -3 & 12 \\ 8 & -6 & 6 \end{pmatrix} \rightarrow \begin{pmatrix} 4 & -3 & 12 \\ 0 & 0 & -18 \end{pmatrix}$; $\emptyset$.

CHAPTER 5

5.1 Linear statements in one variable

1.

3.

5.

7.

9. 0.

11. 25.

13. a) $6 - x$;
   b) $50x$;
   c) $70(6 - x) - 15(6 - x)$;
   d) $50x + 55(6 - x)$, that is, $330 - 5x$;
   e) $\begin{cases} 0 \le x, \\ x \le 6; \end{cases}$
   f) 0.

15. a) $15x + 35(150 - x) - 21(150 - x)$, that is, $x + 2100$;
   b) 150.

5.2 Linear statements in two variables

1.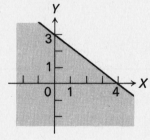

3.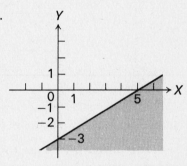

5.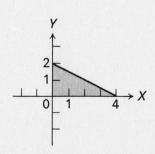

7.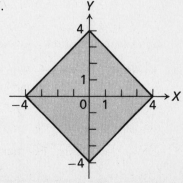

9.

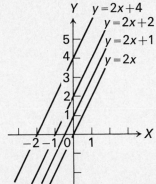

11.

$$\tfrac{1}{2}x + \tfrac{2}{3}y - 4 = 0$$

$$\tfrac{1}{2}x + \tfrac{2}{3}y - 2 = 0$$

$$\tfrac{1}{2}x + \tfrac{2}{3}y - 1 = 0$$

$$\tfrac{1}{2}x + \tfrac{2}{3}y = 0$$

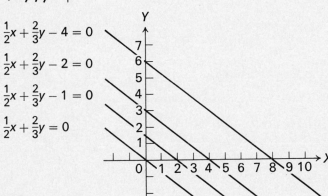

5.3 Linear programs with two variables

1. a) $x = 10, y = 0$ for maximum of 10;
   b) $x = 2, y = 7$ for minimum of -5.

3. a) $x = 3, y = 7$ for maximum of 17;
   b) $x = 2, y = 0$ for minimum of 2.

5. a) $3 \le x \le 10, y = 10 - x$ for maximum of 10;
   b) $x = 2, y = 0$ for minimum of 2.

7. a) $5 \le x \le 7, y = x - 5$ for maximum of 5305;
   b) $x = 0, y = 4$ for minimum of 5260.

9. a) $x = 7, y = 2$ for maximum of 16;
   b) $x = 0, y = 0$ for minimum of 0.

11. $p = 21x + 20y$. For maximum profit of \$63 we take $x = 3$ and $y = 0$.

13. $p = 425x + 490y + (20 - x - y)420 = 5x + 70y + 8400.$ A maximum profit of $88.15 may be made by making 13 puzzles, 5 boats, and 2 chair seats.

15. a)
$$\begin{cases} 0 \le x, \\ 0 \le y, \\ 20x + 25y \ge 1000, \\ 30x + 30y \ge 1260. \end{cases}$$

b)

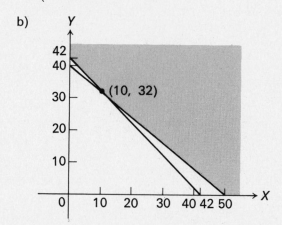

c) $(0, 42)$, $(10, 32)$, $(50, 0)$.

d) Cost of $20x + 30y$ is smallest for 10 units of type I and 32 units of type II.

e) $11.60.

f) 1000 grams of protein, 1260 grams of carbohydrates.

5.4 Slack variables

1. $-x \le 1.$

3. $2x_1 - x_2 - 3x_3 + 4x_4 \le 75.$

5. $\begin{cases} x_1 + x_2 + x_3 = 5, \\ x_3 \ge 0. \end{cases}$

7. $\begin{cases} -x_1 + x_2 + x_3 = 1, \\ x_3 \ge 0. \end{cases}$

9.

Extreme points at $x = 0$ and $x = 5.$

11. Extreme points at $(0, 0)$, $(5, 0)$, $(2, 3)$ and $(0, 3)$.

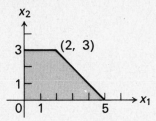

13. a)

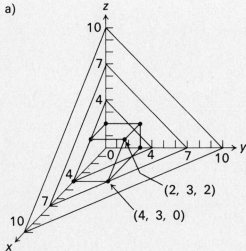

(2, 3, 2)

(4, 3, 0)

b) The maximum value of $x + y + z$ is 7 and occurs at each point of the line segment with endpoints $(4, 3, 0)$ and $(2, 3, 2)$.

5.5 Row transformations for evaluation

1.

	C_1	C_2	
E_1	①	2	1
E_2	1	-1	4
E_3	2	3	3
	-4	1	0

	C_1	C_2	
C_1	1	2	1
E_2	0	-3	3
E_3	0	-1	1
	0	9	4

	C_1	C_2	
C_1	1	0	3
C_2	0	1	−1
E_3	0	0	0
	0	0	13

Thus $4x - y = 13$ at $x = 3, y = -1$.

3. $3x + 2y = 7$ at $x = 3, y = -1$.

5. $3x + 2y = 4$ at $x = 2, y = -1, z = 3$.

7. $2x - 5y = 9$ at $x = 2, y = -1, z = 3$.

9. $x + y + z + w = 10$ at $x = 4, y = 1, z = 2, w = 3$.

11. $x + 2y - 3z + w = 3$ at $x = 4, y = 1, z = 2, w = 3$.

5.6 The simplex algorithm for maximization

1.

	C_1	C_2	E_1	E_2	
E_1	1	2	1	0	7
E_2	0	1	0	1	2
	−1	−4	0	0	0

The pivotal column is selected as C_2; the pivotal row is E_2 since $2 < \frac{7}{2}$.

	C_1	C_2	E_1	E_2	
E_1	1	0	0	−2	3
C_2	0	1	0	1	2
	−1	0	0	4	8

	C_1	C_2	E_1	E_2	
C_1	1	0	0	−2	3
C_2	0	1	0	1	2
	0	0	0	4	11

The maximum of $x + 4y$ is 11 at $(3, 2)$.

3.

	C_1	C_2	E_1	E_2	
E_1	1	2	1	0	7
E_2	0	1	0	1	2
	−3	1	0	0	2

	C_1	C_2	E_1	E_2	
C_1	1	2	1	0	7
E_2	0	1	0	1	2
	0	7	3	0	23

The maximum of $3x - y + 2$ is 23 at $(7, 0)$.

5.

	C_1	C_2	C_3	C_4	E_1	E_2	E_3	E_4	
E_1	1	1	1	2	1	0	0	0	10
E_2	1	-2	0	0	0	1	0	0	5
E_3	3	0	1	-1	0	0	1	0	3
E_4	0	1	-1	2	0	0	0	1	2
	-3	-1	0	-1	0	0	0	0	0

	C_1	C_2	C_3	C_4	E_1	E_2	E_3	E_4	
E_1	0	1	$\frac{2}{3}$	$\frac{7}{3}$	1	0	$-\frac{1}{3}$	0	9
E_2	0	-2	$-\frac{1}{3}$	$\frac{1}{3}$	0	1	$-\frac{1}{3}$	0	4
C_1	1	0	$\frac{1}{3}$	$-\frac{1}{3}$	0	0	$\frac{1}{3}$	0	1
E_4	0	1	-1	2	0	0	0	1	2
	0	-1	1	-2	0	0	1	0	3

	C_1	C_2	C_3	C_4	E_1	E_2	E_3	E_4	
E_1	0	0	$\frac{5}{3}$	$\frac{1}{3}$	1	0	$-\frac{1}{3}$	-1	7
E_2	0	0	$-\frac{7}{3}$	$\frac{13}{3}$	0	1	$-\frac{1}{3}$	2	8
C_1	1	0	$\frac{1}{3}$	$-\frac{1}{3}$	0	0	$\frac{1}{3}$	0	1
C_2	0	1	-1	2	0	0	0	1	2
	0	0	0	0	0	0	1	1	5

The maximum of $3x + y + z$ is 5 at $(1, 2, 0, 0)$.

7.

	C_1	C_2	C_3	C_4	E_1	E_2	E_3	E_4	
E_1	1	1	1	2	1	0	0	0	10
E_2	1	-2	0	0	0	1	0	0	5
E_3	3	0	1	-1	0	0	1	0	3
E_4	0	1	-1	2	0	0	0	1	2
	0	-2	-3	-1	0	0	0	0	0

	C_1	C_2	C_3	C_4	E_1	E_2	E_3	E_4	
E_1	-2	1	0	3	1	0	-1	0	7
E_2	1	-2	0	0	0	1	0	0	5
C_3	3	0	1	-1	0	0	1	0	3
E_4	3	1	0	1	0	0	1	1	5
	9	-2	0	-4	0	0	3	0	9

	C_1	C_2	C_3	C_4	E_1	E_2	E_3	E_4	
C_4	$-\frac{2}{3}$	$\frac{1}{3}$	0	1	$\frac{1}{3}$	0	$-\frac{1}{3}$	0	$\frac{7}{3}$
E_2	1	-2	0	0	0	1	0	0	5
C_3	$\frac{7}{3}$	$\frac{1}{3}$	1	0	$\frac{1}{3}$	0	$\frac{2}{3}$	0	$\frac{16}{3}$
E_4	$\frac{11}{3}$	$\frac{2}{3}$	0	0	$-\frac{1}{3}$	0	$\frac{4}{3}$	1	$\frac{8}{3}$
	$\frac{19}{3}$	$-\frac{2}{3}$	0	0	$\frac{4}{3}$	0	$\frac{5}{3}$	0	$\frac{55}{3}$

	C_1	C_2	C_3	C_4	E_1	E_2	E_3	E_4	
C_4	$-\frac{5}{2}$	0	0	1	$\frac{1}{2}$	0	-1	$-\frac{1}{2}$	1
E_2	12	0	0	0	-1	1	4	3	13
C_3	$\frac{1}{2}$	0	1	0	$\frac{1}{2}$	0	0	$-\frac{1}{2}$	4
C_2	$\frac{11}{2}$	1	0	0	$-\frac{1}{2}$	0	2	$\frac{3}{2}$	4
	10	0	0	0	1	0	$\frac{1}{3}$	1	21

The maximum of $2y + 3z + w$ is 21 at $(0, 4, 4, 1)$.

9. a) $\begin{cases} 0 \le w, 0 \le x, 0 \le y, 0 \le z, \\ 15w + 40x + 25y + 50z \le 1000, \\ w \le 40, \\ x \le 15, \\ y \le 24, \\ z \le 12. \end{cases}$

b) $w + 3x + 3y/2 + 4z$.

c)

	C_1	C_2	C_3	C_4	E_1	E_2	E_3	E_4	E_5	
E_1	15	40	25	50	1	0	0	0	0	1000
E_2	1	0	0	0	0	1	0	0	0	40
E_3	0	1	0	0	0	0	1	0	0	15
E_4	0	0	1	0	0	0	0	1	0	24
E_5	0	0	0	1	0	0	0	0	1	12
	-1	-3	$-\frac{3}{2}$	-4	0	0	0	0	0	0

d)

	C_1	C_2	C_3	C_4	E_1	E_2	E_3	E_4	E_5	
E_1	15	40	25	0	1	0	0	0	-50	400
E_2	1	0	0	0	0	1	0	0	0	40
E_3	0	1	0	0	0	0	1	0	0	15
E_4	0	0	1	0	0	0	0	1	0	24
C_4	0	0	0	1	0	0	0	0	1	12
	-1	-3	$-\frac{3}{2}$	0	0	0	0	0	4	48

	C_1	C_2	C_3	C_4	E_1	E_2	E_3	E_4	E_5	
C_2	$\frac{3}{8}$	1	$\frac{5}{8}$	0	$\frac{1}{40}$	0	0	0	$-\frac{5}{4}$	10
E_2	1	0	0	0	0	1	0	0	0	40
E_3	$-\frac{3}{8}$	0	$-\frac{5}{8}$	0	$-\frac{1}{40}$	0	1	0	$\frac{5}{4}$	5
E_4	0	0	1	0	0	0	0	1	0	24
C_4	0	0	0	1	0	0	0	0	1	12
	$\frac{1}{8}$	0	$\frac{3}{8}$	0	$\frac{3}{40}$	0	0	0	$\frac{1}{4}$	78

The maximum annual dividend is $78 from 10 shares of Handy Holders (cost $400, dividend $30) and 12 shares of Telephone Tapes (cost $600, dividend $48).

Note at each step of part (d) that the selection of the column with the negative indicator with the largest absolute value corresponds to the selection of remaining stock with the largest dividend per share.

5.6 Supplementary Exercises

1. a)

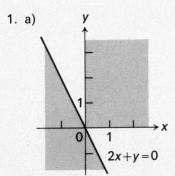

b)

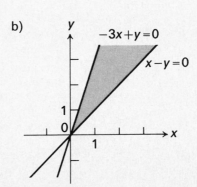

c)

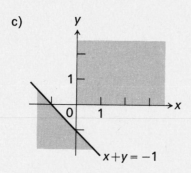

$x+y = -1$

d) $-x-2y=-4$

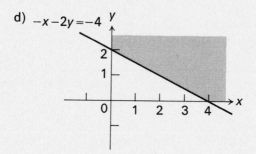

3. b)

	C_1	C_2	E_1	E_2	E_3	
E_1	1	1	1	0	0	7
E_2	1	1	0	1	0	5
E_3	0	1	0	0	1	3
	-2	-1	0	0	0	0

	C_1	C_2	E_1	E_2	E_3	
E_1	0	0	1	-1	0	2
C_1	1	1	0	1	0	5
E_3	0	1	0	0	1	3
	0	1	0	2	0	10

The maximum is 10 at $(5, 0)$. The use of $(5, 0)$ instead of $(7, 0)$ is required by the policy of selecting the smallest of the positive b_i/a_{ij}; that is $\frac{5}{1}$ instead of $\frac{7}{1}$.

5. (a) (b) (c) and (e). The constant terms are not independent and the assumption is not satisfied. (d) The constant terms are independent and the assumption is satisfied.

5.7 The simplex algorithm for minimization

1. a) Maximize $3x + 2y$ subject to the constraints
$$\begin{cases} 0 \le x, 0 \le y, \\ x + 2y \le 5, \\ x \le 3. \end{cases}$$

 b) Minimize $5u + 3v$ subject to the constraints
$$\begin{cases} u \ge 0, v \ge 0, \\ u + v \ge 3, \\ 2u \ge 2. \end{cases}$$

3. a) The extreme points are $(0, 0)$; $(3, 0)$, $(3, 1)$, and $(0, 2\frac{1}{2})$. The values of $3x + 2y$ at these points are $0, 9, 11$, and 5, respectively. The maximum value is 11 at $(3, 1)$.

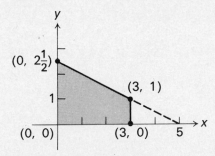

 b) The finite extreme points are $(1, 2)$ and $(3, 0)$. The values of $5u + 3v$ at these points are 11 and 15, respectively. The minimum value is 11 at $(1, 2)$.

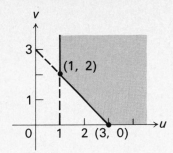

 c)

	C_1	C_2	E_1	E_2	
E_1	0	2	1	−1	2
C_1	1	0	0	1	3
	0	−2	0	3	9

	C_1	C_2	E_1	E_2	
C_2	0	1	$\frac{1}{2}$	$-\frac{1}{2}$	1
C_1	1	0	0	1	3
	0	0	1	2	11

The maximum value of $3x + 2y$ is 11 at $(3, 1)$; the minimum value of $5u + 3v$ is 11 at $(1, 2)$.

5.

	C_1	C_2	C_3	E_1	E_2	E_3	
C_1	1	0	0	1	0	0	5
E_2	0	1	1	0	1	0	4
E_3	0	0	1	-1	0	1	1
	0	-1	-3	5	0	0	25

	C_1	C_2	C_3	E_1	E_2	E_3	
C_1	1	0	0	1	0	0	5
E_2	0	1	0	1	1	-1	3
C_3	0	0	1	-1	0	1	1
	0	-1	0	2	0	3	28

	C_1	C_2	C_3	E_1	E_2	E_3	
C_1	1	0	0	1	0	0	5
C_2	0	1	0	1	1	-1	3
C_3	0	0	1	-1	0	1	1
	0	0	0	3	1	2	31

The maximum of $5x + y + 3z$ is 31 at $(5, 3, 1)$; the minimum of $5u + 4v + 6w$ is 31 at $(3, 1, 2)$.

7. Minimize $5u + 9v + 8w$ subject to the constraints
$$\begin{cases} u \geq 0, v \geq 0, w \geq 0, \\ u \qquad\quad + w \geq 5, \\ \quad\quad v + 2w \geq 9, \\ u + 2v + w \geq 8. \end{cases}$$

9. Maximize $3x + 2y + 6z$ subject to the constraints
$$\begin{cases} 0 \leq x, 0 \leq y \; 0 \leq z, \\ 2x + 2y + 3z \leq 3, \\ 3x - \quad y + 2z \leq 1, \\ \quad\quad\; y + 5z \leq 1. \end{cases}$$

10.

	C_1	C_2	C_3	E_1	E_2	E_3	
E_1	2	$\frac{7}{5}$	0	1	0	$-\frac{3}{5}$	$\frac{12}{5}$
E_2	3	$-\frac{7}{5}$	0	0	1	$-\frac{2}{5}$	$\frac{3}{5}$
C_3	0	$\frac{1}{5}$	1	0	0	$\frac{1}{5}$	$\frac{1}{5}$
	-3	$-\frac{4}{5}$	0	0	0	$\frac{6}{5}$	$\frac{6}{5}$

	C_1	C_2	C_3	E_1	E_2	E_3	
E_1	0	$\frac{7}{3}$	0	1	$-\frac{2}{3}$	$-\frac{1}{3}$	2
C_1	1	$-\frac{7}{15}$	0	0	$\frac{1}{3}$	$-\frac{2}{15}$	$\frac{1}{5}$
C_3	0	$\frac{1}{5}$	1	0	0	$\frac{1}{5}$	$\frac{1}{5}$
	0	$-\frac{11}{5}$	0	0	1	$\frac{4}{5}$	$\frac{9}{5}$

	C_1	C_2	C_3	E_1	E_2	E_3	
C_2	0	1	0	$\frac{3}{7}$	$-\frac{2}{7}$	$-\frac{1}{7}$	$\frac{6}{7}$
C_1	1	0	0	$\frac{1}{5}$	$\frac{1}{5}$	$-\frac{1}{5}$	$\frac{3}{5}$
C_3	0	0	1	$-\frac{3}{35}$	$\frac{2}{35}$	$\frac{8}{35}$	$\frac{1}{35}$
	0	0	0	$\frac{33}{35}$	$\frac{13}{35}$	$\frac{17}{35}$	$\frac{129}{35}$

The maximum of $3x + 2y + 6z$ is $3\frac{24}{35}$ at $(\frac{3}{5}, \frac{6}{7}, \frac{1}{35})$; the minimum of $3u + v + w$ is $3\frac{24}{35}$ at $(\frac{33}{35}, \frac{13}{35}, \frac{17}{35})$.

Review Exercises for Chapter 5

1.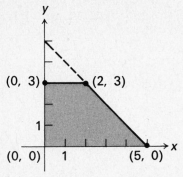

3.

5. a) $-2x \leq 3$;   b) $x \leq -4$;   c) $-x \leq -5$.

7. $\begin{cases} x_1 + 2x_2 + x_3 = 5, \\ \quad\quad\quad\quad x_3 \geq 0. \end{cases}$

9.

	C_1	C_2	C_3	
E_1	1	-2	1	6
E_2	①	-1	0	4
E_3	1	0	2	5
	-7	-5	2	0

	C_1	C_2	C_3	
E_1	0	-1	1	2
C_1	1	-1	0	4
E_3	0	①	2	1
	0	-12	2	28

	C_1	C_2	C_3	
E_1	0	0	③	3
C_1	1	0	2	5
C_2	0	1	2	1
	0	0	26	40

	C_1	C_2	C_3	
C_3	0	0	1	1
C_1	1	0	0	3
C_2	0	1	0	-1
	0	0	0	14

Thus $7x + 5y - 2z = 14$ at $(3, -1, 1)$.

11.

	C_1	C_2	E_1	E_2	
C_1	1	2	1	0	6
E_2	0	1	0	1	2
	0	9	4	0	24

The maximum value of $4x - y$ is 24 at $(6, 0)$.

13. Minimize $6u + 2v$ subject to the constraints
$$\begin{cases} u \geq 0, v \geq 0, \\ u \geq 4, \\ 2u + v \geq -1. \end{cases}$$

15.

	C_1	C_2	C_3	E_1	E_2	E_3	
E_1	1	-2	1	1	0	0	6
E_2	1	-1	0	0	1	0	4
E_3	1	0	2	0	0	1	5
	-5	1	-3	0	0	0	0

17. Minimize $6u + 4v + 5w$ subject to the constraints
$$\begin{cases} u \geq 0, v \geq 0, w \geq 0, \\ \quad u + v + w \geq 5, \\ -2u - v \qquad \geq 1, \\ \quad u \qquad + 2w \geq 3. \end{cases}$$

19. The constraints are
$$\begin{cases} 0 \leq w, 0 \leq x, 0 \leq y, 0 \leq z, \\ w + x \qquad\qquad \leq 100, \\ \qquad\quad y + z \leq 80, \\ \quad x \qquad + z \leq 75. \end{cases}$$
The objective function is $20w + 24x + 25y + 22z$.

CHAPTER 6

6.2 Payoff matrices

1.
$$\begin{array}{cc} & \text{Carl} \\ & \text{heads} \quad \text{tails} \\ \begin{array}{c} \text{heads} \\ \text{Ron} \\ \text{tails} \end{array} & \begin{pmatrix} -1 & 1 \\ 1 & -1 \end{pmatrix}. \end{array}$$

3.
$$\begin{array}{cc} & \text{Carl} \\ & 1 \quad\quad 2 \\ \begin{array}{c} \quad 1 \\ \text{Ron} \\ \quad 2 \end{array} & \begin{pmatrix} -2 & 3 \\ 3 & -4 \end{pmatrix}. \end{array}$$

5.
$$\begin{array}{cc} & \text{Carl} \\ & 1 \quad\ 2 \quad\ 3 \\ \begin{array}{c} 1 \\ \text{Ron } 2 \\ 3 \end{array} & \begin{pmatrix} -2 & 3 & -4 \\ 3 & -4 & 5 \\ -4 & 5 & -6 \end{pmatrix}. \end{array}$$

7. a) Yes, first column dominates second;
   b) yes, third column dominates first;
   c) no;
   d) yes, second column dominates third.

9. a) First column;
   b) third column;
   c) first and second columns are the same in this respect;
   d) first column.

11. a) Yes;
    b) 1, 2, 3, 4, 5, 6 each with probability $\frac{1}{6}$;
    c) heads, tails each with probability $\frac{1}{2}$.

6.3 Pure strategies

1. Second row.

3. None.

5. First column.

7. Third column.

9.
$$\begin{pmatrix} 1 & 2 \\ 2 & 3 \end{pmatrix} \quad \begin{matrix} \text{minimums} \\ 1 \\ 2 \end{matrix} \quad \text{maximin 2}$$

maximums   2   3

minimax 2

Saddle point on the second row and first column. This result agrees with the results obtained in Exercises 1 and 5.

11.
$$\begin{pmatrix} 2 & 1 & -3 \\ 1 & 0 & -1 \\ -2 & 1 & -2 \end{pmatrix} \quad \begin{matrix} \text{minimums} \\ -3 \\ -1 \\ -2 \end{matrix} \quad \text{maximin } -1$$

maximums   2   1   −1

minimax −1

Saddle point on the second row and third column.

13. a) Yes;   b) yes.

15. a) Yes;   b) yes.

17.
$$\begin{pmatrix} 10 & 0 & 23 & -12 \\ 14 & 1 & 2 & 8 \\ -4 & -3 & 14 & -2 \\ 12 & -6 & 6 & 4 \end{pmatrix} \quad \begin{matrix} \text{minimums} \\ -12 \\ 1 \\ -4 \\ -6 \end{matrix} \quad \text{maximin 1}$$

maximums   14   1   23   8

minimax 1

Saddle point on the second row and second column.
Solution: second row, second column. Value of the game; 1.

19.   Carl
$$\text{Ron } \begin{matrix} 1 \\ 2 \end{matrix} \begin{pmatrix} -2 & 0 \\ 0 & 4 \end{pmatrix} \begin{matrix} 1 & 2 \end{matrix}$$

a) Second row;   b) first column;
c) yes, there is a saddle point on the second row and first column;
d) yes.

6.3 Supplementary Exercises

1. a) Yes;   b) yes;   c) yes.
3. a) No;   b) yes;   c) no;   d) yes;   e) no.
5. a) $B \in \overline{AD}$;   b) $C \in \overline{AD}$;   c) $B \notin \overline{AD}$;   d) $C \notin \overline{AD}$.
7. No.
9. Each element of the dominant column is a minimum of the elements in its row. Each element of the dominant row is a maximum of the elements in its column.

6.4 Mixed strategies

1. Row strategy $(\frac{2}{3}, \frac{1}{3})$, column strategy $(\frac{2}{3}, \frac{1}{3})^t$, value $\frac{2}{3}$.
3. Row strategy $(\frac{1}{2}, \frac{1}{2})$, column strategy $(\frac{1}{4}, \frac{3}{4})^t$, value $\frac{5}{2}$.
5. a) $\begin{pmatrix} 3 & 0 \\ -1 & 0 \end{pmatrix}$;

   b) row strategy $(1, 0)$, column strategy $(0, 1)^t$, value 0;
   c) row strategy $(0, 1, 0)$, column strategy $(0, 0, 1)^t$, value 0.
7. a) $\begin{pmatrix} 1 & -4 \\ -2 & 0 \end{pmatrix}$;

   b) row strategy $(\frac{2}{7}, \frac{5}{7})$, column strategy $(\frac{4}{7}, \frac{3}{7})^t$, value $-\frac{8}{7}$;
   c) row strategy $(\frac{2}{7}, 0, \frac{5}{7})$, column strategy $(0, \frac{4}{7}, 0, \frac{3}{7}, 0)^t$, value $-\frac{8}{7}$.
9. $\begin{pmatrix} -1 & 1 \\ 1 & -1 \end{pmatrix}$,

   row strategy $(\frac{1}{2}, \frac{1}{2})$, column strategy $(\frac{1}{2}, \frac{1}{2})$, value 0.
11. Numerator and denominator of each fraction are multiplied by k; the values of the fractions are not changed.
13. $\dfrac{(ad - bc)k^2}{(a - b - c + d)k} = kv.$

6.5 Game theory and linear programming

1. $\begin{pmatrix} 10 & 7 & 4 \\ 1 & 6 & 9 \end{pmatrix}$.
3. Take $k = 4$, $\begin{pmatrix} 10 & 7 & 4 \\ 1 & 6 & 9 \end{pmatrix}$

	C_1	C_2	C_3	E_1	E_2	
E_1	10	7	4	1	0	1
E_2	1	6	9	0	1	1
	-1	-1	-1	0	0	0

	C_1	C_2	C_3	E_1	E_2	
C_1	1	$\frac{7}{10}$	$\frac{2}{5}$	$\frac{1}{10}$	0	$\frac{1}{10}$
E_2	0	$\frac{53}{10}$	$\frac{43}{5}$	$-\frac{1}{10}$	1	$\frac{9}{10}$
	0	$-\frac{3}{10}$	$-\frac{3}{5}$	$\frac{1}{10}$	0	$\frac{1}{10}$

	C_1	C_2	C_3	E_1	E_2	
C_1	1	$\frac{39}{86}$	0	$\frac{9}{86}$	$-\frac{2}{43}$	$\frac{5}{86}$
C_3	0	$\frac{53}{86}$	1	$-\frac{1}{86}$	$\frac{5}{43}$	$\frac{9}{86}$
	0	$\frac{3}{43}$	0	$\frac{4}{43}$	$\frac{3}{43}$	$\frac{7}{43}$

$(p_1, p_2) = (\frac{43}{7})(\frac{4}{43}, \frac{3}{43}) = (\frac{4}{7}, \frac{3}{7})$;
$(q_1, q_2, q_3)^t = (\frac{43}{7})(\frac{5}{86}, 0, \frac{9}{86})^t = (\frac{5}{14}, 0, \frac{9}{14})^t$;
$v = \frac{43}{7} - 4 = \frac{15}{7}$.

5. The second column is dominated by the third.

	C_1	C_3	E_1	E_2	E_3	
E_1	5	1	1	0	0	1
E_2	2	4	0	1	0	1
E_3	1	3	0	0	1	1
	-1	-1	0	0	0	0

	C_1	C_3	E_1	E_2	E_3	
C_1	1	$\frac{1}{5}$	$\frac{1}{5}$	0	0	$\frac{1}{5}$
E_2	0	$\frac{18}{5}$	$-\frac{2}{5}$	1	0	$\frac{3}{5}$
E_3	0	$\frac{14}{5}$	$-\frac{1}{5}$	0	1	$\frac{4}{5}$
	0	$-\frac{4}{5}$	$\frac{1}{5}$	0	0	$\frac{1}{5}$

	C_1	C_3	E_1	E_2	E_3	
C_1	1	0	$\frac{2}{9}$	$-\frac{1}{18}$	0	$\frac{1}{6}$
C_3	0	1	$-\frac{1}{9}$	$\frac{5}{18}$	0	$\frac{1}{6}$
E_3	0	0	$\frac{1}{9}$	$-\frac{7}{9}$	1	$\frac{1}{3}$
	0	0	$\frac{1}{9}$	$\frac{2}{9}$	0	$\frac{1}{3}$

$(p_1, p_2) = 3(\frac{1}{9}, \frac{2}{9}, 0) = (\frac{1}{3}, \frac{2}{3}, 0)$;
$(q_1, q_2, q_3)^t = 3(\frac{1}{6}, 0, \frac{1}{6})^t = (\frac{1}{2}, 0, \frac{1}{2})^t$;
$v = 3$.

7. a) $(\frac{1}{6}, \frac{1}{6}, \frac{1}{6}, \frac{1}{6}, \frac{1}{6}, \frac{1}{6})$;
   b) $(\frac{1}{2}, \frac{1}{2})^t$;

c) $\left(\frac{1}{6}, \frac{1}{6}, \frac{1}{6}, \frac{1}{6}, \frac{1}{6}, \frac{1}{6}\right)\begin{pmatrix} 1 & -1 \\ -2 & 2 \\ 3 & -3 \\ -4 & 4 \\ 5 & -5 \\ -6 & 6 \end{pmatrix}\left(\tfrac{1}{2}, \tfrac{1}{2}\right)^t$

$= \left(-\tfrac{1}{2}, \tfrac{1}{2}\right)\left(\tfrac{1}{2}, \tfrac{1}{2}\right)^t = 0,\ v = 0;$

d) yes.

9. a)

	C_1	C_2	E_1	E_2	E_3	E_4	E_5	E_6	
E_1	8	6	1	0	0	0	0	0	1
E_2	5	9	0	1	0	0	0	0	1
E_3	10	4	0	0	1	0	0	0	1
E_4	3	11	0	0	0	1	0	0	1
E_5	12	2	0	0	0	0	1	0	1
E_6	1	13	0	0	0	0	0	1	1
	-1	-1	0	0	0	0	0	0	0

b)

	C_1	C_2	E_1	E_2	E_3	E_4	E_5	E_6	
E_1	$\frac{98}{13}$	0	1	0	0	0	0	$-\frac{6}{13}$	$\frac{7}{13}$
E_2	$\frac{56}{13}$	0	0	1	0	0	0	$-\frac{9}{13}$	$\frac{4}{13}$
E_3	$\frac{126}{13}$	0	0	0	1	0	0	$-\frac{4}{13}$	$\frac{9}{13}$
E_4	$\frac{28}{13}$	0	0	0	0	1	0	$-\frac{11}{13}$	$\frac{2}{13}$
E_5	$\frac{154}{13}$	0	0	0	0	0	1	$-\frac{2}{13}$	$\frac{11}{13}$
C_2	$\frac{1}{13}$	1	0	0	0	0	0	$\frac{1}{13}$	$\frac{1}{13}$
	$-\frac{12}{13}$	0	0	0	0	0	0	$\frac{1}{13}$	$\frac{1}{13}$

c) For the second row $\dfrac{1}{13} + \dfrac{12}{13} \times \dfrac{-9}{56} = -\dfrac{1}{14}$;

for the fourth row $\dfrac{1}{13} + \dfrac{12}{13} \times \dfrac{-11}{28} = -\dfrac{2}{7}$.

d)

	C_1	C_2	E_1	E_2	E_3	E_4	E_5	E_6	
C_1	1	0	0	0	0	0	$\frac{13}{154}$	$-\frac{1}{77}$	$\frac{1}{14}$
C_2	0	1	0	0	0	0	$-\frac{1}{154}$	$\frac{6}{77}$	$\frac{1}{14}$
	0	0	0	0	0	0	$\frac{6}{77}$	$\frac{5}{77}$	$\frac{1}{7}$

$(p_1, p_2, p_3, p_4, p_5, p_6) = \left(0, 0, 0, 0, \tfrac{6}{11}, \tfrac{5}{11}\right);$

$(q_1, q_2)^t = \left(\tfrac{1}{2}, \tfrac{1}{2}\right)^t;\ v = 7 - 7 = 0.$

e)

	C_1	C_2	E_1	E_2	E_3	E_4	E_5	E_6	
C_1	1	0	$\frac{13}{98}$	0	0	0	0	$-\frac{3}{49}$	$\frac{1}{14}$
C_2	0	1	$-\frac{1}{98}$	0	0	0	0	$\frac{4}{49}$	$\frac{1}{14}$
	0	0	$\frac{6}{49}$	0	0	0	0	$\frac{1}{49}$	$\frac{1}{7}$

$(p_1, p_2, p_3, p_4, p_5, p_6) = (\frac{6}{7}, 0, 0, 0, 0, \frac{1}{7})$;
$(q_1, q_2)^t = (\frac{1}{2}, \frac{1}{2})^t$; $v = 0$.

Note that there are several possible optimum strategies for the row player in this game.

Review Exercises for Chapter 6

1.

	penny	dime
penny	-1	5
dime	5	-10

3. a) No;   b) no.

5. a) No;   b) no.

7.

$$\begin{pmatrix} 0 & 3 \\ 1 & 2 \end{pmatrix} \qquad \begin{matrix} 0 \\ 1 \end{matrix} \quad \text{maximin 1}$$

minimums

maximums   1 2

minimax 1

Row strategy $(0, 1)$; column strategy $(1, 0)^t$; value of the game 1

9.

minimums

$$\begin{pmatrix} 0 & 0 & -1 & 1 \\ 0 & 0 & -1 & 0 \\ 0 & -2 & 0 & -1 \\ 2 & 1 & 0 & 1 \end{pmatrix} \qquad \begin{matrix} -1 \\ -1 \\ -2 \\ 0 \end{matrix} \quad \text{maximin 0}$$

maximums   2   1   0   1

minimax 0

Row strategy $(0, 0, 0, 1)$; column strategy $(0, 0, 1, 0)^t$; value of the game 0.

11.

	C_1	C_2	E_1	E_2	
E_1	3	0	1	0	1
E_2	2	④	0	1	1
	-1	-1	0	0	0

	C_1	C_2	E_1	E_2	
E_1	③	0	1	0	1
E_2	$\frac{1}{2}$	1	0	$\frac{1}{4}$	$\frac{1}{4}$
	$-\frac{1}{2}$	0	0	$\frac{1}{4}$	$\frac{1}{4}$

	C_1	C_2	E_1	E_2	
C_1	1	0	$\frac{1}{3}$	0	$\frac{1}{3}$
C_2	0	1	$-\frac{1}{6}$	0	$\frac{1}{12}$
	0	0	$\frac{1}{6}$	$\frac{1}{4}$	$\frac{5}{12}$

$(p_1, p_2) = (\frac{12}{5})(\frac{1}{6}, \frac{1}{4}) = (\frac{2}{5}, \frac{3}{5})$;
$(q_1, q_2)^t = (\frac{12}{5})(\frac{1}{3}, \frac{1}{12})^t = (\frac{4}{5}, \frac{1}{5})$;
$v = \frac{12}{5}$.

13. $(p, 1 - p)\begin{pmatrix} -1 & 5 \\ 5 & -10 \end{pmatrix} = (5 - 6p \quad 15p - 10)$

The row player receives $5 - 6p$ cents if the column player guesses a penny and $15p - 10$ cents if the column player guesses a dime.

15. $(p_1, p_2) = (\frac{5}{7}, \frac{2}{7})$; $(q_1, q_2)^t = (\frac{5}{7}, \frac{2}{7})^t$; $v = \frac{5}{7}$.

index